NORSE
MYTHOLOGY

NORSE MYTHOLOGY

Tales of the gods, sagas and heroes

Abbie Farewell Brown, Sarah Powers Bradish,
Mary Litchfield and others

ARCTURUS

ARCTURUS

This edition published in 2018 by Arcturus Publishing Limited
26/27 Bickels Yard, 151–153 Bermondsey Street,
London SE1 3HA

ISBN: 978-1-78828-084-6
AD005783UK

Printed in China

CONTENTS

TALES FROM THE SAGAS

INTRODUCTION

THE legendary tales of the Norse gods Odin, Thor, Loki and their companions, as they fight amongst each other, battle fierce enemies and meddle with troublesome humans, are some of the most entertaining and fascinating stories of all mythology. Their names remain with us in the days of the week: for example, Wednesday is "Wodan's Day" (Wodan being an alternative name for Odin). The myths and legends of the Norsemen were shared by all the Germanic peoples of Europe, and provided a unique alternative to the two competing cultures of the continent in the early centuries CE – the increasingly powerful and prescriptive Christianity, and the slowly fading, if widely known, tales of Greek and Roman mythology.

The old stories of the men and women of Scandinavia have been retold countless times and inspired many works of fiction. Fantasy and science fiction owe much to Norse mythology, with its characters, creatures and deities worming their way, in altered forms, into J R R Tolkien's *Lord of the Rings* and Neil Gaiman's *American Gods*. In music, Norse mythology has inspired as diverse creations as Richard Wagner's *Ring Cycle* and modern heavy metal. While the names of Mjöllnir, Asgard, the Valkyries and Ragnarök have crept into modern usage.

The tales found their first written expression in two Icelandic "Eddas". The elder of the two is known as the *Poetic Edda* and derives from the medieval manuscript of the *Codex Regius*, often attributed to the twelfth-century priest Saemund. The younger collection is the *Prose Edda*, written by Snorri Sturluson in the early thirteenth century. It is from these two sources that almost all knowledge of the Norse mythological world derives.

The gods of the Norsemen were strangely complicated. Like the Greek inhabitants of Mount Olympus, they were often selfish, petty and quick to anger, but they could also display great generosity and were prepared for immense sacrifice. Thor, with his trusty hammer Mjöllnir, held immense power, but could easily be tricked; Loki was the trickster, but he was far more than the mere personification of evil; the one-eyed Odin was a wise and cunning deity locked in pursuit of knowledge. In short, the gods were not so different from men.

In Norse cosmology, the world began after Ymir, the first giant, was formed from the meeting of the frost of Niflheim and the flames of Muspelheim. The cow Audhumbla uncovered a group of gods known as the Æsir that included Odin, who slew Ymir and created the earth from his corpse. The Ash Tree of Life, Yggdrasil, sat at the centre of the Nine Worlds. The gods resided in the upper world of Asgard while humanity dwelt in the central world of Midgard. Mary Litchfield explained more about this in the Introductory Chapter (*see* page 14). Through these worlds were found creatures such as elves, dwarves and frost giants. In death, men might be condemned to Hel; be carried away by the Valkyries to Valhalla, a heavenly feasting hall reserved for the brave who died in combat; or chosen by Freyja to dwell in the field of Folkvangr. In Valhalla, the martial heroes of Midgard joined Thor in preparation for Ragnarök. Also known as "The Twilight of the Gods", Ragnarök consisted of a great battle between the gods and the frost giants, culminating in the destruction of the world before its eventual rebirth.

War beset the divine world just as it did the mortal one. The Norse gods divided into two tribes – the Æsir and the Vanir, who were often at odds with each other. Gods, such as Thor, Heimdall and Frigg, belonged to the Æsir, with Odin as their leader. The Vanir included Njörd and his children Freyr and Freyja, amongst others. The Æsir were known for their warlike qualities and the Vanir for fertility and wisdom.

In the myths collected here, we discover how the world began and how Odin lost his eye. We follow Loki's adventures, his courting of Idunn and his troublemaking, to the cost of the beloved god Baldr. We learn of Thor's adventures and his efforts to recover the famous hammer Mjöllnir. We hear of Freyr and Freyja, of the great wolf Fenris, of the Æsir–Vanir war and of the origin of poetry. And of course, we learn of Ragnarök, the Twilight of the Gods.

The fabulous tales of the Viking world do not end with the occurrences in Asgard. Unlike early literary accounts from many other cultures, the storytelling tradition of the Eddas found its way into the recording of history. For centuries, the men of the North recounted the tales of their heroes, their kings and their great adventures in the Sagas. Pages are filled with legendary figures, such as Ragnar Lodbrok, the man who rose from obscurity to become perhaps the most famous Viking of all time, terrorizing the shores of Anglo-Saxon England and West Francia and fathering a crop of sons who would dominate European history in the ninth century CE; and Halfdan the Black, who carved out a great kingdom in Norway over a series of violent battles. These men, who may well have been true historical figures, take on mythical proportions as they overcome trials and tribulations with which even the gods struggled.

Some of the tales from the Sagas are short, self-contained stories, such as "The Tale of Thidrandi". Others are detailed epics, telling the whole life story of an individual. Of these, a few have been reproduced in full. The story of Sigurd, recorded in the "Völsunga Saga", has everything to recommend it – power struggles, a battle with a dragon, heartwarming romance, a cursed ring and even moral lessons to take away. The tale of Frithiof the Bold and Ingeborg the Fair is one of the latest of this volume, recorded in *c.* 1300 in *The Saga of Thorstein Vikingsson*. In a story of star-crossed lovers long before Shakespeare, the titular Frithiof rages against the kings who prevent him from attaining his love, before eventually realizing his destiny. "The Story of Gunnlaugh the Worm-tongue" – considered one of the masterpieces of Old Norse literature – is unlike most of the other sagas in that it takes two poets as its protagonists; gift-giving, courts and honour are at the centre of this fascinating and emotional tale.

Like the fairy-tales of medieval Europe, the legends are often infused with moral lessons. They explain to men and women how they should behave but they are also used to provide a sense of history. It is from the Sagas that we derive most of our knowledge of Scandinavian and Icelandic history in the era before Christianity took hold. Sometimes literal, sometimes allegorical, they are both entertaining and powerful reminders of a half-forgotten world.

For centuries, the stories of the Norsemen vanished into obscurity. In the late nineteenth century, however, a determined effort was made to restore them to public view.

This was largely thanks to the work of writers like Mary Litchfield, Sarah Bradish, Edward Ernest Kellett and William Morris – whose interpretations and translations are included in this collection, in all their variety of writing styles and viewpoints, sometimes overlapping or contradicting but ultimately combining to create a charismatic picture of a world both familiar and mysterious. As evidenced by its influence in so many fields of literature and creativity today, Norse mythology has, deservedly, never been more popular.

TALES FROM THE EDDAS

INTRODUCTORY CHAPTER

as told by Mary Litchfield

 OUR ancestors who lived hundreds of years ago believed in many gods. The stories of these gods, however, were written, not in sacred books, but in the memories of the people; for in those early days the Teutons living in northern Europe had no written language.[1] For centuries the fathers handed down to their children the traditions they had received from former generations; until finally Christianity took the place of the old religion.

Even after this, the belief in the gods lingered long in out-of-the-way places; and, at last, in Iceland, some of the stories about them were collected and written down. The books in which they are written are called the Eddas. There are two of them – *The Elder*, or *Saemund's Edda*, which consists of poems, and *The Younger*, or *Snorre Sturluson's Edda*, which is prose.

Probably these stories collected in Iceland are not just like those told hundreds of years before in Europe, because things handed down by word of mouth are sure to change a little with each generation. Still, they give us, in the main, a true idea of the gods our warlike forefathers believed in. The stories that follow in this book are for the most part based upon the Eddas.

---

1   They had a few characters called runes, which were supposed to possess magic properties.

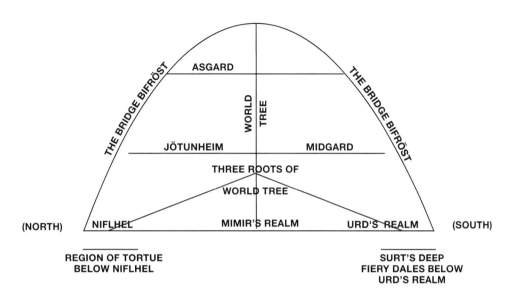

A cross-section of the Nine Worlds

Our ancestors knew but little of the world, and what they saw made them think that it was flat – a great flat region encircled by a river, called the Ocean. They believed that there were nine worlds instead of one, arranged in some such way as this:[2]

Highest of all was Asgard, the home of the Æsir, or gods, ruled over by Odin, or Wodan. Next below came Midgard, the world of men, with the river Ocean around it. Beyond the Ocean, on the same plane, was Jötunheim, the upper giant-world. Far below these stretched the under-world, vast compared with the regions above it, and containing four of the nine worlds. In the north was Niflheim (or Niflhal), the lower giant-world, cold, dark and misty. In the south Urd and her two sisters ruled over the kingdoms of the dead. Between these two regions lay Mimir's land, where, besides the wise old giant, there dwelt many mighty beings, among whom were Night (the ancient mother), bright Day and Delling, the elf of the dawn. Even the Sun and Moon had resting-places there; and in some parts there were elves and dwarfs. West of Mimir's land was the home of the Vanir, a noble race akin to the Æsir. Some of the Vanir lived in Asgard.

---

2   In the plan of the nine worlds Rydberg has been followed.

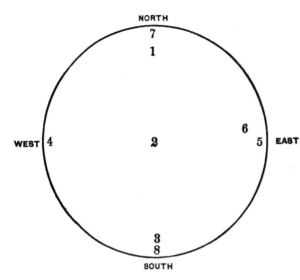

(1) Spring Hvergelmir, in Niflhel or Niflheim, under Yggdrasil's northern root

(2) Well of Wisdom in Mimir's Realm, under Yggdrasil's middle root

(3) Urd's Well in her Realm, under Yggdrasil's southern root

(4) Home of the Vanir

(5) Home of the Elves in Mimir's Realm

(6) Castle where Baldr dwelt with the Asmégir

(7) Northern End of Bifröst, guarded by Heimdall

(8) Southern End of Bifröst, near Urd's Well

Plan (from above) of the Nine Worlds

There were regions lower still – the land of subterranean fire ("Surt's deep fiery dales"), below Urd's realm, and the world of torture under Niflheim.

Two things, a bridge and a tree, united all these worlds.

Bifröst,[3] the trembling bridge, threw its mighty arch over Asgard, while its northern end rested upon the mountains of Niflheim and its southern end reached to the land of Urd. It was very useful to the gods, who crossed it daily on their way to the judgment hall in Urd's realm; but it had to be carefully watched lest hostile giants should, by its help, find their way to Asgard. Heimdall, a pure and wise Van, guarded its northern end. His ears were so good that he could hear the grass pushing up through the ground and the wool growing on the backs of the sheep; and he needed less sleep than a bird.

The tree which connected the nine worlds was called Yggdrasil.[4] Its three main roots were watered by three fountains in the under-world, and the rootlets went down to Surt's deep dales and to the world of torture. The branches of this wonderful tree reached to the most remote regions, and its sap carried life everywhere. Serpents gnawed

---

3 Rydberg maintains that the Milky Way, and not the rainbow, is the original of Bifröst.
4 Yggdrasil was an ash tree.

its roots; stags, squirrels and birds lived among its branches; and on its topmost bough, far above Asgard, the cock Vidofnir glittered. It was indeed a "tree of life".

They had a strange story of the creation, these northern people – a story that is interesting because it is so very old.

In the beginning there were two worlds – a world of freezing mists in the north, and a world of raging fire in the south. Between these two regions was a yawning abyss – Ginungagap, dark and empty.

In Niflheim, the cold world, a mighty spring sent down twelve rivers; and some of the rivers flowed into the abyss, filling the part that was next to Niflheim with layers of frozen vapour. The flames raged so fiercely in Muspelheim, the world of fire, that they blew over into Ginungagap, taking many sparks with them. At last the sparks met the frozen vapour, and a huge giant was formed. His name was Ymir.

The following lines are from a translation of one of the old poems:

> There was in times of old
> where Ymir dwelt
> nor sand nor sea
> nor gelid waves;
> earth existed not,
> nor heaven above,
> 'twas a chaotic chasm
> before Bur's sons
> raised up heaven's vault,
> they who the noble mid-earth shaped.[5]

Not long after the creation of Ymir, a cow, Audhumla, was formed; and the giant Ymir fed upon her milk. The cow licked the masses of frozen vapour, for they were salt. And as she was licking, the first evening, a man's hair appeared; and the second day his head; and the third day the whole man could be seen. His name was Bur. He was very large and fair and had great strength. He had a son called Bor.

---

5   From "Völuspa" in Thorpe's translation of *Saemund's Edda*.

From under the arm of the huge giant Ymir there grew two children, a boy and a girl. They were giants, but still they were good, and from them descended many wonderful beings. Mimir, the boy, grew to be the wisest person in all the nine worlds. Unfortunately he lost his life in a great war. Odin cut off his head and preserved it; and it kept on giving good advice, as though it were Mimir himself. The great goddess Night was Mimir's daughter. The girl who came from under Ymir's arm was called Bestla. She was the mother of Odin.

While a race of good and wise giants descended from Mimir and Bestla, a race of evil giants and monsters came from a six-headed son of Ymir's. This monster grew from Ymir's feet. His descendants were so powerful that in the end they were to conquer Odin and cause the destruction of the world. The ruin of the gods, however, was to be brought about in part by their own shortcomings: they were not strong and noble enough to resist the evil forces arrayed against them.

Odin and his two brothers slew the giant Ymir, dragged his body into the middle of the abyss, and from it formed the world.

> From Ymir's flesh
> the earth was formed,
> and from his bones the hills,
> the heaven from the skull
> of that ice-cold giant,
> and from his blood the sea.[6]

The "melancholy clouds" were formed from Ymir's brains. Some of the sparks that flew over into Ginungagap were placed in the heavens, and men called them stars.

One day Odin and his brothers[7] were walking near the sea, when they came upon two trees, an ash and an elm. From these trees they created the first human beings – a man and a woman. An old poem says:

---

6 From "The Lay of Vafthrûdnir" in Thorpe's translation of *Saemund's Edda*.
7 Rydberg maintains that Hoenir and Lodur are identical with Vili and Ve, Odin's brothers.

They found on earth,
nearly powerless,
Ask and Embla,
void of destiny.
Spirit they possessed not,
sense they had not,
blood nor motive powers,
nor goodly colour.
Spirit gave Odin,
sense gave Hoenir,
blood gave Lodur
and goodly colour.[8]

The elves and dwarfs swarmed in Ymir's body after he was killed: they were not created by the gods.

In Europe there are still ancient customs and old sayings that go back to the time when men believed in Thor and Odin. In some parts of Germany, until recently, the peasants left a clump of grain standing for Odin's horse when they gathered the harvest. Even in English there is something to remind us of the old gods. Tuesday is named for Tyr, the god who gave his right hand to save his people from the dangerous wolf. Wednesday is Odin's, or Wodan's, day. He placed wisdom above everything else, being willing to give even his eye for one drink from Mimir's well. Thursday belongs to Thor, the fierce thunder-god; and Friday to Frigg, Freyr or Freyja – we are not sure which.

How did people come to believe in all these gods? No one will ever know just how the belief began and how it grew, but it is possible to learn something about it.

We who live now have had so many things found out for us that we cannot imagine how the world seemed to people who knew very little, and who had to find out everything for themselves or make their own guesses about things. In the early ages men lived in a world of mystery; the sun, the moon, the sea, the wind – everything was strange and wonderful. Life was a struggle. In the north it was hard to provide for the

---

8   From "Volüspa" in Thorpe's translation of *Saemund's Edda*.

needs of the long, cold winter. Man had not learned how to control the forces of nature, and he was continually warring against them. The mountains shut him in; the forests were dark and awful; the snow and the ice and the desolate wastes set themselves against him to thwart his best endeavours. Was it strange that these hostile forces seemed like cold, heartless giants opposed to all that was joyous and gentle and human? Thus began the belief in frost giants and mountain giants.

There were kindly powers, however, and chief among these was the sun, man's best friend. He gave man light and heat. Through his influence the rivers burst their bonds, the grass grew green and the crops ripened. While the sun reigned, life was happy. But in the north, at a certain time of the year, the sun lost his power; and in the extreme north, he sank out of sight and left the world in darkness. As men saw him disappearing, what anxiety must have filled their hearts! How could they be sure that this mysterious being, upon whom their very lives depended, would ever return? How eagerly they must have watched for him; and when the first faint flush appeared, what rejoicing! No wonder they hailed the returning sun as a god – the god who gave light and joy.

The character of Odin is said to have come from men's feeling about the sun. Some books say that Odin gave one of his eyes for the drink from Mimir's well, and that the sun represents Odin's single eye. We can easily see that the story of Idunn has something to do with the going and coming again of the summer.

Baldr is the god who represents most fully the feeling that men had for the sun in the far north. Baldr was the pure and shining god. And as the sun sank out of sight and left the world in darkness, so he died, and went to the under-world, causing untold grief in Asgard and Midgard.

The thunder was pictured as a strong, fierce god, with fiery hair and beard, who rode in his iron chariot and flung his mighty hammer at the rocks and mountains – Thor, the foe of the giants.

All the gods cannot be easily traced back to something in nature; indeed, most of them lost their original character as the years rolled on, and became very human in their attributes; and we must not think of them as representing to their worshippers simply some object in nature. Men and women lived hard lives in those rude times, and thought much about life and death and the unknown future. What they believed and hoped was expressed in the character of their gods, and in the pictures they made for themselves of the unseen worlds. As we read their poems and stories, we feel that they were trying to get at the secret of life, the great open secret that no one has wholly guessed, even with the "light" that has come into the world since those days.

It was a fighting age. The hero looked forward to death on the battle-field as the greatest of blessings. He believed that so dying meant the Valkyries would come and take him to Odin's palace of Valhalla, where the fighting and the feasting would go on for ages. Still, with all their love of war, these people did not believe that force was to be victorious, or that evil was to triumph over good. The strong gods were to have their day, but were to be defeated at Ragnarök; then Baldr was to come – the ruler of a new and better world. Goodness and purity were to conquer in the end.

All this has passed away, and those warlike people have left little to remind us that they once lived here. Yet one heritage we have – not a few pyramids of stone, but nine worlds built of that airy stuff that outlasts solid granite, and peopled with beings strange and wonderful. Surely, he who loves the past will care sometimes to wander amid the shadows of those ancient worlds.

ODIN SEEKS WISDOM FROM MIMIR

as told by Mary Litchfield

 IT was night in Asgard, the home of the gods. A soft light fell upon the sleeping city, showing its vine-clad hills and glittering palaces, and touching even the deep, still valleys that lay between. For the trembling bridge, Bifröst, spanned the city like a rainbow of silver, meeting the horizon at the north and south. Toward the south, as far as the eye could reach, rose mountains, with castles upon their tops and sides; while toward the north stretched the level and grassy plains of Ida.

From a structure upon the highest place of the city, a shaft shot up, slender and glittering, as a tall spire rises from some great cathedral. It rose high above all the castles and towers, so high as almost to touch the arch of the celestial bridge. This slender shaft was Odin's High Seat. From its top could be seen not only Asgard, but also a large part of the worlds below.

Here the Allfather sat alone, buried in thought. Alone except for two wolves that lay sleeping at his feet, and two ravens[1] perched upon his shoulders, weary after their journey through the nine worlds.

After sitting a long while in meditation, Odin looked down upon the stately homes of his children, and upon the fields that stretched away, beyond the high walls and the dark, rushing river that surrounded the city of the gods. Then his eyes tried in vain to pierce the dense blackness that shrouded a land far below him toward the north. He gazed long and earnestly, and at last rose up and descended quickly to the palace just below his High Seat. The vast halls resounded as he strode through them.

---

1 Odin's ravens were Hugin (thought) and Munin (memory); each day they flew over the nine worlds, bringing back tidings to Odin.

He hastened to a building nearby, and soon appeared again, leading a grey horse. This horse was well fitted to bear the father of the gods; for he had a powerful frame and eight legs. As he stood waiting for Odin to mount, he trembled with eagerness, and flames poured from his nostrils. In an instant Odin was on his back, and the wonderful horse was carrying him toward the north with the speed of the wind.

The high wall and the dark river surrounding the city were no obstacle to Sleipnir. He leaped easily over them, and kept on his swift way across the fields on the other side, which stretched green and level to the distant horizon. Here and there were groves in whose quiet depths a less rapid traveller might have heard the trickling of fountains. And occasionally a lake reflected on its dark surface the silvery arch of Bifröst.

At last they reached the point where the celestial bridge touched the outer edge of Asgard. The eight-footed horse rushed unhesitatingly upon the bridge, although it trembled beneath his weight, sending up fitful flames. Like a comet among the stars, Sleipnir sped on, bearing Odin over the black depths.

At length a faint light reached them from the north; and soon Odin saw a horseman, clad in a white garment, coming towards him. The horse had a mane of gold, which, shining full upon the rider, revealed his pure, pale face. Approaching, he said, "Welcome, Father Odin. I have been watching for you ever since I heard Sleipnir's eight hoofs strike the bridge. Doubtless some deep purpose brings you across Bifröst at night?"

"Yes, Heimdall, you have judged rightly," said Odin; "a great matter urges me on; and many days must I journey ere I return home. I must go through the dark land of our enemies, the frost giants of the lower world; and then far beyond, to regions that few have visited. Fortunate are the gods that Heimdall guards for them the trembling bridge. Were it not for your keen ears that hear the grass growing and the wool thickening on the backs of the sheep, our enemies might, ere this, have crossed the abyss, and have stormed Asgard."

As he spoke, they both looked down upon the land beneath them, dark, except for the light that streamed from Heimdall's far-shining castle at the bridge-head. And they could see the glistening tops of ice mountains rising above the mists.

As Odin looked he said, "Our enemies are strong, and I fear the treacherous Loki, who is ever going between Asgard and the giant-world. We have need of all your watchfulness, Heimdall, and of all the strength of Thor, the dread foe of the giants, to keep our enemies at bay. What great wisdom do I need to protect the realm of Asgard, and the world of men!"

They kept on their way toward Heimdall's castle, which was on a high mountain near the bridge-head. The castle was apparently made of the same material as the bridge, and, as it rose toward the sky, might have been taken for a structure of cloud bathed in moonlight. But in truth it shone with a soft fire of its own; for radiance streamed from it in all directions, lighting up, as we have seen, a part of the cold, foggy land of the giants. The approach to the bridge was in this way made so clearly visible that it would have been impossible for anyone to get near without Heimdall's knowledge, even had his hearing been less keen. Then, too, the castle was strongly fortified, surrounded by a high wall and a moat, the waters of which, like those of the Asgard river, were covered with a mist that flashed into flames when disturbed by an enemy of the gods.

"Come in, Odin," said Heimdall, as they reached the castle; "your journey has been long, and a hard road lies before you."

They entered a large hall whose walls were made of something that resembled white marble or alabaster. All the decorations were of silver. Vines bearing clusters of silver grapes ran along the walls, and curious horns and lamps hung from the arches above. Tall youths, clad, like Heimdall, all in white, brought in tankards of foaming mead.[2]

The two gods drank the mead, and talked earnestly together, until at last Odin rose, saying, "One favour I ask of you, Heimdall: keep Sleipnir for me until my return. There are few to whom I would entrust him, but he will be safe with you. I wish to journey, unknown, through the world of cold and darkness, and the horse would betray me."

Heimdall accompanied Odin a short distance down the steep mountain, and then returned to his post, to guard the bridge of the gods.

As Odin went down into Niflheim,[3] a chilly fog closed about him, shutting out the light from Heimdall's castle, and making it hard for him to keep to the path. As he got lower, the cold became intense, and his foot slipped on the icy road which broadened into a river of ice. There were sounds of creaking and crashing, and in the distance

---

2 Honey and water, fermented and flavoured.
3 The giant-world in the northern part of the great under-world.

could be heard the moaning of waves as they broke upon the desolate shore. As he made his way he could just distinguish through the mist and darkness the enormous mountains of ice surrounding him. Some of these seeming ice mountains were really frost giants whose huge heads would slowly turn to follow him. Once an iceberg in the sea went to pieces with the noise of distant thunder, and he could long hear the booming and crashing, Sometimes a deluge of icy water would rush upon him from a cascade that he had not perceived; and then he would hear the slow, heavy laughter of the giants, sounding like the roar of hoarse winds. At one point in his journey he came upon a field of ice; and as the fog lifted, he could see that it stretched on all sides, level and white, covered with snow. Here the sounds of creaking and crashing ceased, and he no longer heard the laughter of the giants: the silence was absolute. He stood alone under the stars.

After a long journey through the ice region, Odin reached a country where dark, savage mountains took the place of icebergs, and here and there on their peaks loomed up the strongholds of the mountain giants. As he kept on his way, he could sometimes distinguish the giants themselves, looking like huge, moving masses of rock. This land was as dreary as the land of ice; for although there was no fog, and a faint twilight glimmered, it was very desolate. Not a green thing was to be seen; nothing but grim mountains and dark abysses, at the bottom of which rushed rivers, finding their way from the spring Hvergelmir to the cold northern sea. The mountains, at times, gave place to level wastes of great extent, where boulders lay heaped one upon another, with deep, still pools lurking among them. Often heavy clouds rolled across the sky, enveloping the mountains.

After journeying long, Odin stood upon a high place from which he could look down upon a morass stretching as far as the eye could reach. In the dim light he could just distinguish a narrow footpath of solid ground leading across it. When he was partly over, one of the giants saw him; and soon a troop of the monsters came stumbling after him. Finding it impossible to reach him, they filled the air with their shouts, and brandished their great clubs. Upon this a fearful wind arose, threatening to blow Odin from the narrow path. Clouds shaped like dragons blew gusts at him from their open mouths; and when he got safely over, howls of disappointed rage resounded long in the air behind.

He came next to a river, whose dark, swift current bore with it sharp stones and bits of iron, and no bridge spanned the deadly stream; but Odin crossed it safely on some driftwood.

Higher mountains than any he had yet seen now loomed up toward the south; and one, higher than the others, down whose sides rushed twelve rivers. On the top of this mountain was the ice-cold spring Hvergelmir. One of the three roots of the great World Tree, Yggdrasil, was bathed by the waters of this spring; and the rivers that flowed from it went in all directions; some flowing through the cold, foggy land of the giants to the northern ocean, while others flowed toward the south, through the vast realms where Mimir[4] and Urd[5] guarded their wells under the other two roots of the World Tree.

As Odin neared the mountain, his way led through a gloomy cave, where he could hear the baying of a dog and the creaking of an iron gate. This gate, he knew, barred the descent to the world of torture below Nilfheim – a world far more dark and dreadful than that through which he had just passed. Once out of the cave, the road led over the mountain. On the highest peak stood a solitary watchman, the trusty guardian of the spring and the dread foe of the giants.

As Odin came near, he greeted him: "Did the monsters try to harm you, Odin? The hateful crew would be glad enough to crush the father of the gods and get possession of Asgard. And your Loki is too much with them. I often see him there. He thinks himself well hidden by the darkness; but my eyes are trained to see in the dark."

"Yes, Egil," replied Odin; "your eyes and Heimdall's ears are the best defence we have against our foes. I came through safely, as you see. Their attacks would have been more fierce had they known me. As for Loki, I am well aware how dangerous he has become. Still, I may not yet turn him out of Asgard, for I am bound by an oath made when we both were young – when I thought him innocent. But I must hasten, Egil; a great purpose urges me on."

As Odin went down the southern slope of the mountain, a pleasant prospect greeted his eyes, wearied with the gloomy sights upon which they had been looking for so many days. The country was still mountainous, but it was not black and sterile. Rich metals

---

4   The giant who grew from under Ymir's arm.
5   Urd and her two sisters were Norns, or Fates, representing the past, present and future.

seamed the rocks, and here and there were the mouths of caves where sparkled crystals and gems. When Odin stopped and listened, he could hear the picks and hammers of the dwarfs. Twilight still hung over the scene, but at intervals lights streamed across the sky, their rich colours playing upon the mountains.

Odin had now to cross a broad river, and then he could see in the distance a castle of fantastic shape, which was ornamented in an unusual manner. Stone dragons grinned from its corners, their large jewelled eyes gleaming like fire as the lights flashed upon them. About the slender columns twined golden snakes and lizards of copper; and metal vines ran thickly along the walls, bearing gems for flowers. A fire shone from one part of the building, and it was evident that work of some kind was going on.

This strange castle was the home of Sindri and his brothers – dwarfs and famous artists, who had made wonderful weapons and ornaments for the gods. None approached them in skill except the sons of Ivaldi. The latter were partly of giant blood, and were said to be magicians as well as artists. Between them and the dwarfs there was some rivalry, but, as yet, no hard feeling. Odin passed near the castle, but did not enter.

As he went on, the mountains lost all their savage wildness, and rose in gentle outlines against the sky. They were clothed with forests and vineyards. Down their slopes rushed brooks, changing into cascades of mist. Peaceful valleys stretched between the mountains; while high above all were clouds, glowing with the colours of an eternal sunset. For this was a land where dark night and glaring midday never came.

The mountains gradually softened into hills, and these, at last, were lost in broad stretches of level fields covered with golden grain or tall, waving grass. The rivers glided along, deep and peaceful. Flowers bloomed everywhere, their bright colours reflected in the still waters of little ponds. Herds of deer came timidly up to Odin, and birds sang to him as he passed. Only the gentlest breeze stirred the leaves, and all sounds were low and sweet.

Along the southern horizon there now appeared a bank of white clouds, piled high, one upon another. But as Odin neared them, they changed to mountains of marble, evidently enclosing some sacred spot. Like pure white sentinels they stood, bathed with rich colours.

There seemed to be no entrance through this marble wall; but when Odin reached it, he knocked with his staff, and a door was opened. A man of grave and reverend aspect greeted him, and led the way through a spacious cave sparkling with crystals that reflected the light of his torch. At the further end of the cave was a door, larger than the one by which Odin had entered, opening into a circular valley.

The sides of the valley were formed by the marble mountains; but they did not look like mountains on the inside; for they had been carved into beautiful shapes, and delicate vines ran over them, veiling the whiteness of the marble.

From the centre of the valley grew the root of the enormous World Tree; and the waters of the deep well of wisdom bathed the root of the tree. At the further end of the valley rose a stately palace. Here and there were groups of trees, and rare plants bloomed on all sides. Near a pool a large turtle, his back covered with the incrustations of ages, basked lazily in the light. Harmless serpents with brilliant eyes twined about the trunks of trees. Dragons slept with folded wings, while many ancient and uncouth monsters rested amid the groves, or sunned themselves in the niches of the marble walls. Gay-coloured birds flitted in and out among the branches, and peacocks walked proudly about, spreading their tails. The scene was made more fair by the light that fell upon it. It was not sunlight, and one could not tell whence it came; but it flooded the peaceful valley with the softest radiance.

Odin stood for a few moments looking at the scene before him, and then walked slowly toward the centre of the valley. Under the root of the World Tree sat a man of giant stature, apparently absorbed in watching the waters of the well. Long silver locks floated over his shoulders, and a white beard fell upon his breast. There was no look of old age in his face, although, as he raised his head, the wisdom of the centuries gleamed from his deep blue eyes, and his whole aspect expressed perfect peace. His hand rested upon the edge of the well, which was thickly overlaid with gold. Near him stood an immense chest, curiously carved, containing treasures from bygone ages. A large horn of silver lay upon the chest, bearing Heimdair's name in runic characters of gold.

As Odin came near, Mimir rose, saying, "Welcome, Odin! You come from the north, I see. This time you have chosen the hard road, and on foot too!"

"Yes, Mimir," answered Odin; "I chose that road because I wished to explore the land of my enemies, and I have come to you for counsel and help."

"Gladly will I help you, as you know," said Mimir.

"I know your readiness," replied Odin; "but this time I ask what no one has ever asked of you. My realm is beset with dangers. Loki grows in wickedness. He has taken for his wife the witch of the iron-wood, and their children threaten to prove our most formidable foes. And the frost giants and the mountain giants, as you know, are only too ready to attack us whenever there is a chance of success. I need great wisdom rightly to govern and protect Asgard, and Midgard, the world of men."

Both were silent for a moment; and then Odin said, looking earnestly at Mimir, "In order that I may gain this wisdom, I ask for one drink from your deep well."

After a long silence, Mimir said slowly, "You have asked a great thing, Odin! Are you prepared to pay the price for it?"

"Yes," replied Odin, eagerly; "all the gold of Asgard, our best swords, our jewelled shields! Even Sleipnir will I give you for one draught of the precious water!"

"These things will not buy what you desire," said Mimir; "wisdom can be gained only by suffering and sacrifice. Would you give one of your eyes for wisdom?"

A cloud came over the bold face of Odin, and he pondered long. Finally he said slowly, "I will give one of my eyes, and I will suffer whatever else is necessary, if I may thereby gain the wisdom I need."

No one ever knew all that Odin suffered and learned in that mysterious valley. Some say that he really gave one of his eyes in return for the drink from Mimir's well. But as nothing is said of that in the old song called "Odin's Rune Song", and as the fact of his being one-eyed is not mentioned in some of the oldest poems, it seems doubtful whether that sacrifice was required of him. Odin says in his "Rune Song":

> I know that I hung
> on a wind-rocked tree,
> nine whole nights,
> with a spear wounded

and to Odin offered,
myself to myself;
on that tree,
of which no one knows
from what root it springs.

Bread no one gave me,
nor a horn of drink;
downward I peered,
to runes applied myself,
wailing learnt them,
then fell down thence.

Potent songs nine
from the famed son,
I learned, of Bolthorn, Bestla's sire,
and a draught obtained
of the precious mead
drawn from Odhraerir.

Then I began to bear fruit,
and to know many things,
to grow and well thrive:
word by word
I sought out words,
fact by fact
I sought out facts.[6]

---

6   From "Odin's Rune Song" in Thorpe's translation of *Saemund's Edda*.

THE GIANT BUILDER

as told by Abbie Farewell Brown

AGES AND ages ago, when the world was first made, the gods decided to build a beautiful city high above the heavens, the most glorious and wonderful city that ever was known. Asgard was to be its name, and it was to stand on Ida Plain under the shade of Yggdrasil, the great tree whose roots were underneath the earth.

First of all they built a house with a silver roof, where there were seats for all the twelve chiefs. In the midst, and high above the rest, was the wonder-throne of Odin the All-Father, whence he could see everything that happened in the sky or on the earth or in the sea. Next they made a fair house for Queen Frigg and her lovely daughters. Then they built a smithy, with its great hammers, tongs, anvils and bellows, where the gods could work at their favourite trade, the making of beautiful things out of gold; which they did so well that folk name that time the Golden Age. Afterwards, as they had more leisure, they built separate houses for all the Æsir, each more beautiful than the preceding, for of course they were continually growing more skilful. They saved Father Odin's palace until the last, for they meant this to be the largest and the most splendid of all.

Gladsheim, the home of joy, was the name of Odin's house, and it was built all of gold, set in the midst of a wood whereof the trees had leaves of ruddy gold – like an autumn-gilded forest. For the safety of All-Father it was surrounded by a roaring river and by a high picket fence; and there was a great courtyard within.

The glory of Gladsheim was its wondrous hall, radiant with gold, the most lovely room that time has ever seen. Valhalla, the Hall of Heroes, was the name of it, and it was roofed with the mighty shields of warriors. The ceiling was made of interlacing spears, and there was a portal at the west end before which hung a great grey wolf, while over him a fierce eagle hovered. The hall was so huge that it had 540 gates, through each of which 800 men could march abreast. Indeed, there needed to be room, for this was the hall where every morning Odin received all the brave warriors who had died in battle on the earth below; and there were many heroes in those days.

This was the reward which the gods gave to courage. When a hero had gloriously lost his life, the Valkyries, the nine warrior daughters of Odin, brought his body up to Valhalla on their white horses that gallop the clouds. There they lived forever after in happiness, enjoying the things that they had most loved upon earth. Every morning they armed themselves and went out to fight with one another in the great courtyard. It was a wondrous game, wondrously played. No matter how often a hero was killed, he became alive again in time to return perfectly well to Valhalla, where he ate a delicious breakfast with the Æsir; while the beautiful Valkyries who had first brought him thither waited at table and poured the blessed mead, which only the immortal taste. A happy life it was for the heroes, and a happy life for all who dwelt in Asgard; for this was before trouble had come among the gods, following the mischief of Loki.

This is how the trouble began. From the beginning of time, the giants had been unfriendly to the Æsir, because the giants were older and huger and more wicked; besides, they were jealous because the good Æsir were fast gaining more wisdom and power than the giants had ever known. It was the Æsir who set the fair brother and sister, Sun and Moon, in the sky to give light to men; and it was they also who made the jewelled stars out of sparks from the place of fire. The giants hated the Æsir, and tried all in their power to injure them and the men of the earth below, whom the Æsir loved and cared for. The gods had already built a wall around Midgard, the world of men, to keep the giants out; built it of the bushy eyebrows of Ymir, the oldest and hugest of giants. Between Asgard and the giants flowed Ifing, the great river on which ice never formed, and which the gods crossed on the rainbow bridge. But this was not protection enough. Their beautiful new city needed a fortress.

So the word went forth in Asgard, "We must build us a fortress against the giants; the hugest, strongest, finest fortress that ever was built."

Now one day, soon after they had announced this decision, there came a mighty man stalking up the rainbow bridge that led to Asgard city.

"Who goes there?" cried Heimdal the watchman, whose eyes were so keen that he

Loki and Svadilföri

could see for a hundred miles around, and whose ears were so sharp that he could hear the grass growing in the meadow and the wool on the backs of the sheep. "Who goes there? No one can enter Asgard if I say no."

"I am a builder," said the stranger, who was a huge fellow with sleeves rolled up to show the iron muscles of his arms. "I am a builder of strong towers, and I have heard that the folk of Asgard need one to help them raise a fair fortress in their city."

Heimdal looked at the stranger narrowly, for there was that about him which his sharp eyes did not like. But he made no answer, only blew on his golden horn, which was so loud that it sounded through all the world. At this signal all the Æsir came running to the rainbow bridge, from wherever they happened to be, to find out who was coming to Asgard. For it was Heimdal's duty ever to warn them of the approach of the unknown.

"This fellow says he is a builder," quoth Heimdal. "And he would fain build us a fortress in the city."

"Ay, that I would," nodded the stranger. "Look at my iron arm; look at my broad back; look at my shoulders. Am I not the workman you need?"

"Truly, he is a mighty figure," vowed Odin, looking at him approvingly. "How long will it take you alone to build our fortress? We can allow but one stranger at a time within our city, for safety's sake."

"In three half-years," replied the stranger, "I will undertake to build for you a castle so strong that not even the giants, should they swarm hither over Midgard – not even they could enter without your leave."

"Aha!" cried Father Odin, well pleased at this offer. "And what reward do you ask, friend, for help so timely?"

The stranger hummed and hawed and pulled his long beard while he thought. Then he spoke suddenly, as if the idea had just come into his mind. "I will name my price, friends," he said; "a small price for so great a deed. I ask you to give me Freyja for my wife, and those two sparkling jewels, the Sun and Moon."

At this demand the gods looked grave; for Freyja was their dearest treasure. She was the most beautiful maid who ever lived, the light and life of heaven, and if she should leave Asgard, joy would go with her; while the Sun and Moon were the light and life of the Æsir's children, men, who lived in the little world below. But Loki the sly whispered that they would be safe enough if they made another condition on their part, so hard that the builder could not fulfil it. After thinking cautiously, he spoke for them all.

"Mighty man," quoth he, "we are willing to agree to your price – upon one condition. It is too long a time that you ask; we cannot wait three half-years for our castle; that is equal to three centuries when one is in a hurry. See that you finish the fort without help in one winter, one short winter, and you shall have fair Freyja with the Sun and Moon. But if, on the first day of summer, one stone is wanting to the walls, or if anyone has given you aid in the building, then your reward is lost, and you shall depart without payment." So spoke Loki, in the name of all the gods; but the plan was his own.

At first the stranger shook his head and frowned, saying that in so short a time no one unaided could complete the undertaking. At last he made another offer. "Let me have but my good horse to help me, and I will try," he urged. "Let me bring the useful Svadilföri with me to the task, and I will finish the work in one winter of short days, or lose my reward. Surely, you will not deny me this little help, from one four-footed friend."

Then again the Æsir consulted, and the wiser of them were doubtful whether it were best to accept the stranger's offer so strangely made. But again Loki urged them to accept. "Surely, there is no harm," he said. "Even with his old horse to help him, he cannot build the castle in the promised time. We shall gain a fortress without trouble and with never a price to pay."

Loki was so eager that, although the other Æsir did not like this crafty way of making bargains, they finally consented. Then in the presence of the heroes, with the Valkyries and Mimer's head for witnesses, the stranger and the Æsir gave solemn promise that the bargain should be kept.

On the first day of winter the strange builder began his work, and wondrous was the way he set about it. His strength seemed as the strength of a hundred men. As for his horse Svadilföri, he did more work by half than even the mighty builder. In the night he dragged the enormous rocks that were to be used in building the castle, rocks as big as mountains of the earth; while in the daytime the stranger piled them into place with his iron arms. The Æsir watched him with amazement; never was seen such strength in Asgard. Neither Týr the stout nor Thor the strong could match the power of the stranger. The gods began to look at one another uneasily. Who was this mighty one who had come among them, and what if after all he should win his reward? Freyja trembled in her palace, and the Sun and Moon grew dim with fear.

Still the work went on, and the fort was piling higher and higher, by day and by night. There were but three days left before the end of winter, and already the building was so tall and so strong that it was safe from the attacks of any giant. The Æsir were delighted with their fine new castle; but their pride was dimmed by the fear that it must be paid for at all too costly a price. For only the gateway remained to be completed, and unless the stranger should fail to finish that in the next three days, they must give him Freyja with the Sun and Moon.

The Æsir held a meeting upon Ida Plain, a meeting full of fear and anger. At last they realized what they had done; they had made a bargain with one of the giants, their enemies; and if he won the prize, it would mean sorrow and darkness in heaven and upon earth. "How did we happen to agree to so mad a bargain?" they asked one another. "Who suggested the wicked plan which bids fair to cost us all that we most cherish?" Then they remembered that it was Loki who had made the plan; it was he who had insisted that it be carried out and they blamed him for all the trouble.

"It is your counsels, Loki, that have brought this danger upon us," quoth Father Odin, frowning. "You chose the way of guile, which is not our way. It now remains for you to help us by guile, if you can. But if you cannot save for us Freyja and the Sun and Moon, you shall die. This is my word." All the other Æsir agreed that this was just. Thor alone was away hunting evil demons at the other end of the world, so he did not know what was going on, and what dangers were threatening Asgard.

Loki was much frightened at the word of All-Father. "It was my fault," he cried, "but how was I to know that he was a giant? He had disguised himself so that he seemed but a strong man. And as for his horse – it looks much like that of other folk. If it were not for the horse, he could not finish the work. Ha! I have a thought! The builder shall not finish the gate; the giant shall not receive his payment. I will cheat the fellow."

Now it was the last night of winter, and there remained but a few stones to put in place on the top of the wondrous gateway. The giant was sure of his prize, and chuckled to himself as he went out with his horse to drag the remaining stones; for he did not know that the Æsir had guessed at last who he was, and that Loki was plotting to outwit him. Hardly had he gone to work when out of the wood came running a pretty little mare, who neighed to Svadilföri as if inviting the tired horse to leave his work and come to the green fields for a holiday.

Svadilföri, you must remember, had been working hard all winter, with never a sight of four-footed creature of his kind, and he was very lonesome and tired of dragging stones. Giving a snort of disobedience, off he ran after this new friend towards the grassy meadows. Off went the giant after him, howling with rage, and running for dear life, as he saw not only his horse but his chance of success slipping out of reach. It was a mad chase, and all Asgard thundered with the noise of galloping hoofs and the giant's mighty tread. The mare who raced ahead was Loki in disguise, and he led Svadilföri far out of reach, to a hidden meadow that he knew; so that the giant howled and panted up and down all night long, without catching even a sight of his horse.

Now when the morning came the gateway was still unfinished, and night and winter had ended at the same hour. The giant's time was over, and he had forfeited his reward. The Æsir came flocking to the gateway, and how they laughed and triumphed when they found three stones wanting to complete the gate!

"You have failed, fellow," judged Father Odin sternly, "and no price shall we pay for work that is still undone. You have failed. Leave Asgard quickly; we have seen all we want of you and of your race."

Then the giant knew that he was discovered, and he was mad with rage. "It was a trick!" he bellowed, assuming his own proper form, which was huge as a mountain, and towered high beside the fortress that he had built. "It was a wicked trick. You shall pay for this in one way or another. I cannot tear down the castle which, ungrateful ones, I have built you, stronger than the strength of any giant. But I will demolish the rest of your shining city!" Indeed, he would have done so in his mighty rage; but at this moment Thor, whom Heimdal had called from the end of the earth by one blast of the golden horn, came rushing to the rescue, drawn in his chariot of goats. Thor jumped to the ground close beside the giant, and before that huge fellow knew what had happened, his head was rolling upon the ground at Father Odin's feet; for with one blow Thor had put an end to the giant's wickedness and had saved Asgard.

"This is the reward you deserve!" Thor cried. "Not Freyja nor the Sun and Moon, but the death that I have in store for all the enemies of the Æsir."

In this extraordinary way the noble city of Asgard was made safe and complete by the addition of a fortress which no one, not even the giant who built it, could injure, it was so wonder-strong. But always at the top of the gate were lacking three great stones that no one was mighty enough to lift. This was a reminder to the Æsir that now they had the race of giants for their everlasting enemies. And though Loki's trick had saved them Freyja, and for the world the Sun and Moon, it was the beginning of trouble in Asgard which lasted as long as Loki lived to make mischief with his guile.

HOW THIASSI CAPTURED LOKI

as told by Mary Litchfield

ODIN, Loki and another god set out upon a journey. The road lay through thickets, where they could scarcely make their way, and up steep hills; so that fatigue and hunger at last compelled them to stop. They threw themselves down on the edge of a field where some oxen and cows were grazing. Loki, whose appetite was always keen, suggested that one of the oxen would make a good meal. In a few moments the creature was captured and killed. While Loki was preparing the meat for boiling, the other gods brought boughs and small trees to make the fire. Then they retired into the shade.

Loki watched the fire with delight. The red flames sent their forked tongues up around the huge iron kettle, the steam rose in clouds, and the water hissed as the pot boiled over. He laughed gleefully, and cried, "Burn, fire, hot and high, and cook us a dinner fit for gods!" And he threw on more wood.

Soon it was time for the meat to be done. So Loki found a forked stick and fished out a piece, which he examined and tasted. To his astonishment, it was as raw as when first put in. He stared at the pot, and at the fire, with a look of bewilderment. Then he piled on wood till the fire roared.

In a little while he again tried the meat, but with no better success: it was still raw. The fooler of others, the knave among the gods, was at his wits' end. He gazed at the kettle, exclaiming, "The evil powers are at work! The frost giants have got into the fire!"

Just then he heard a mocking laugh, which seemed to come from above. And looking up, he saw an enormous eagle that returned his gaze with a steady stare that nearly put him out of countenance; for the eagle's eyes shone like stars.

Finally the bird spoke: "Well, friend Loki, why doesn't your meat cook? You seem to lack skill, or else bad luck attends you. Give me my share of the feast, and the meat will be done soon enough."

Loki was already out of patience, and the words of the eagle made him angry. "Stop your jeering," he cried, "or you shall feel the might of an Asa!"

Then the mocking laugh sounded again; and the eagle said, "Keep your threats, Loki, for those whom you can reach. You are 'little pot, soon hot', unlike your big kettle there."

The god was now thoroughly enraged; but knowing himself to be helpless, he controlled his anger, and said mildly, "Suppose we stop our jesting and get the meat cooked. Take your portion, if it will help matters. The meat is bewitched."

Upon this, the eagle swooped down, and seizing a leg and two shoulders of the ox – which might certainly be called the lion's share – was about to fly off with them, when Loki, seeing what he had done, quickly seized a long pole that was lying near, and struck him a hard blow. But, alas for Loki! The pole stuck fast to the eagle's back, and the other end would not leave Loki's hands. The bird sailed up into the air, carrying with him the astonished god. He soon lowered his flight, so that Loki was dragged over trees and sharp rocks till he howled with pain.

After a while the eagle, tired from carrying so heavy a burden, stopped on the crest of a hill and looked around at his captive. The latter was nearly dead with fright and pain; but he got his breath in a moment, and began to beg for mercy.

The bird listened to him, and laughed his mocking laugh again, as he said, "Don't you know me yet, Loki? Do you forget your friends so soon?"

Loki stared for a moment, and then cried, "You are Thiassi!"

"Of course I am Thiassi," replied the bird. "I did not think you could be so easily deceived. But I have no desire to harm you. It is the other gods I wish to reach – those who pronounced in favour of the dwarfs.

"Dearly shall they pay for the insult done to us! They shall yet feel the edge of the fatal sword!" And the eagle's eyes flashed.

"How can I serve you? " said Loki. "Do not count me an enemy, I beg of you."

"I know you of old, Loki," replied Thiassi; "and I know that mischief delights you whether the victim be friend or foe. The game I am going to play will be after your

Thiassi carrying Loki

own heart. Idunn,[1] as you may remember, is a kinswoman of mine. I saw her the day the judgment was pronounced – the first time in years. I fancy she must at times weary of the charming monotony of Asgard, and long for a peep at her giant kin. I intend to gratify her unspoken wish. In so doing I shall cause some discomfort to my enemies, the fair gods. Their brows will soon be wrinkled and their forms bent, if the charming Idunn, with her golden apples, leaves them."

At the picture of the happy gods careworn and wrinkled, Loki laughed aloud, forgetting his recent pain. "Thiassi, your plan is excellent, and I will help you carry it out!" he cried. "But in return promise to do one thing for me. It will hurt your foes more than the loss of Idunn."

"Speak," said Thiassi. "I will do anything for revenge."

"To injure the gods most deeply," said Loki, "one must hurt Baldr. He is their idol. They worship him, as though he were a higher kind of being – even Odin does. I do not share this enthusiasm, as you may imagine. So far as I can remember, I have never

---

1 Idun or Idunn, usual form, sometimes Anglicized as Iduna; the goddess of early spring.

found anyone in all the nine worlds to admire; and I hate their meek Baldr as much as they love him. Some time ago their favourite had bad dreams, and had them so repeatedly that Father Odin and Mother Frigg, becoming alarmed for their darling, called a council of the gods, consulted wise giants, and finally made all living creatures, and even the plants and metals, swear not to harm Baldr.

"Not satisfied with this, Odin visited the lower world and consulted a Vala, long since dead, concerning his son's fate. I overheard him telling Frigg about his journey. He rode on Sleipnir. When he was near the cave that leads to the world of torture, a dog met him, and barked furiously – a bad sign, I believe. I lost what came next. But at last he reached the grave of the Vala, who, I assure you, was not pleased to be disturbed after her long sleep under the dew and the snow. She told Odin that a place was being made ready for his son in the lower world. I did not hear all, but I am convinced that Odin got little comfort from his journey.

"This meek Baldr now parades his superiority by standing up as a mark for the Æsir. He thinks himself safe now; but I happen to possess a little secret of great importance. Mother Frigg, in her innocence, confided it to me, taking me for a beggar-woman. When she made all creatures swear not to harm Baldr, there was one she neglected because it was so weak, so powerless to harm anyone. It was the little shrub mistletoe that grew on the eastern side of Valhalla. Of course, I at once secured the plant, and here it is." And Loki drew from his bosom the withered mistletoe.

"Now for my plot, friend Thiassi! From this weak plant, you, with your wonderful skill, can make an arrow that will kill the fair-faced Baldr, the darling of the gods." Thiassi pondered a moment, and then said, "I would not do so much to please you. You are in my power, and I can compel you to help me whether you will or not. But I like your plot. Give me the mistletoe. The arrow I make shall be deadly; for it shall be poisoned by hate. I have already made a fatal sword whose edge the Æsir shall feel some day. Mimir the wise took it from me while I slept. I know not where it is; but it will surely fulfil the end for which it was made."

Before they parted, it was arranged that Loki should entice Idunn outside the walls of Asgard, so that Thiassi could carry her off to Jötunheim. And Thiassi, as he flew towards the north, bore with him the withered mistletoe from which he was to make the fatal arrow.

THIASSI CARRIES OFF IDUNN

as told by Mary Litchfield

 IDUNN was sitting in her garden one afternoon, when Loki wandered in, and threw himself down on a low seat. All the gods came often to see Idunn. It was a charming spot, this garden, with its fountains and bowers, and Idunn was a lovely goddess. But the gods had another reason for coming – they came to get Idunn's apples.

These apples were the most delicious fruit. They were golden in colour, just touched with red; and one seemed to be eating whatever one liked best in the world when one tasted them. And there was something still more wonderful about them. Whoever ate them, if old, grew young, and if tired, felt as fresh as though just awaking from sleep. Because of these virtues, the Æsir prized them above all their treasures.

As Loki sat there, Thor, the strong god of thunder, came for refreshment after fighting with the giants in Jötunheim. Baldr the Beautiful came; for even he needed to taste the wondrous fruit. In a moment Tyr walked up, strong and cheerful in spite of the loss of his right hand. Later came Frigg and some of the other goddesses. And all talked pleasantly together as they strolled about among the trees, or rested in the shady bowers.

Loki chuckled as he thought to himself, "How will mighty Thor feel when his hand is too weak to fling the hammer at the giants? And how will Frigg look, when she can no longer stand erect, queen of the gods, but must totter about, a bent old woman? Oh, it will be rare sport!"

The gods came and went, and the shadows lengthened, but still Loki lingered. When at last he was alone with Idunn, he said carelessly, "Let me see one of your apples a moment; I wish to examine it." After looking at it critically, he smelt it and tasted it. Then he said, in a decided tone, "Yes, it is as I thought; those apples are much finer!"

Idunn looked at him with an expression of bewilderment.

He continued: "The gold is brighter, and the red a more beautiful shade; and the flavour is beyond that of anything I have ever tasted. I would never have believed there were apples better than yours in all the nine worlds, had I not seen and tasted them myself."

As Loki talked, amazement and anxiety were pictured on Idunn's face; and when he finished, she burst out, "Why, Loki! What do you mean? There cannot be apples better than mine! All the gods say so – even Odin himself; and he has been everywhere."

"So the gods say, but how can they prove it?" said Loki, smiling. "I have seen finer ones and have eaten them. They grow just beyond the wall and river of Asgard, in a grove. No one would ever think of looking there for apples. I found them by chance, the other day, when searching for something I had lost."

"O Loki!" cried Idunn, with tears in her eyes. "I cannot bear to think there are apples better than mine. I wonder if they are also apples of youth?"

"As to that I cannot say," replied the god; "I only know that I was quite exhausted when I came upon them, and the first taste made me feel as fresh as a lark. So I presume they surpass your apples in their youth-giving and refreshing qualities as well as in other things. However," he added, seeing Idunn's look of distress, "you need not be alarmed. I know how sad a thing it would be for you to lose your position as sole possessor of the wonderful fruit. And so, out of consideration for you, I have spoken to no one of my discovery. You, charming Idunn, who have always been so gracious and so generous in dispensing your treasure, you alone must have the new golden apples!"

"How kind you are, Loki!" said Idunn, the tears still in her eyes. "Won't you get me some of them, so that I can see for myself how much better they are? I feel as though I cannot wait!"

"Let me think," said Loki, meditatively; "I must start for Midgard tonight. How can I manage it?" Then in a moment, he added: "I should not have time to get the apples and come back here with them; but this is what we can do. You go with me. I shall have time to see you safely into Asgard again; and once inside the walls, you will not mind coming home alone. Or, if you prefer, you need not go outside at all. I will get the apples while you wait inside. You can decide which you would rather do when we get there."

The unsuspecting Idunn prepared to go with Loki. She threw over her shoulders a light green mantle, her flower-embroidered robe showing gaily below it. Then she said, "I wonder whether I had better hide my apples, or take them with me."

"Oh, take them," Loki replied, "and then you won't be worrying about them."

They started off, Idunn half frightened and half pleased at the prospect of so long a trip; for she rarely left her own home, and had not been beyond the walls for years.

"I wonder what Bragi will say if he comes back and does not find me," she murmured. "I hope I shall get home before dark!" And she was almost ready to turn back. But Loki was very gay, and his jests and stories soon made her forget her fears.

After a long walk – and gods walk much faster than mortals – they reached the walls of the city.

"Now," said Loki, "which will you do? Stay here or go with me? It makes no difference, unless you would like to see the apples growing; and possibly you may not fancy being left by yourself in such a lonely spot."

"I am a little afraid to stay here alone," said Idunn, "and I should like to see the apples growing. I think I will go with you. There can't be any harm in my going if it is so near."

Loki helped her over the high wall. And, strange to say, there was a curious boat just where they got down on the other side. Had Idunn been in the least suspicious, she might have wondered at its being there. She did not stop to wonder, but stepped in with Loki. The boat went over the rushing river with its dangerous mists as easily as a swan crosses a smooth lake. For, in truth, it was no common boat, but one made by Thiassi for this very occasion.

As they stepped on shore, Loki pointed to a grove of trees, saying, "The apples are in there."

They went toward the grove, and soon the long rays of the afternoon sun were shut out by the trees and the thick undergrowth.

Idunn was tired, and said in a weary tone, "Is it much further, Loki?"

"No, only a little way," he replied; "but if you are tired, here is a nice mossy seat in this little opening. You can rest a few moments, while I go and get some water from the spring that bubbles out from the other side of the large rock yonder."

Idunn sat down, holding her basket of golden apples in her lap, and leaning her beautiful head against a tree. Looking up through the opening, she could see the white clouds sailing lazily in the deep blue sky. In a few moments her eyes closed, and she was fast asleep.

She was suddenly awakened by a whirring sound, and when she looked up, the blue sky had vanished, and a dark thunder cloud was coming rapidly towards the opening.

"Loki! Loki! Come back!" she cried.

There was no reply, and the cloud came swiftly down. As it touched the tree-tops, a few feathers fell into Idunn's lap; and as she gazed in fear and wonder, it took the form of a large eagle with shining eyes. Idunn screamed with terror, and sank back helpless upon the mossy seat. As the eagle seized her, a small arrow dropped upon the ground near where she had been sitting.

Idunn was borne rapidly away toward Jötunheim. When the eagle was so far up that he looked no larger than a swallow, a form appeared from behind the large rock, and Loki, a look of malicious triumph in his face, picked up the mistletoe arrow.

THE GODS GROW OLD

as told by Mary Litchfield

 **WHEN** Bragi,[1] Idunn's husband, came home that night, his wife was not at the gate to meet him with her happy face and her golden hair. He searched for her in the garden and in the palace; he enquired of the people about the place, of her maidens and finally of all the gods and goddesses; but no one had seen Idunn since they left her, as well and as happy as ever, in the afternoon. Thor did remember that when he left the garden, Loki sat on a low seat, half asleep.

"Thor," said Bragi, "if there is mischief, Loki is at the bottom of it! Let us find him!"

They went to Loki's home, and found him sitting by a large fire. He seemed surprised to see them, and opened his eyes wide when they told him that Idunn had disappeared.

"That is very strange!" said he. "I was the last one to leave the garden, and everything was all right then. I have seen nothing that looked suspicious near Asgard." Then, after a short pause, he added, "I did notice a large eagle as I walked home; but I do not think he came very near."

Loki seemed so innocent that they could not suspect him of knowing anything more of Idunn's whereabouts than they did.

That night and the day following, and every day, the search for Idunn was kept up; but no trace of her could be found. Great sorrow was felt throughout the city of the gods. With her, the warm summer, which never left that happy home, departed, giving place to dreary November. Cold winds blew from the north, chilling the delicate flowers. A look of decay came over the hills and fields; and yellow leaves fell from the trees, leaving them bare and brown. Vines that had always borne fruit and flowers during every month of the year rattled their lifeless stems against the tottering walls. A cold breath touched the ponds and streams, covering them with a thin coating of ice.

---

1   The god of poetry; the best of *skalds*.

And the birds left for the first time the summer-land of the gods and flew toward the south. The sun itself shone with a pale, sickly light, scarcely warming the blood even at noon. And the nights grew long and dark.

But if nature mourned for Idunn, the gods felt her loss still more. As long as she gave them her golden apples, weariness and old age could not touch them. Each one enjoyed the fullest life. After Idunn's going, Odin, the wise All-Father, grew older: his beard became as white as the beard of Mimir, and there was a look of sadness on his kingly features. Stately Frigg, the mother of the gods, became wrinkled and grey. Even Thor, the mighty thunder-god, showed signs of age, although his spirit was unbroken. Matters were fast becoming so desperate that Odin decided to call a council to consider what could be done to remedy the evil.

The gods and goddesses assembled – those whose homes were far away as well as those who lived in Asgard. All came except Heimdall, who could not leave his post as guardian of the bridge Bifröst. Niord came from his wind-blown palace by the sea, "on a strand outside of which the swans sing", in the western part of the lower world. Freyr came from Alfheim, the land of the light elves; and Vidar the Silent left his lonely vine-grown home, deep in the mountains, at the call of Odin. All came, and all showed the signs of weakness and of age.

One alone was absent when the Æsir were assembled. Loki was not there. And it had been remarked that he seemed little affected by Idunn's absence. His hair gleamed red and fiery, unmixed with grey; and his restless eyes had lost none of their brightness.

All were silent until Odin arose, feeble yet majestic, his countenance lit by the wisdom for which he had paid so dear. "My children," he said, "Idunn has gone, and the world is growing old. The gods grow feeble. Winter winds already howl around Gladsheim. The shadow of death is upon us. Who will bring back Idunn?"

As he finished speaking, a god rose from his seat. He was one that was not often among them; for he lived far from Gladsheim, near the high wall of Asgard.

"May I speak, father Odin?" he asked.

Odin bowed his head; and he went on: "I heard in my lonely home that Idunn had gone; but it did not occur to me until recently that certain strange things I had seen could have anything to do with her disappearance. What I have to say may unravel the mystery.

"One afternoon, rather late, I climbed the high wall which is near my castle, and looked down upon the dark Asgard river. Suddenly my attention was attracted by a peculiar whirring sound, such as is made by a bird in rapid flight. Looking up, I saw an enormous eagle carrying something in his talons. I could not tell what. I watched him until he became a mere speck and at last vanished on the northern horizon. On looking down, I saw another strange sight – a singular boat that crossed the dangerous river as easily as though it had been a common stream. Night was coming on, but I could distinguish Loki as he leaped from the boat, concealed it amid some bushes, and then quickly climbed the wall and went towards the centre of Asgard. I do not see Loki here, and that makes it seem still more probable that he had something to do with Idunn's disappearance."

As the god sat down, Thor sprang up, the old fire flashing in his eyes. "Odin," he cried, "shall not Bragi and I seek Loki? He shall pay dearly for it, if he is the cause of all this!"

Odin gave his permission, and they left the hall. They soon came back bringing Loki, who put on an air of careless gayety, ill-suited to the occasion. Odin calmly repeated what the god had said, and Loki, finding it useless to deny that he had crossed the river with Idunn, told the whole story: how he was captured by Thiassi on the day when he suddenly disappeared while travelling with Odin and the other god, and how to save himself he had betrayed Idunn into Thiassi's hands.

Thor advanced towards the guilty god with his hammer raised; and then Loki, thoroughly frightened, begged for mercy, saying he would surely find a way to bring back Idunn, if they would only give him time.

"Loki," said Odin, sternly, "we will give you time; but if at the end of one month you do not bring her back, you shall be put to death with terrible tortures."

Loki asked for a moment's silence, that he might think of some way in which he could outwit Thiassi. This was not an easy thing to do, because the latter was a great magician. He buried his face in his hands, but in an instant looked up, saying: "I have a plan, but a disguise is needful. If Freyja will lend me her falcon plumage, I will match Thiassi with his eagle feathers." And he laughed gleefully at the thought of outwitting the great artist. Then he continued: "I know some runes by which I can change Idunn into a nut, so that I can easily bring her back. Let me go; I long to fool the giant who trailed me over the rocks and trees."

The gods looked coldly on Loki; for they saw that his chief desire was not to rescue Idunn.

A little later a falcon might have been seen flying towards the desolate mountains of Jötunheim.

LOKI BRINGS BACK IDUNN

as told by Mary Litchfield

THE home where Thiassi now lived was in Jötunheim, a land inhabited by giants. This region was separated from Midgard by the great river, Ocean, and lay between Asgard and the lower world. After the gods pronounced in favour of the dwarfs, Thiassi came here and shut himself up in a grim stone castle, where he spent most of his time making weapons to be used against his foes. His dwelling was near the sea, and rose like a jagged mountain amid the grey rocks of the coast. A few stunted trees and bushes clung to crevices in the rocks, and in the valleys were scanty patches of coarse grass. A dull twilight reigned always, and over all hung a leaden sky.

Loki's flight was very rapid, and it did not take him long to reach Jötunheim, although it was so far from Asgard. As he neared the coast, he made large circles, flying far out to sea. There he saw Thiassi fishing – a most fortunate thing; for had he been at home, it would have been hard for Loki to reach Idunn without his knowledge.

Next he circled around the castle, coming nearer each time, and examining it carefully on every side. As he passed by one of the rude openings that served as windows, a gleam like sunshine shot out into the grey twilight. Loki alighted on the edge and looked in. There, on a rough couch, lay Idunn, sleeping. There were tears on her cheeks, and the basket of golden apples was clasped firmly to her breast. Her long yellow hair filled the bare room with radiance, and the light streamed out through the opening, making a little sunshine in that land of gloom. In her sleep she sobbed, and Loki caught the word "Asgard".

Losing no time, he flew into the room, and taking his proper shape, gently awakened her. She stared vacantly for a moment, and then fear and reproach pictured themselves upon her face. "False Loki!" she cried. "Why are you here? Through you I am a prisoner far from Asgard!"

"Do not waste time in reproaches, fair Idunn," said Loki. "I alone can save you; and I will, if you do as I bid you." Seeing the look of distrust still on Idunn's face, he added: "You may trust me; for if I do not carry you safely back to Asgard, I am to be put to death with dreadful tortures. All the gods are growing old, and Asgard is desolate. You may thank me, after all; they will think more of you than ever when you go back with your precious fruit."

So Idunn's fears were quieted; and as there was no other hope of escape, she decided to trust herself to Loki.

"Now," said he, "grasp your basket firmly, while I say some runes that will make you as small as a nut. In that way, I can carry you safely home." Idunn did as Loki bade her, although she trembled as she felt herself growing smaller and smaller. Loki again put on his falcon plumage, and in an instant was flying towards the south. He felt quite sure that Thiassi had not seen him.

He flew more swiftly than the hawk that seeks his prey, or than the eagle that returns to her young. From time to time he turned his head to see if Thiassi, in his eagle plumage, were following him. He had gone so far that the huge castle could hardly be seen on the horizon, when above it appeared a small black speck. It was Thiassi.

The race now began in earnest. Both flew steadily for hours, high up among the leaden clouds of the cheerless sky. Loki put forth his godlike strength, and Thiassi his giant force. At last the glittering towers of Asgard gleamed against the southern sky. Would Loki reach it in time?

In the city of the gods all was expectancy from the time Loki set forth. Wily and skilful they knew him to be, but Thiassi was fierce and powerful. The result was doubtful. The gods gathered near the wall of Asgard that looked toward Jötunheim. Odin, only, sat apart, far up in his High Seat. In the dim distance he could see the mountains and castles of Jötunheim. Cold winds blew, and Asgard looked cheerless in the waning light of the afternoon. Beautiful as ever rose the stately homes of the gods; but the plains of Ida lay brown and bare, except for a few scattered snowflakes. No summer sounds were in the air; for all the birds had flown, and even the song of the cricket was hushed.

Odin kept his eyes fixed upon the distant mountains, that he might catch the first glimpse of the returning Loki. He knew, better than anyone else, the vast importance of

Loki's errand; and his face, grown old and lined with care, expressed the great anxiety he felt. His ravens had not come back from their daily journey, but the two wolves lay at his feet, watching his countenance with eager eyes: near him stood Hermod, the messenger god.

Suddenly a gleam shot across the stern face of the All-Father, and a light like the fire of battle shone in his eyes. "Go, Hermod!" he cried. "Tell the Æsir, Loki comes! But stay," he added; and then in a moment, "say Thiassi, clad in his eagle plumage, pursues him! The gods will soon see them from the wall of Asgard."

Hermod hastened to tell the gods, and more eagerly than ever did they scan the northern horizon for the wished-for sight.

Hermod went back to Odin, but soon rejoined the gods, saying: "The All-Father gave Loki important instructions before he left Asgard. He bade him lower his flight as he neared the city, for the mists of the rushing river cannot harm him; but should Thiassi fly low enough, they will burst into flames, since he is now an enemy to the Æsir."

In a moment two specks could be seen in the north. Then what suspense was felt by the gods! Every eye was fixed upon the swiftly advancing birds. The Æsir showed signs of weakness, as they stood there, and looked older by years than when Idunn left them. The chill wind whistled through their garments; but they did not feel it. Nor

did they see the sun as he sank wearily behind the dark clouds in the west, as though he too had grown old. One thought alone filled all their minds – could Loki hold out? Would he reach Asgard before the powerful Thiassi, who seemed to be gaining upon him?

Nearer and nearer comes Loki. His flight is very swift; and although the eagle is gaining upon him, the distance is short. Will he remember to lower his flight? Yes; he suddenly swoops down as he nears the dark river. The gods stand breathless, with outstretched arms. Thiassi, too, lowers his flight, forgetting the dangerous mists. At last Loki is over the river and over the wall, and now he falls exhausted to the ground. But the gods heed him not, so intently are they watching Thiassi. As the eagle flies over the river, the mists burst into fierce flames, burning his wings; but he can neither stop nor turn back, his headway is so great. His scorched wings bear him over the wall, and he falls dead in their midst.

As the gods turn to look at Loki, they behold him in his natural form, and near him stands Idunn, radiant with joy, holding out with her old gracious smile her basket of golden apples. The sun, as though suddenly grown young, sends a parting stream of radiance from the west; the clouds are turned to gold; Gladsheim glitters in the distance. Youth and summer have come back to the home of the gods.

SKADI'S CHOICE

as told by Abbie Farewell Brown

 THE giant Thiassi, whom Thor slew for the theft of Idunn and the magic apples, had a daughter, Skadi, who was a very good sort of girl, as giantesses go. Most of them were evil-tempered, spiteful and cruel creatures, who desired only to do harm to the gods and to all who were good. But Skadi was different. Stronger than the hatred of her race for the Æsir, stronger even than her wish to be revenged for her father's death, was her love for Baldr the Beautiful, the pride of all the gods. If she had not been a giantess, she might have hoped that he would love her also; but she knew that no one who lived in Asgard would ever think kindly of her race, which had caused so much trouble to Baldr and his brothers. After her father was killed by the Æsir, however, Skadi had a wise idea.

Skadi put on her helm and corselet and set out for Asgard, meaning to ask a noble price to pay for the sorrow of Thiassi's death. The gods, who had all grown young and boyish once again, were sitting in Valhalla merrily enjoying a banquet in honour of Idunn's safe return when Skadi, clattering with steel, strode into their midst. Heimdal the watchman, astonished at the sight, had let this maiden warrior pass him upon the rainbow bridge. The Æsir set down their cups hastily, and the laughter died upon their lips; for though she looked handsome, Skadi was a terrible figure in her silver armour and with her spear as long as a ship's mast brandished in her giant hand.

The nine Valkyries, Odin's maiden warriors, hurried away to put on their own helmets and shields; for they would not have this other maiden, ten times as huge, see them meekly waiting at table, while they had battle-dresses as fine as hers to show the stranger.

"Who are you, maiden, and what seek you here?" asked Father Odin.

"I am Skadi, the daughter of Thiassi, whom your folk have slain," answered she, "and I come here for redress."

At these words the coward Loki, who had been at the killing of Thiassi, skulked low behind the table; but Thor, who had done the killing, straightened himself and clenched his fists tightly. He was not afraid of any giant, however fierce, and this maiden with her shield and spear only angered him.

"Well, Skadi," quoth Odin gravely, "your father was a thief, and died for his sins. He stole fair Idunn and her magic apples, and for that crime he died, which was only just. Yet because our righteous deed has left you an orphan, Skadi, we will grant you a recompense, so you shall be at peace with us; for it is not fitting that the Æsir should quarrel with women. What is it you ask, O Skadi, as solace for the death of Thiassi?"

Skadi looked like an orphan who was well able to take care of herself; and this indeed her next words showed her to be. "I ask two things," she said, without a moment's hesitation: "I ask the husband whom I shall select from among you; and I ask that you shall make me laugh, for it is many days since grief has let me enjoy a smile."

At this strange request the Æsir looked astonished, and some of them seemed rather startled; for you can fancy that none of them wanted a giantess, however handsome, for his wife. They put their heads together and consulted long whether or not they should allow Skadi her two wishes.

"I will agree to make her laugh," grinned Loki; "but suppose she should choose me for her husband! I am married to one giantess already."

"No fear of that, Loki," said Thor; "you were too near being the cause of her father's death for her to love you overmuch. Nor do I think that she will choose me; so I am safe."

Loki chuckled and stole away to think up a means of making Skadi laugh.

Finally, the gods agreed that Skadi should choose one of them for her husband; but in order that all might have a fair chance of missing this honour which no one coveted, she was to choose in a curious way. All the Æsir were to stand in a row behind the curtain which was drawn across the end of the hall, so that only their feet were seen by Skadi; and by their feet alone Skadi was to select him who was to be her husband.

Now Skadi was very ready to agree to this, for she said to herself, "Surely, I shall know the feet of Baldr, for they will be the most beautiful of any."

Amid nervous laughter at this new game, the Æsir ranged themselves in a row behind

Skadi, daughter of Thiassi

the purple curtain, with only their line of feet showing below the golden border. There were Father Odin, Thor the thunderer and Baldr his brother; there was old Njörd the rich, with his fair son Freyr; there were Týr the bold, Bragi the poet, blind Höd and Vidar the silent; Vali and Ull the archers, Forseti the wise judge and Heimdal the gold-toothed watchman. Loki alone, of all the Æsir, was not there; and Loki was the only one who did not shiver as Skadi walked up and down the hall looking at the row of feet.

Up and down, back and forth, went Skadi, looking carefully; and among all those sandalled feet there was one pair more white and fair and beautiful than the rest.

"Surely, these are Baldr's feet!" she thought, while her heart thumped with eagerness under her silver corselet. "Oh, if I guess aright, dear Baldr will be my husband!"

She paused confidently before the handsomest pair of feet, and, pointing to them with her spear, she cried, "I choose here! Few blemishes are to be found in Baldr the Beautiful."

A shout of laughter arose behind the curtain, and forth slunk – not young Baldr, but old Njörd the rich, king of the ocean wind, the father of those fair twins, Freyr and Freyja. Skadi had chosen the handsome feet of old Njörd, and thenceforth he must be her husband.

Njörd was little pleased; but Skadi was heartbroken. Her face grew longer and sadder than before when he stepped up and took her hand sulkily, saying, "Well, I am to be your husband, then, and all my riches stored in Noatûn, the home of ships, are to be yours. You would have chosen Baldr, and I wish that this luck had been his! However, it cannot be helped now."

"Nay," answered Skadi, frowning, "the bargain is not yet complete. No one of you has made me laugh. I am so sad now, that it will be a merry jest indeed which can wring laughter from my heavy heart." She sighed, looking at Baldr. But Baldr loved only Nanna in all the world.

Just then, out came Loki, riding on one of Thor's goat steeds; and the red-bearded fellow cut up such ridiculous capers with the grey-bearded goat that soon not only Skadi, but all the Æsir and Njörd himself were holding their sides with laughter.

"Fairly won, fairly won!" cried Skadi, wiping the tears from her eyes. "I am beaten. I shall not forget that it is Loki to whom I owe this last joke. Some day I shall be quits with you, red joker!" And this threat she carried out in the end, on the day of Loki's punishment.

Skadi was married to old Njörd, both unwilling; and they went to live among the mountains in Skadi's home, which had once been Thiassi's palace, where he had shut Idunn in a prison cell. As you can imagine, Njörd and Skadi did not live happily ever after, like the good prince and princess in the story-book. For, in the first place, Skadi was a giantess; and there are few folk, I fancy, who could live happily with a giantess. In the second place, she did not love Njörd, nor did he love Skadi, and neither forgot that Skadi's choosing had been sorrow to them both. But the third reason was the most important of all; and this was because Skadi and Njörd could not agree upon the place which should be their home. For Njörd did not like the mountain palace of Skadi's people – the place where roaring winds rushed down upon the sea and its ships. The sea with its ships was his friend, and he wanted to dwell in Noatûn, where he had greater wealth than anyone else in the world – where he could rule the fresh sea-wind and tame the wild ocean, granting the prayers of fisher-folk and the seafarers, who loved his name.

Finally, they agreed to dwell first in one place, then in the other, so that each might be happy in turn. For nine days they tarried in Thrymheim, and then they spent three in Noatûn. But even this arrangement could not bring peace. One day they had a terrible quarrel. It was just after they had come down from Skadi's mountain home for their three days in Njörd's sea palace, and he was so glad to be back that he cried:

"Ah, how I hate your hills! How long the nine nights seemed, with the wolves howling until dawn among the dark mountains of Giant Land! What a discord compared to the songs of the swans who sail upon my dear, dear ocean!" Thus rudely he taunted his wife; but Skadi answered him with spirit.

"And I – I cannot sleep by your rolling sea-waves, where the birds are ever calling, calling, as they come from the woods on the shore. Each morning the sea-gull's scream wakes me at some unseemly hour. I will not stay here even for three nights! I will not stay!"

"And I will have no more of your windy mountain-tops," roared Njörd, beside himself with rage. "Go, if you wish! Go back to Thrymheim! I shall not follow you, be sure!"

So Skadi went back to her mountains alone, and dwelt in the empty house of Thiassi, her father. She became a mighty huntress, swift on the skis and ice-runners which she strapped to her feet. Day afterday she skimmed over the snow-crusted mountains, bow in hand, to hunt the wild beasts which roamed there. "Ski-goddess" she was called; and never again did she come to Asgard halls. Quite alone in the cold country, she hunted hardily, keeping ever in her heart the image of Baldr the Beautiful, whom she loved, but whom she had lost forever by her unlucky choice.

GEIRRÖD AND AGNAR

as told by Sarah Powers Bradish

I. THE LITTLE PRINCES

ODIN and Frigg from their lofty seat often looked down into the palace of a certain king. They came to be very fond of the two little sons of this king.

One day the little princes went out in a boat to fish. A storm came up suddenly. Their boat drifted out to sea. It was thrown by the waves on an island, where an old couple lived in a cottage. The old people, who were Odin and Frigg in disguise, took the princes home and cared for them.

They were very kind to both children; but the elder, Geirröd, was Odin's favourite; while the younger, Agnar, appealed to Frigg's motherly heart. They lived contentedly with their friends during the cold, dark winter. But when the long, bright days of spring came, and the sea grew calm, and the skies were blue, they longed for their father and mother and the playmates in their distant home. So Odin gave them a boat, and sent them away under favourable winds.

They made the voyage quickly; but, when the boat touched the shore of their native land, Geirröd leaped out; and, pushing the boat back into the water, left Agnar to the mercy of the waves.

Geirröd hastened to his father's house, where he was welcomed as one brought back from the dead. But little Agnar drifted away to the land of the giants.

He fell into the hands of good giants, who gave him a home, where he lived many years. When he became a man, he married a young giantess, and settled down to stay with his benefactors. But, after a time, he longed to see his own people. So he built a boat, and sailed away over the sea.

He found his native land; but the king, his father, was dead; and his brother, Geirröd, was king instead. Geirröd received his brother as a subject, and made him a servant in his father's palace.

II. THE SELFISH KING

FRIGG had been watching the two princes all the time. She saw how unjust and cruel Geirröd was to his younger brother. Odin knew only of Geirröd's success, and admired him as a great king.

One day, when Odin and Frigg were sitting on their lofty seat, looking out over the world, Odin said, "See what a mighty king Geirröd has become, while your little pet, Agnar, is nothing but the little husband of a giantess."

"True," said Frigg, "but Geirröd, with all his grandeur, is mean and selfish. He is even guilty of inhospitality, an offence most shameful in a Norseman. But Agnar, in his poverty, is still kind and generous."

Odin said he would test Geirröd's hospitality. He put on his cloud cloak and broad-brimmed hat, and set out to visit Geirröd. In the meantime, Frigg sent word to Geirröd that he must be watchful, because a wicked enchanter was approaching his palace.

When Odin arrived, he gave his name as Grimnir, and refused to tell who he was or whence he came. Thinking that the old man must be the wicked enchanter, Geirröd ordered his servants to bind him and place him between two fires that were burning on the floor of his great hall. The fires scorched the old man's face, but did not burn his garments. There he stayed eight days and nights, in silence and without food. He would have had nothing to drink, but for Agnar, who secretly brought him a drinking horn containing a refreshing draught.

III. AGNAR'S REWARD

AT the close of the eighth day, Geirröd was seated on his throne, enjoying the sight of his guest's sufferings, when the old man began to sing. The song was faint at first, but grew louder and louder, until the chains dropped away, the fires went out, and the feeble old man stood up in the beauty and strength of a god. In his song, Odin told how the king, who had been so blessed by the gods, should fall by his own sword.

Geirröd was about to slay the unwelcome guest; but, as he rose from his seat, his foot slipped, and he fell on his sword, as had just been foretold.

Odin placed Agnar on the throne, and blessed him with great wealth and happiness.

Frigg, the wife of Odin, spins thread

FREY

as told by Sarah Powers Bradish

I. FREYR'S GIFTS

NJORD had two children: a boy named Freyr, and a girl named Freyja. Freyr was the god of sunlight and gentle showers, and Freyja was the goddess of beauty.

It was the custom in the Northland to make every child a present when he cut his first tooth. When Freyr's first tooth came through, the gods gave him Elfheim, the home of the light elves, or fairies, for a tooth gift. The little god was king of Elfheim, or Fairyland, and lived there with his tiny subjects, whenever he could be spared from Asgard. The little creatures loved their king, and obeyed his lightest wish; and he was much happier there than in his mother's icy palace at Thrymheim.

Little Freyr soon became a tall, handsome youth. Then the gods gave him a magic sword, which, as soon as it was drawn from the sheath, won every battle of its own accord. But Freyr seldom used it, except to fight the cruel frost giants, who dreaded his glittering sword, because it held the softening power of the sunbeams.

Freyr had also a fine horse called Blodughofi. This horse could go through fire and water.

II. FREYR IN ODIN'S SEAT

FREYR was very busy during the summer months. He looked after the sunshine and the warm showers. Sometimes he helped his father direct the gentle winds. But, when the sunshine went away, Freyr's work went away too. The dark northern winter seemed very long to the young god.

One day, when wandering about the city of Asgard, he came to the foot of Odin's lofty throne, Hlidskialf. No one ever ascended this throne, except the All-Father and his wife Frigg. But the gods all knew that the whole world could be seen from its summit. Freyr wanted to see the whole world. So he began to climb the steps. No one saw him, and he soon came to the top. He sat down on Odin's seat, and looked toward the north. He saw a maiden standing in the doorway of her father's castle. She was the most beautiful maiden in the world. She was Gerda, daughter of Gymir, the frost giant. When she raised her hand to open the door, many-coloured lights blazed in the northern sky, and shot out toward the southern heavens. Frery longed to win Gerda for his bride.

But he knew that her father, Gymir, would never consent to their marriage, because Gymir was cousin to Thiassi, the storm giant, whom the gods had killed in Asgard. Slowly and sadly Frey left Hlidskialf. He walked up and down the city streets as usual; but he was silent, and never joined in the sports of the young gods. At the feasts his cup of sparkling mead was left untasted. No one could find out any reason for his strange conduct. His father, Njörd, was greatly alarmed, and sent for his stepmother Skadi, who was then at their winter home in Thrymheim.

III. HOW SKADI HELPED HER STEPSON

SKADI came at once. She, too, was greatly concerned about her stepson. She knew there must be some trouble; but he refused to tell his stepmother what it was that made him so miserable.

One day Skadi called Skirnir, their most trusted servant. She said: "Skirnir, you played with Freyr in childhood; you were his friend in youth; you have served him faithfully in manhood. He trusts you. Find out his secret, and help him in his trouble. You alone can save his life."

Skirnir went to Freyr, and learned from him the story of his visit to the lofty throne, how he had seen Gerda, the most beautiful of maidens, and how he wished to make her his wife. This, Freyr said, could never be done, because Gerda was the daughter of Gymir, the frost giant, who hated him. Besides, the giant's castle was surrounded by a barrier of fire, and at the approach of any stranger the flames leaped as high as the sky.

"If that is all," said Skirnir, "I can win fair Gerda for you. Lend me your horse, Blodughofi, and give me your magic sword to be my own."

Freyr lent him the horse and gave him the sword; and Skirnir promised to hasten on his journey.

Freyr sent eleven golden apples and a magic golden ring, as gifts to Gerda. Still Skirnir lingered.

One day, as Freyr was sitting near a pool, his face was reflected in the surface. Skirnir caught the reflection in his drinking horn, and covered it carefully. Then he started on his journey; for, with these three gifts, the golden apples, the magic ring and the portrait of his handsome master, he was confident that he could win the beautiful maiden.

IV. SKIRNIR'S JOURNEY

SKIRNIR rode away to the land of the frost giants as fast as Freyr's swift steed could carry him. As he came near Gymir's castle, he was stopped by the terrible howling of the giant's watchdogs, Winter Winds.

He spoke to the shepherd who was watching the flocks in Gymir's fields. The shepherd said: "You cannot reach the castle. Even if you pass the dogs, it will be impossible for you to enter the gates, for the whole place is surrounded by fire. Don't you see how the flames light up the sky?"

Still Skirnir pressed on. He put spurs to his horse, and outran the dogs. Then he gave rein to Blodughofi, who plunged into the fire and bore his rider safely to the steps of Gymir's castle. A servant opened the door and led the daring horseman into the presence of Gerda.

Skirnir offered her the golden apples and the magic ring, and showed her the portrait of his master, which he had taken from the pool. But she said, "My father has gold enough for me," and she did not care at all for the picture.

Then Skirnir threatened to cut off her head with the magic sword. He did not intend to do this, because he knew his master would not want a bride without a head. But she was not at all frightened. Then he cut runes in his stick, so that he could weave a magic spell about her. He told her that she would be married to an old frost giant, who would keep her hidden in his cold, dark castle. He kept on cutting runes until she said: "Perhaps it would be better to marry handsome young Freyr and live in Asgard, than to marry an ugly old frost giant and live in a dungeon. When spring comes, I will be Freyr's bride."

Skirnir hurried back toward Asgard. But Freyr, impatient to learn how he had succeeded, met him at Elfheim, and there, among the fairies, he learned that, when the trees budded and flowers bloomed and grass grew green again, he might go to the land of Buri, or green groves, to meet his bride.

Gerda met him in the land of Buri, as she had promised. They were married, and went to Freyr's new palace in Asgard, where they lived happily ever after, and blessed the homes of married pairs who wished to live without strife.

V. PEACE-FRODI

FREYR had a son named Frodi. Frodi lived in Midgard, or the world of men. He was good and wise, and men were glad to have him for a king. He began to reign in Denmark, when there was peace throughout the world. That was the time when Christ was born in Bethlehem. He was called Peace-Frodi.

He had a pair of magic millstones. They could grind anything he wished, but there was no one in all his kingdom strong enough to turn them. He went to visit the king of Sweden, and saw, near the royal palace, two captive giants, who were eight feet tall. They could lift heavy weights, and hurl javelins to a great distance. He thought they would be able to turn his enchanted millstones. He bought the giants from their master. Their names were Menia and Fenia.

As soon as they came to Denmark, Frodi led them to the magic stones and bade them grind gold, peace and prosperity. They turned the stones easily, and sang as they worked:

> "Let us grind riches for Frodi!
> Let us make him happy

> In plenty of substance
> On our magic Quern."[1]

They worked on hour after hour until their backs ached, and they could hardly stand from weariness. There was peace in the world, prosperity in the land, and the king's treasuries were filled with gold. The king had always been kind and gentle, but he was maddened by the sight of the gold, and, when the women begged to be allowed to rest, he sharply bade them work on. "Rest as long as the cuckoo is silent in the spring," he said. "Alas," they replied, "the cuckoo is never silent in the spring." When they could work no longer, he gave them as much time to rest as would be required to sing one verse of their song.

But while Frodi slept, they changed their song, and began to grind an armed host, instead of gold.

---

1 Longfellow's translation, *Grotta Savngr*.

They sang:

> "An army must come
> Hither forthwith,
> And burn the town
> For the prince."[2]

A viking landed with his soldiers, and surprised the Danes. He defeated Prodi's army, and carried away the Danish treasure. He took Menia and Fenia, with their magic millstones, on board his own ship. He ordered them to grind salt, instead of gold. But he was as greedy as Frodi had become. He kept the giants at work until they were worn out. But they had already ground so much salt that its weight caused the ship to sink, and all on board perished. As the millstones sank, the water, rushing in, gurgled through the holes in the millstones, and made a great whirlpool. This whirlpool is off the northwestern coast of Norway, and is still known as the Maelstrom.

The salt dissolved and made all the water very salt, and the water of the sea is salt to this day.

VI. YULETIDE

SKIRNIR kept Freyr's magic sword for his own, and he did not bring back the borrowed horse, Blodughofi. So, for a long time, Freyr had neither sword nor horse. The dwarfs kindly supplied him with a swift steed, as we shall see. This was a boar called Gullinbursti, or Golden-bristle, which was, ever after, Freyr's constant attendant. The golden bristles gave light, and were the rays of the sun; or, some say, the golden grain, which grew in Midgard, at the sun-god's bidding. Gullinbursti, by tearing up the earth with his tusks, taught men to plough. Sometimes Freyr rode on his back; and sometimes he harnessed him to his chariot, from which he scattered fruits and flowers, as he drove over the world. Sometimes his sister Freyja rode with him in his chariot, and helped him in blessing men with fruits.

---

2 Longfellow's translation, *Grotta Savngr*.

Boar's flesh was eaten at the festivals sacred to Freyr. The roasted boar's head, crowned with laurel and rosemary, was brought into the dining room with great ceremony. The head of the household laid his hand upon it, and swore that he would be faithful to his family and true to his promises. Then everyone present followed his example.

The boar's head was then carved by a man of good character and great courage.

The helmets of Northern warriors were often ornamented with boars' heads, because that emblem of the conquering sun-god was supposed to strike terror into the hearts of the enemy.

The longest night of the year was called Mother Night. It was a time of rejoicing, because the sun was then beginning his homeward journey. It was called Yuletide, or Wheeltide, because the sun was thought to be like a wheel rolling across the sky. A large wooden wheel was taken to the top of a high hill, wound well with straw, set on fire, and, when all ablaze, rolled down into the water, because the sight of the burning wheel suggested the sun's course through the heavens.

This Yule festival was kept in England for many years. As it occurred in the month of December, it was easily united with the festivities of Christmas.

At Yuletide, a huge log was brought in and burned in the great fireplace. It was a bad omen if it did not burn all night. In the morning, the charred pieces were gathered and saved to light the Yule log the following year.

FREYJA

as told by Sarah Powers Bradish

I. HOW GOLD CAME TO BE HIDDEN IN THE ROCKS

 FREYJA was the daughter of Njörd. She was the goddess of beauty. She had golden hair and blue eyes. She had a commanding figure, and was clad in flowing robes. She wore a corselet and helmet, and carried a shield and a spear. She rode in a chariot drawn by two large grey cats. She admired brave men, and liked nothing so well as to reward a deed of valour. She visited battle-fields, to choose, from the slain heroes, those who should be her guests at Folkvang, her palace in Asgard. The other slain warriors were taken to live with Odin in his great hall, Valhalla.

Folkvang was always filled with heroes and their wives and sweethearts. Northern women often rushed into battle, or fell upon swords, or were burned on the funeral pyre with their beloved dead, hoping that their courage and devotion would win Freyja's favour, so that they might enjoy the society of their husbands and lovers in Folkvang.

Freyja was married to Odur, god of the summer sun. They had two daughters, who were so beautiful that all lovely and precious things were called by their names. All beautiful creatures were said to belong to Freyja. Butterflies were called Freyja's hens. Freyja was always happy when she had her family together. But her husband, Odur, was too fond of travel. He always spent the winter in the Southland. This was a source of great grief to Freyja. Once he left home without saying where he intended to go. Freyja was heartbroken. She wept constantly. All nature wept with her. Hard rocks softened when her tears fell upon them! They opened their stony hearts to receive every shining drop, and hid it as pure gold. The sea treasured her tears, and threw them back upon the shore as clearest amber.

After long waiting, Freyja went in search of her husband. She wandered through every part of the earth, weeping as she went. The earth kept her tears as fine gold. This is the reason that gold is found in all parts of the world.

II. WHY NORTHERN BRIDES WEAR MYRTLE

FREYJA found the missing Odur far away in the sunny Southland. He was sitting under a flowering myrtle tree, watching the fleecy clouds change colour in the rays of the setting sun. He was well and happy, and did not think how lonely his beautiful wife must be in the dark winter of the frozen North. But when she stood before him, he was glad to see her; and she was almost beside herself with joy.

Hand in hand, they returned to the Northland. Birds sang and flowers bloomed along their pathway, and spring followed their footsteps. Freyja wore a garland of myrtle leaves; and to this day Northern brides wear myrtle wreaths instead of orange blossoms.

III. BRISINGA-MEN

FREYJA was forid of ornaments and jewels. One day, when passing through the land of the dark elves, she saw four dwarfs at work on a wonderful necklace. It was called Brisinga-men. It was an emblem of the fruitfulness of the earth. It was made of the most precious gems, which sparkled like stars. She begged the dwarfs to give her the beautiful necklace.

They said it should be hers if she would promise to grant them her favour forever. This was a great deal to ask; but the necklace was a masterpiece of art, and priceless in value. So she promised all they asked, and they clasped the necklace about her neck. She wore it night and day. Once she lent it to Thor, when he went to the land of the giants; and once she lost it; but she always regarded it as her choicest treasure.

IV. HEIMDAL SAVES BRISINGA-MEN

THE gods had just finished the rainbow bridge, which they built to connect Asgard with Midgard and Urdar Fountain. This bridge was made of fire, air and water. These

  71

three things can still be seen in the rainbow; fire in the red, air in the blue and water in the green. All the gods except Thor passed over the bridge every day, on their way to their council chamber at Urdar Fountain. Thor was still obliged to harness his goats to his iron chariot and drive in the old way, because they all feared that his heavy tread and the heat of the lightnings, which always attended him, would destroy the beautiful bridge. They feared also that the giants would take advantage of the new bridge to force an entrance into Asgard. So they decided to appoint a guard for the rainbow bridge.

Heimdal was the son of the nine wave daughters of Ægir, ruler of the sea. His nine mothers fed him on the strength of the earth, the moisture of the sea and the heat of the sun. He grew very fast and could do many remarkable things. He could hear the grass growing in the fields, and the wool on the sheep's backs. He could see at a distance of one hundred miles, as clearly by night as by day. He needed less sleep than a bird. He was very beautiful, and had gold teeth which flashed when he smiled. He was always clothed in pure white, and carried a glittering sword.

The gods decided to take Heimdal to Asgard, and then they appointed him to be guard of the rainbow bridge. They built him a palace on the highest point of the bridge, and gave him a golden-maned horse called Gull-top, and a wonderful trumpet called Giallar-horn. The trumpet was to be used only when he saw the enemies of the gods approaching. Then he would know that the Twilight of the Gods was near at hand, and the sound of the trumpet would arouse all creatures in heaven and earth and the land of the mist.

One night Heimdal was disturbed by the sound of footsteps in the direction of Freyja's palace. He soon found that the noise was made by Loki, who had just changed himself into a fly, in order to enter Freyja's chamber window. Once within her room, he resumed his usual form, and tried to take the precious necklace, Brisinga-men, from her neck, as she lay asleep. Her head was turned so that he could not reach the clasp without waking her. He stepped back and muttered magic runes. He began to shrink, and shrank and shrank until he shrank into the size and shape of a flea. Then he made his way under the cover and bit Freyja's side until she turned in her sleep. He became Loki again, unclasped the necklace, and stole away.

Heimdal mounted Gull-top and galloped over the rainbow bridge. He met the robber just outside the gates of Asgard, and drew his sword. Quick as thought, Loki became a faint blue flame. Heimdal changed himself into a cloud, and poured torrents of rain upon the flame. Then the flame became a great white bear, which drank up the water. The cloud became a bear also, and the two bears fought until Loki slipped into the water in the form of a seal. Heimdal became a seal, and pursued Loki until he gave up the necklace, which was sent back to Freyja so quickly that she never knew it had been stolen.

But Heimdal had been badly hurt in his struggle with Loki. Idunn came and bound up his wounds, and healed them with a golden apple.

LOKI AND SKYRMSLI

as told by Sarah Powers Bradish

I. THE PEASANT'S TROUBLE

LOKI was not always bad. He was fond of mischief, and his pranks soon grew into practical jokes. But he was kind sometimes, and generous when it did not cost too much.

Once a peasant played chess with a giant. The stake was the peasant's only son. The giant, whose name was Skrymsli, won the game, and said he would come for the boy the next day. But if the parents could hide the child so that he could not find him, he would give up his claim.

In their distress the peasants prayed to Odin for help. The All-Father came to earth, changed the boy into a kernel of wheat, hid him in an ear of grain in a large field, and assured the anxious father and mother that the giant would not be able to find him.

The following day the giant came, searched the house, but failed to find the boy. Then he took the scythe and mowed the field of wheat. He selected a handful of ears, and chose the ear that held the enchanted kernel. He was picking out the right grain of wheat when Odin, hearing the cry of the child, snatched him from the giant's hand and returned him to his parents. But, he said, they must take care of him now, for he could do no more.

Then they called on Odin's brother, Hoenir, who changed the boy into down, and hid him in the breast of a swan that was swimming in a pond nearby.

When the giant came, he went to the pond, caught the swan, bit off its head, and was about to swallow the down, when Hoenir wafted it away from his lips and sent it into the cottage. He gave the boy back to his parents, but declared that he could do no more.

II. LOKI COMES TO THE RESCUE

IN despair, they invoked the aid of Loki, who came at once, carried the boy out to sea, changed him into a tiny egg, and hid him in the roe of a flounder. Then he rowed back to shore, where he found the giant preparing for a fishing excursion.

"Come with me," said Loki. "I will show you a good place to fish for herring."

But Skrymsli wanted to fish for flounders, and thought he could do very well alone. Loki, therefore, insisted on going with him. Skrymsli rowed as far as he wished to go, baited his hook, caught several fish, and, at last, drew up the flounder in which Loki had concealed the precious egg. Then he rowed back to shore. Loki snatched the egg and set the boy on the landing, saying, "Run home now; but go through the boat house and shut the door behind you."

The frightened boy obeyed, and the giant rushed after him. But Loki had fixed a spike in the boat house so that it should strike Skrymsli's head as he passed through. He fell; and Loki, following, cut off one of his legs.

To Loki's surprise, the pieces grew together again. He saw that it was the work of magic, but he cut off the other one, and threw a flint and steel between the leg and the body, which broke the charm, and the giant died.

The thankful parents ever after regarded Loki as the greatest of the three gods, because he had delivered them from their trouble, while the others had only helped them for a little time.

LOKI MAKES TROUBLE BETWEEN THE ARTISTS[1] AND THE GODS

as told by Mary Litchfield

LOKI once cut off the beautiful hair of Sif, Thor's wife. And when Thor found out that Loki was the culprit, he threatened to crush every bone in his body if he did not repair the mischief he had done. Loki promised to do this, for he feared Thor. He went at once to the sons of Ivaldi for help. They were famous artists, these sons of Ivaldi. Many were the weapons and ornaments they had made for the gods. They quickly spun some golden hair for Sif. This wonderful hair grew to her head, becoming like her own hair, except that it was gold.

Besides this they sent a spear to Odin, and a ship to Freyr. The spear was sure to hit the mark each time; and the ship, called *Skidbladnir*, could be folded up like a napkin and put into the pocket when not in use: it would always have fair winds.

It has been told how Odin, on his journey to Mimir's well, passed near the singular hall of the dwarf Sindri and his brothers. One day when Loki was near there, it occurred to him that it would be an easy matter to stir up jealousy between the two sets of artists. Perhaps, too, he could, at the same time, make trouble between them and the gods.

One of Sindri's brothers was outside the castle as Loki came near; and the latter at once began to talk with him about the making of beautiful and curious objects. Loki described the wonderful gifts the sons of Ivaldi had sent the gods by him, and then said, "I will wager my head that you cannot make, you and your brothers, three treasures as good as those I have just described!"

---

1   The artists, the productive forces of vegetation.

The dwarf was angry at this disparagement of their skill, and hurried into the hall to tell Sindri of Loki's wager. Loki went in after him, and repeated what he had said, adding that, if they would make the gifts, the gods themselves should be the judges, and pronounce upon the merits of the rival artists.

They went to the smithy, which was in another part of the castle. The heat from the great furnace was so intense that even Loki, who loved fire, could hardly bear it. Sindri took down a pigskin that was hanging on the wall, and putting it into the furnace, told his brother Brok to blow the bellows, and not stop blowing until he took the pigskin out.

Loki stepped behind some iron-work, and instantly a fly appeared upon the hand of Brok as he was blowing the bellows, and stung him badly; but he bore the pain, and did not stop blowing. Very soon Sindri drew from the furnace a boar with golden bristles.

Next, Sindri put some gold into the furnace, giving his brother the same directions. This time the fly settled upon Brok's neck, and stung him so that he lifted his shoulders, but still kept on blowing. The result was a ring.

The next time, Sindri put iron into the furnace; and as Brok was blowing, the fly buzzed angrily, and settling between his eyes, stung him so severely on the eyelid that the blood ran down into his eye, and he could not see. He stopped blowing for an instant and brushed the fly away. A hammer came out this time; but the handle was a little too short.

The three treasures were now finished, and Loki left the dwarfs, naming a day for them to meet him in Asgard. He set out at once for the home of the sons of Ivaldi. One of these artists, Thiassi, who was as large as a giant, and who was said to have great skill as a magician, went with him to Asgard. The treasures made by the last-named artists were already in the possession of the god.

It was a fair morning in the beautiful city when the judgment was to be pronounced. Gladsheim glittered in the sun. Upon its marble walls were pictured the wonders of the nine worlds, and the mighty deeds of gods and heroes in the earliest times. Mimir's mysterious valley, Urd's pure fountain, Mount Hvergelmir with its ice-cold spring – all could be seen on those vast walls. And there, too, were Surt's fiery dales below the realms of Urd, the dark, misty regions of Niflheim and even the world of torture with its stagnant sea. In other pictures lived again the strange beings and huge, uncouth monsters of the ancient world.

The great hall of Gladsheim was to be the scene of the judgment. "There was Odin's throne. Over it rose the arch of Bifröst, so like the real bridge that it sent forth fitful flames. Behind the throne was a golden tree, representing Yggdrasil, the World Tree. The trembling leaves flashed in the sunlight that streamed in through the eastern openings. Sif, with her golden hair, sat near a table in the centre of the hall. And upon the table lay Odin's spear and Freyr's ship, made by the sons of Ivaldi.

The hour had come, and all eyes were turned toward the wide door, as Loki entered, accompanied by the enormous Thiassi. Loki's eyes sparkled with malicious pleasure; and, after making his reverence to Odin, he began talking gaily with the other gods. Thiassi came in awkwardly, as though unused to scenes of such grandeur and beauty. He saluted Odin and the greater gods, and then seated himself near Sif, who tried in vain to make him talk with her.

In a few moments, two diminutive figures appeared at the great entrance, and with them a large boar whose golden bristles dazzled the eyes. One of the dwarfs led the boar, while the other carried a small hammer. They paid their respects to Odin and the other gods in a peculiar, jerky manner, and then stood looking about with eager, inquisitive faces.

Odin rose, and said, in a deep voice, "We are here to decide upon the comparative skill of two sets of artists. They are both very skilful, and we are indebted to both for many rare and valuable gifts. It will be a difficult task to judge rightly, and we regret that Loki has made a judgment necessary. He, however, has promised to forfeit his head to Sindri and his brothers should the decision be in their favour."

He paused a moment, and all looked at Loki's head on which the stiff, red hair gleamed like fire; a smile lurked about his treacherous mouth, and his eyes twinkled.

Odin went on: "Let Thiassi state the peculiar properties and special merits of his work and that of his brothers; and then Sindri shall follow him, and speak of his gifts."

Thiassi rose up, a sullen, defiant look in his face; evidently he was forced to play a part ill-suited to him. Pointing to Sif, he said, "There is Thor's wife; you can all see her golden hair; it needs no praise." Taking up the spear that lay on the table, he went on,

Sif, the wife of Thor, was famed for her beautiful hair

"This is a good spear; it never misses the mark."

He next took from the table what seemed to be a white napkin; but as he held it, it bloomed and spread, until a ship appeared that grew larger and larger while he talked. "This ship is like no other," he said; "it can be made small enough to be carried in the pocket, or large enough to hold many men; it always has a fair wind."

Thiassi did not raise his eyes as he talked, but uttered every sentence as though it cost him an effort, making long pauses between. When he had finished speaking, he put the ship – which again looked like a napkin – upon the table, and with a sigh of relief sat down.

Sindri then came forward, his small, bright eyes peering everywhere, and his face eager and excited. His brother stood by his side, watching him intently and imitating all his gestures. Sindri pointed to the boar, saying: "This boar is worthy of higher praise than I can give him. You see how his golden bristles flash in the sunlight; but in the darkest night their brightness is the same. On this boar Freyr can ride through Nilfheim itself and still have day; and so swift is he that Sleipnir with his eight legs cannot outrun him. He can fly through the air, or skim over the sea, as his rider wills." As he said this, Sindri looked keenly at Thiassi, as though searching in his face for a look of conscious defeat.

He next drew from his bosom a ring,[2] and as he held it up in the sunlight, all could see the stones of many colours that sparkled in the setting of yellow gold. After gazing upon it for a moment as though fascinated by the beautiful object, Sindri spoke: "Were

---

2   The ring Draupnir, said to represent fertility.

this ring merely what it seems, it would need no words of mine; but it has a most marvellous property. Every ninth night, eight rings of equal size and beauty drop from it. There is not another treasure like it in all the nine worlds!" And Sindri put the ring down slowly, as though loath to part with it.

He then took the hammer from his brother. As he raised it, that it might be seen by all, it grew larger and larger, until the strength of both dwarfs was needed merely to hold it upright on the floor. With a look of triumph, Sindri cried: "This mighty hammer, called Mjöllnir, will be more useful to Thor when he meets the frost giants than his wife's golden hair! It will strike whatever it is aimed at, without fail, let the thing be large or small; and it will always return to the hand that flings it. Besides, it can be easily carried; for it can be made so small as to go into the pocket." He glanced at Loki as he added, "To be sure, the handle is a little too short."

As Sindri finished speaking, he and his brother looked around exultingly. Thiassi's face was expressionless, except for a haughty curl of the lip.

After a short pause, Odin rose, saying, "Let Sif come here, and let all the treasures be brought. We will examine them carefully and then pronounce our judgment."

While the gods were examining and consulting, the dwarfs watched them intently, their quick glance going from one to another; but Thiassi sat motionless, his head buried in his hands, apparently half asleep.

After a long consultation, silence was commanded. As Odin rose, every eye was fastened upon him. "It has been a hard task", he began, "to decide between such wonderful and useful gifts; but the decision must be given. We consider that the gifts made by the dwarfs, Sindri and his brothers, surpass in some respects those made by the sons of Ivaldi." Then, turning to Loki, he added, "Loki, you have forfeited your head; defend yourself as best you can!"

As Odin pronounced the judgment, a look of disappointment came into Thiassi's countenance, followed by an expression of fierce hatred, and bitter words escaped through his closed teeth. But the faces of the two dwarfs beamed with triumph and delight.

Sindri instantly sprang towards Loki, crying: "Your head belongs to me, you crafty god! Never again shall you turn yourself into a fly to spoil the work of Sindri! Your red hair will make bristles for my next boar!" He tried to seize Loki, while he drew from beneath his mantle a large knife.

The nimble god slipped from his grasp, however, and was instantly out of the hall and speeding like the wind over the plains of Ida.

Sindri called for help. Then Thor, laughing mightily at the frantic rage of the dwarf, took up his hammer, and cried in a voice of thunder, "Come back, you coward, or I'll try my hammer on you! Remember, it always hits!" The sound of Thor's voice produced a quick effect upon the runaway. He stopped, and came slowly back to the palace.

"Try your wits, now your heels have failed you," said Thor.

As the dwarf again approached Loki, prepared to cut off his head, the latter cried, "The head is yours, but not the neck!" Sindri stopped, and looked questioningly at the gods.

And they all said, "Loki is right! Not the neck!" "I am cheated," yelled the angry dwarf. And quickly seizing his brother's awl, he sprang toward Loki, and in an instant had sewed his lips together with a stout thread. Thereupon he and his brother left the hall. Thiassi was nowhere to be seen. He had disappeared while Sindri and Loki were disputing.

Well had Loki succeeded in stirring up jealousy and hatred where all had been peace and good-will. Thiassi had left the great palace, full of rage against the gods, and with plans for revenge already seething in his brain; while Sindri and his brother were equally angry at the loss of their wager and at the mirth of the gods at their expense. Besides, the bitterest jealousy was now aroused between the two sets of artists.

BALDR AND LOKI

as told by Mary Litchfield

NONE of the gods stood so high in the judgment hall of the dead as Baldr. While he was not famed as a fighter, or noted for his strength, his pure heart and righteous life made his judgment so clear that his decisions were absolutely just, and once spoken were never questioned.

Besides being a perfect judge, Baldr had other qualities that made everyone love him, even the strong and fierce. He was so full of kindness and sympathy that wherever he went the sun shone more brightly, and joy filled all hearts. From the first his life had been blameless, and his one aim had been to make others happy. The loveliness of his character was expressed in his face and in his form; he was the most beautiful of all the gods: indeed, they often called him Baldr the Beautiful; and in Midgard, men named the whitest flower they could find Baldr's brow.

But dearly loved as he was, Baldr had one deadly enemy – the false, vindictive Loki. Loki secretly hated all the gods, but none so much as Baldr. His fierce jealousy was stirred because Baldr held such a high place in Asgard. He hated him as the darkness hates the light, and as evil abhors good; and all his plots and schemes tended to one end – the destruction of this hated being. He had long hoped to bring about in some way the downfall of Odin and the ruin of Asgard; but first he would kill Baldr, for well he knew that nothing would cause such universal grief as his death.

BALDR'S DREAMS

as told by Mary Litchfield

BALDR, the beloved of the gods, had grown sad. His palace, the "Hall-of-broad-shining-splendour"[1], no longer gave him pleasure, and Nanna, his wife, could not comfort him. His voice was not heard in the council hall of the gods. Finally, after suffering long in silence, he confided to Odin and Frigg the cause of his sorrow. Every night, for a long while, he had been tormented by dreams which told him that the day of his death was not far distant, that he must leave the home he loved so well, to dwell in the under-world, apart from all his brethren. This thought made him so sad that the most joyous sights and sounds could not drive away his melancholy.

Odin at once called a council of all the gods and goddesses, and after conferring together, they sent some of their number to consult wise giants and other beings who knew more of the future than they themselves knew. All said that Baldr must die.

Then it was determined that from every living creature, and from all plants and metals, the oath not to harm Baldr should be exacted. Frigg received their oaths; and for days Asgard was thronged with the multitude of beings who came to take the solemn oath; until, finally, all had sworn.

But even this did not satisfy Odin. He resolved to go to the lower world and there seek information about the fate of his son. Sleipnir was saddled; and the All-Father took the same road that he had travelled when he visited the realms of Mimir in search of wisdom. Again he crossed the celestial bridge, going towards the north, and passed again the shining castle of Heimdall, the sleepless watchman. But this time Sleipnir bore him swiftly through the dark ice region and the gloomy land of the mountain giants.

As he was going toward the south, a dog met him, having come evidently from the cave near Mount Hvergelmir. The breast of the dog was bloody, and so were his

---

1   Breidablik.

throat and his lower jaw. He barked furiously at Odin, and howled long after he had passed; but the All-Father rode on, not heeding him.

In the eastern part of Mimir's realm, near the home of Delling, the elf of the dawn, Odin came to a dense forest[2] that he could not remember having seen before.

Yet the locality was familiar to him, and he knew that a little farther to the east was the grave of the Vala,[3] whom he wished to consult. After penetrating for a long distance into the silent depths of the wood, he came to a wall, higher than the one around Asgard. However, Sleipnir was not daunted by this obstacle; and in an instant Odin found himself in a large garden, from the midst of which rose a castle of singular beauty. The doors stood hospitably open: evidently no enemies were anticipated in this charmed spot, protected by forest and wall. The All-Father dismounted and entered.

Tall men and fair women walked about the castle, or talked together in small groups; and there were preparations as for some honoured guest whose coming was expected. At the upper end of the hall was a throne of gold, and near it benches, strewn with rings and ornaments; while on the table the mead stood ready; but it was covered with a shield.

As Odin entered, a graceful youth came forward, saying reverently, "Are you the

---

2   The forest and castle have been introduced into the Baldr myth on Rydberg's authority. Mimir saved some pure mortals at the time of an impending catastrophe, and placed them in this castle. Baldr came, after his death, and ruled over them. After the destruction of the world, at Ragnarök, Baldr was to rule, and these mortals, who had long served him, were to re-people the earth. These lines from "The Lay of Vafthrudnir" in *Saemund's Edda* refer to the subject:

> What mortals will live,
> when the great Fimbul-winter
> shall from men have passed?"
> Vafthrûdnir: "Lîf and Lîfthrasir;
> but they will be concealed
> in Hoddmimir's holt.
> The morning dews
> they will have for food.
> From them shall men be born.

3   A prophetess.

good king, and the wise, that Mimir has long promised us? You see that everything is in readiness, and your subjects await you with impatience."

And Odin answered, "I am indeed the king of a fair realm, but not your king. What is the name of him who is to rule over you? "

And the youth replied, "Mimir has not told us his name; but we know he is to come ere long; and he will be so noble and so pure that we shall all love him and serve him gladly."

Odin sighed, thinking of Baldr. After talking a little with the inhabitants of the castle, the All-Father left them, and made his way out of the forest.

Upon reaching the grave of the Vala, Odin chanted a magic song, compelling her to rise and answer him. She rose, and with a deathlike voice, said, "What man is this, to me unknown, who has for me increased an irksome course? I have with snow been decked, by rain beaten and with dew moistened; long have I been dead."

Odin did not give his real name, but said, "Vegtam is my name; I am Valtam's son. Tell me what I wish to know of the realms of death; from earth I call on you. For whom are those benches strewn o'er with rings, and those costly couches o'erlaid with gold?"

And the Vala answered, "Mead stands for Baldr brewed; over the bright potion a shield is laid; but the Æsir race are in despair. By compulsion I have spoken; I will now be silent."

Then Odin spoke again: "Be not silent, Vala; I will question you until I know all. I must yet know who will Baldr's slayer be; who will kill the son of Odin?"

The Vala said, "Hödur[4] will thither his glorious brother send; he will the slayer of Baldr be; he will kill the son of Odin. By compulsion I have spoken; I will now be silent."

However, Odin kept on questioning the Vala, until he asked something that revealed his true character; and she said, "Not Vegtam are you, as I before believed; you are Odin, lord of men! Homeward ride, Odin, and exult! Nevermore shall man thus visit me, until Ragnarök, the Twilight of the Gods, has come."

As she said this, the Vala sank back into the earth. And Odin rode again to Asgard, little comforted by what he had learned in the lower world.

---

4 Said to be blind. He may have represented winter, the slayer of summer.

THE MISTLETOE

as told by Abbie Farewell Brown

IT seemed as though death could not come near Baldr now; for all beings had sworn that they would not hurt him. The purest of the gods was surely saved. One day he chanced to be hit by an arrow; and, had another been in his place, the wound would have been fatal; but when the arrow touched him, it was blunted, and he was not hurt. Seeing this, some of the gods begged him to stand as a mark, while they amused themselves by hurling things at him; stones, spears, arrows and swords – nothing could harm him.

Loki passed by as the Æsir were enjoying this game, and fierce jealousy filled his heart when he saw Baldr so calm in a position that would have meant death to any other being. Taking the form of a decrepit old woman, Loki went to the mansion of Frigg, and asked alms. Frigg gave the seeming beggar something, and then asked what the gods were doing as she crossed the plains of Ida. The woman replied that they were throwing stones and weapons at Baldr, who stood there, unhurt.

"Ah!" exclaimed the queen. "They cannot harm him now, whatever his dreams may be, for I have exacted an oath from all things!"

"What!" said the woman, in a weak, shaky voice. "Have all things sworn not to harm him?"

"Yes," replied Frigg; "all things." Then she added carelessly, "There was one little shrub, the mistletoe, that grows on the eastern side of Valhalla, too weak to do any harm. I did not exact an oath from that."

Had Frigg been watching the old woman narrowly, she would have seen a look of triumph come into her face as she heard these words. But the queen of the gods scarcely noticed her, so absorbed was she in thinking of her dear son. And the beggar crept quietly out of the palace, and disappeared behind a clump of bushes.

In a few moments Loki was talking gaily with the gods on the plains of Ida, and

congratulating Baldr on his ability to stand unhurt amid a shower of weapons.

After dark, when all Asgard was asleep, a form might have been seen creeping stealthily towards the eastern side of Valhalla. It was Loki. When he found the slender mistletoe, he pulled it up by the roots and hid it in his bosom. From that time it never left him; and he was continually planning to get some skilful maker of weapons to form from it an arrow fatal to Baldr.

THOR AND THRYM

as told by Mary Litchfield

 THOR and Loki went to Jötunheim, in search of adventures. On the way home, night overtook them, and they lay down and slept on the edge of a forest. When Thor awoke, he felt for his hammer, and it was gone. His wrath was terrible. His fiery eyes and beard darted forth lightnings, and he struck his forehead as though he would awaken from a dream.

"Loki! Loki!" he cried. "Awake! Hear what I tell you! No one on earth or in heaven knows this! The Æsir's hammer is stolen!"

Loki's face showed surprise and bewilderment. "Stolen!" he replied. "Your hammer? That cannot be!"

Then they looked all about them in the grass; but no hammer could be found. "Thor," said Loki, "if I had Freyja's feather garment, I might find out where the hammer is. Do you think she would lend it to me?"

"The hammer must be found," said Thor; "if not, the giants of Jötunheim may prevail against us. Freyja will not refuse to help me."

Very early in the morning they entered the city and went to Freyja's palace. Many warriors feasted there each day – mortals who had died on the field of battle, and lovers who had been faithful unto death. As they entered the wide hall, Freyja rose to greet them. And seeing that Thor's brow was dark, she said, "What ails you, Asa-Thor? Some trouble is surely in your heart!"

And Thor answered, "The hammer, Mjöllnir, is stolen; it is in the hands of our enemies!"

"Mjöllnir stolen!" cried Freyja. "How can that be? Who could take the hammer from mighty Thor?"

"I slept," said Thor, "and when I awoke, the hammer was gone. I can tell you no more."

Freyja knew well what this meant. She pondered a moment, and then said, "How can I help you, Thor?"

"Will you lend me your feather garment?" said Thor. "With the help of that, the hammer may be found."

"I would give it to you if it were made of gold, and trust it to you if it were of silver," replied Freyja.

Thor and Loki left Freyja's palace, taking with them the feather garment. When they had gone a little way, they stopped, and Loki put on the plumage and flew towards Jötunheim. He flew so swiftly that the plumage rattled.

When he reached the icy land, he saw Thrym, the Thursar's lord, sitting on a mound, plaiting gold bands for his greyhounds, and smoothing his horses' manes. He knew Loki in spite of his disguise, and said, "How are the Æsir getting on? And the elves? Why have you come alone to Jötunheim?"

"The Æsir are in a bad plight; and so are the elves," Loki replied. "Where have you hidden Thor's hammer?"

Thrym laughed aloud, and said, "I have hidden Thor's hammer eight miles beneath the earth; and no man shall get it again unless he brings me Freyja for my wife."

When Loki heard this, he too laughed; for he was not sorry that Thor had lost his hammer.

He flew back to Asgard in the rattling plumage.

When he came near to Thor's palace, the latter saw him, and called out, "Have you had success as well as labour? Tell me your story from the air. The man who sits down leaves out too much; and he who lies down speaks falsely."

Loki answered from the air: "I have had labour and success. Thrym, the Thursar's lord, has your hammer. And no man can get it again unless he bring him Freyja for his wife." Then Loki flew to the ground and took off the feather garment; and he and Thor went to Freyja's palace.

When Freyja saw them, she welcomed them. Glad was she to get her falcon plumage again. But Thor's brow was dark, and he said, "Put on your bridal garments, Freyja; for we two must drive to Jötunheim."

Freyja did not understand him. So he told her that unless she became the wife of the giant Thrym, Mjöllnir would never be returned.

"Make ready, therefore, and come with me!" said Thor. "Or the giants will storm Asgard; and without the hammer, who can defend it against them?"

Freyja grew very angry as Thor talked. She was a mighty goddess, tall and powerful. And as her anger raged, the hall where they were trembled, and the great Brisinga[1] necklace shivered into pieces. "Never will I drive with you to Jötunheim!" cried Freyja. "Never will I be the bride of Thrym!"

Thor and Loki left the palace, and sought Odin, the wise All-Father. As soon as

---

1 A famous necklace made by the dwarfs.

Thor is disguised in Freyja's garments

Odin heard what had happened, he called a council of all the gods and goddesses; for the safety of Asgard depended upon their getting back Thor's hammer.

The council met. When many had spoken to no purpose, Heimdall arose. He had the wisdom of the Vanir.

"I think I know how we may get back the hammer," he said. "Let Thor be clothed in Freyja's garments; let keys jingle at his side; place precious stones on his breast; around his neck put the famed Brisinga necklace; and set a neat coif[2] on his head. Clad thus, he may deceive the giant, and get again the mighty hammer, Mjöllnir."

These words did not please Thor. He said, "The Æsir will call me womanish if I let myself be clad in bridal raiment."

Loki rejoiced secretly at the thought of Thor in woman's robes, and he said, "Speak not such words, Thor! The giants will soon rule in Asgard if you do not get back Mjöllnir."

The Æsir all agreed that Heimdall's words were wise. And after much urging, Thor allowed them to clothe him in Freyja's garments. They put the famed Brisinga necklace around his neck; keys jingled at his side; precious stones sparkled upon his breast; and on his head was a neat coif.

Loki was delighted, and he said to Thor, "I will go as your serving-maid; we two will drive to Jötunheim together."

The goats were found in their rocky pastures. They were quickly driven home, and hurried into the traces; and Thor and Loki leaped into the chariot. Like mountain winds let loose the goats sped on. The rocks were shivered, and the earth was in a blaze; for the mighty thunder-god drove in his wrath to Jötunheim.

When Thrym, the Thursar's lord, saw them coming, he was glad; for he thought the desire of his heart was won – Freyja was to be his wife.

"Rise up, Jötuns!" he cried. "And deck the benches; for they bring Freyja, Njörd's daughter, from Noatûn, to be my wife. Bring hither gold-horned cows and all-black oxen for the joy of the Jotuns. I had many necklaces and many treasures; but Freyja I lacked. With her I shall want nothing."

Early in the evening, many giants came to the wedding feast; and much beer was

---

2 A kind of cap.

brought out for them. Thor alone devoured an ox and eight salmon, and all the sweet-meats women like. He also drank three barrels of mead.

Thrym, the king of the giants, was astonished to see a woman eat so much, and he said, "Did you ever see such a hungry bride? I never saw a bride eat so much, nor a maiden drink so much mead!"

The crafty serving-maid sat close by, and she found a ready answer. She said to the Jotun, "For eight days Freyja has eaten nothing, she has longed so for Jötunheim."

Then the giant stooped to kiss the bride under her veil; but he suddenly sprang back, saying, "Why are Freyja's looks so piercing? Methinks fire comes from her eyes."

The crafty serving-maid found again fitting words.

"Well may her eyes be piercing; Freyja did not sleep for eight nights, so eager was she for Jötunheim."

The sister of the giant then came in. She, luckless woman, dared ask for a bride-gift. "Give me the ruddy rings from your hands," she said, "if you would gain my friendship and my love."

Thrym, the Thursar's lord, then said: "Bring in the hammer to consecrate the bride. Lay Mjöllnir on the maiden's knees. Unite us with each other in the name of Var."[3]

When he saw the hammer, Thor's heart leaped within him. Fierce joy filled his soul at the sight of Mjöllnir. He rose in his might and slew Thrym, the Thursar's lord, and crushed all the race of giants. Last of all he slew the giant's aged sister. For a bridal gift she got the stroke of Mjöllnir – blows of the hammer instead of many rings.

Thus did Odin's son get back his mighty hammer.

---

3   Var or Vor, the goddess of betrothals and marriages.

THOR AND SKRYMIR

as told by Mary Litchfield

 Thor sat in his great palace, of which Odin said, "Five hundred floors, and forty eke, I think, has Bilskirnir, with its windings. Of all the roofed houses that I know, is my son's the greatest." The thunder-god was uneasy; for his fierce, restless spirit could never be satisfied unless warring against the giants or seeking adventures in some distant land. He went from one hall to another, and at last, with a sigh, threw himself upon a couch that was covered with the skin of a wild beast. His powerful frame showed the muscles of an athlete, and his red beard gleamed like fire.

The walls of the hall where he lay were thickly hung with shields of rare workmanship, and between them were spears and swords that flashed in the sunlight. But the glories of his great palace had no charm for Thor now; he yawned, and cast wistful glances towards the north, as though he could discern even at that distance the dreary mountains of his foes.

Suddenly a form darkened the doorway, and Loki stood before him. The thunder-god did not like Loki; he distrusted him. The love of adventure was so strong in both, however, that it sometimes drew them together.

"Thor," said Loki, as he entered, "order your chariot, and let us drive to Jötunheim. Asgard may do for Baldr, but I am tired of it; I long for something new."

Fire flashed from Thor's listless eyes; and he sprang up, saying, "Well spoken, Loki! Get ready; we will go at once."

They started off towards the north in Thor's heavy, rumbling chariot, drawn by the famous goats. Thor had with him three things that he never meant to leave behind: the hammer, Mjöllnir, which always returned to him when he flung it, and never missed the mark; the iron gloves which enabled him to grasp the hammer more firmly; and the belt of power.

They journeyed all day over barren fields and plains, and as night fell, found themselves in an almost uninhabited country. A tiny house standing on the edge of a forest was the only dwelling in sight. As they came near, some heads appeared at the doorway and suddenly disappeared. Evidently the inmates were frightened: and well they might be; for the rumbling of Thor's iron chariot sounded like thunder, and his red beard and fiery eyes flashed so in the gathering darkness that they might have been mistaken for lightning.

Thor was about to drive on, not heeding the house, when Loki cried imploringly: "Do stop, I pray you, Thor! With your great strength you forget that ordinary gods may get tired and hungry after rattling about in your chariot all day with nothing to eat!"

Thor laughed heartily, and said: "I forgot who was with me; Loki and food may not long be parted. This is a small house, but it may give us food and shelter."

They alighted from the chariot and went in. The peasants cowered in one corner of the room, on seeing the wonderful strangers, so tall that they could not stand upright in the small house.

Loki spoke: "Do not be frightened, good people. We are hungry travellers who desire rest and food. We will not harm you, but will reward you generously for your hospitality."

Reassured by Loki's mild words, and Thor's good-natured smile, they came forward, still trembling. The woman made a deep curtsey, and said: "My good lords, we welcome you, and would gladly give you some supper; but the little food we had is eaten, and there is nothing left in the house; we are very poor."

"Never mind," said Thor; "do as I bid you, and I will manage the rest." Then, turning to the man, he said, "Go and unharness my goats, while your wife makes the fire and gets the pot ready; we will cook some meat."

The peasants did as Thor bade them, though they could not imagine where the meat was coming from.

Loki helped the woman make the fire, while Thor followed the man out. As soon as the goats were unharnessed, he knocked them both on the head with his hammer, and told the peasant to prepare them for cooking. Soon an enormous platter of goats' flesh was smoking on the table.

As Thor helped the peasants and their two children to the meat, he said: "Eat all you will, good people, but beware of breaking the bones. I have a special reason for wishing them to be kept whole."

Thialfi, the son, had rarely tasted meat, so this was a great feast for him. As he was picking the meat from one of the thigh-bones, Loki whispered, "The marrow inside the bone is best of all!" and Thialfi, forgetting Thor's command, cracked the bone and sucked out the marrow.

Raska, his sister, ate but little. She spent her time in gazing with open-mouthed wonder at the tall strangers who ate with such evident relish the goats that served them as horses. And she asked herself what they would do on the morrow, with the heavy iron chariot, and no goats to draw it.

After the hearty meal all were soon fast asleep.

Thor awoke as the first rays of the early dawn shot into the little room. Jumping up quickly, he gathered together the bones of the goats and put them into the skins. Then lifting his mighty hammer, he repeated some magic words, called runes. Instantly the two goats were skipping about as lively as if they had enjoyed a good meal and a night's rest instead of having served as food for others; but Thor noticed that one of them limped. Suspecting the cause, he became furious with anger, and called out in a loud voice, "Wake up, you wretched peasants! See what you have done to my goats!"

The peasants started as though waked by a thunder-clap, and cowered, trembling, before the angry god.

"Who broke the thigh-bone of my goat?" roared Thor, clutching Mjöllnir till his knuckles grew white, while flashes of light came from his eyes and beard, threatening to burn the room.

Then Thialfi, who was a brave lad, plucked up his courage, and said: "Oh! Mighty sir, I broke the thigh-bone of your goat. I forgot what you said; the meat was so good; and I wanted to get the marrow. Punish me, but do not harm the others; they have done nothing."

The boy's courage and honesty touched Thor, who was really kind at heart. And he said: "You have done a very bad deed, but I will forgive you, because you are brave and speak the truth. A liar and a coward I cannot abide. But you are too good a fellow to spend your life in this hut like a beast. Come with me, and you shall see the world. Your sister shall come too. You shall live in a big house. If this little hut were put into it, you might hunt all day and not find it."

Then Thor gave the peasant and his wife a handful of gold, saying, "Your children shall come and see you when they will." And when they were starting off, he said, "I leave the goats and the chariot in your care until my return. Do not break any bones!" And he laughed heartily.

So the four started into the thick forest. Thialfi, who was very fleet of foot, carried the bag containing food for the journey; and Raska, who was a stout peasant-girl, kept up easily with the others. After a long walk through the forest, they came to the great river, Ocean, on the other side of which lay Jötunheim. They crossed the sea without much trouble, although it was a long distance over it.

On the other side was a land much wilder than the one they left behind. Everything was enormous in size; the stones being as large as rocks, and the trees reaching to the clouds. After crossing a barren stretch of country, strewn with huge bowlders, they came to a deep forest where perfect silence reigned, and where there was nothing green underfoot, for the ground was covered with pine-needles. It was like twilight in this forest even at noon, the thick branches let so little sunlight through; and besides, the sun never shone brightly in any part of Jötunheim.

All day they travelled on, and one part of the wood was so exactly like another that they might have gone about in a circle had not Thialfi now and then climbed to the top of a tall tree to make sure that they were going in the right direction.

As night fell, the little light that filtered through the branches faded away, leaving them in utter darkness. It was impossible to go on without running against the trees. Thor, impatient as he was to proceed, decided to stop and wait for the morning. In the darkness they felt around for a good place to sleep. As Loki was groping about, he touched something that was not a tree; and, as he ran his hand up, it seemed like the entrance to a house.

"This is very strange!" he exclaimed. "Strike a light, Thialfi! Here is some kind of a house, but whoever lives in it must be fond of the woods!"

Thialfi did as Loki requested, and by the flaring light of a dry stick they could distinguish a large opening. A dwelling of some kind it was, certainly, but of a new pattern; for the door was the size of the whole front of the house.

"There's nothing like travelling to see strange sights!" said Loki. And as they went in, he remarked, "This house is of an odd shape, but it seems to be a good place to sleep in."

They threw themselves down on the floor of the large entrance hall, and were soon fast asleep.

About midnight they were awakened by a terrible shaking of the earth, together with a rumbling noise like thunder. They started up, expecting to feel another shock in a moment, for apparently it was an earthquake. But all was still. Thor placed himself in the main door of the house, while the others found some smaller rooms that promised greater quiet.

As soon as the first rays of the sun struggled through the branches, so that Thor could distinguish one object from another, he fastened on his belt of strength, drew on his iron gauntlets and, grasping his hammer firmly, strode out into the forest to seek the cause of the noise and the shaking that had so disturbed their slumbers. He expected to find a mighty chasm yawning nearby – the result of the earthquake.

He had not gone far, when he saw a hill rising in an opening amid the trees; and at the same time he heard a loud sound that evidently came from the further side of the hill. When Thor reached that side, he could just distinguish in the dim light the enormous head of a giant from whose open mouth came the sounds he had heard. What Thor had taken for a hill was the giant's body. His eyes were closed, and his eye-brows stood out like lines of bushes from above them. His hair looked more like a forest of trees than like the hair of a common person.

Thor looked at the sleeping giant for a moment and then aimed his hammer at his forehead. But instead of flinging it, he stopped short, and reaching up, put his mouth near his ear, and roared in a voice of thunder, "What is your name?"

The giant stretched his huge limbs, and slowly opened his eyes. At first he seemed dazed; but gradually a look of intelligence came into his face, and he said, slowly, "Did anybody speak?"

"Yes," roared Thor, "I did. What's your name?"

As the giant heard Thor's voice, he turned his large head slowly around and looked at him. After a long stare, he replied, "Skrymir." Then he added, "I know you; you are Asa-Thor."

"You had better thank me," said Thor; "I seldom begin my acquaintance with giants in so polite a manner, as some of your friends have learned to their cost."

Skrymir smiled, but it took a good while. After another pause he broke the silence with, "What have you done with my glove?" And he slowly stretched out his hand and picked up the house where they had spent the night. Luckily Loki and the others had just left it. There was a look of amusement on Skrymir's enormous features that irritated Thor greatly; but he tried to look unconcerned.

At last the giant got up, shook his huge limbs, and said, good-naturedly: "Will you little people accept of the company of such a large person as myself? I should like to join you; and we may be useful to one another, although we differ in size."

Thor accepted Skrymir's offer, but his words angered him so that he clutched Mjöllnir. The giant next untied an immense provision sack in which he carried his food, and began to eat his breakfast. Thor, who could enjoy the society of giants only when he was fighting them, went off to a little distance and ate with his companions.

As they were finishing their meal, the giant came crashing through the woods to where they were, and said: "Here, friends, I am big, and you are small. Put your provisions into my sack. I can carry everything easily."

There was no reason for refusing the offer of the good-natured giant, so they put all the food into his sack. He flung the bag over his shoulder, and led the way with long strides.

It was a hard day's journey. But Thor was too proud to own that they could not easily keep up with a giant; so instead of asking him to slacken his pace, they ran all the way.

Toward night, Skrymir stopped under a large oak. Flinging himself down, he handed the provision sack to Thor, saying, "Here, Asa-Thor, take this. I am more sleepy than hungry, and do not care for food." In an instant he was sound asleep, and snoring so loudly that the woods resounded and the earth trembled.

Thor took the bag and started to untie the strings; but with all his efforts not a knot would come undone, nor could he even loosen one. At this his blood began to boil; and seizing Mjöllnir, he flung it with all his might at the head of the sleeping giant.

Skrymir stirred a little, put his hand to his head, and slowly opened his large blue eyes, saying, "Did a leaf fall on my head? I thought I felt something." Then looking at Thor, he asked, "Have you eaten your supper yet? Aren't you going to bed?"

"Yes," replied Thor; "we are going to bed." And as he would not ask Skrymir to untie the sack, they lay down, hungry and tired, under a tree, not very far from the giant.

Skrymir made such a roaring that it was almost impossible to sleep. As Thor lay there, hearing the dreadful noise, he grew more and more furious. At last he started up with an oath, and going to where the giant lay, swung Mjöllnir with all his Asa-might, and plunged it into his forehead up to the handle.

The giant stopped snoring, and turning uneasily, muttered, "What is the matter now? Did an acorn fall upon my forehead? Where are you, Thor?"

Then, with a sigh, he was fast asleep again, and snoring as loudly as ever.

Thor was by this time so angry that, even had all been quiet, he could not have slept. He sat for hours leaning against the tree, his comrades asleep near him. Instead of growing calmer, he grew more enraged as the hours went by.

When the morning light showed again the outlines of the giant's huge form, he went over to where he lay. This time he swung Mjöllnir as he had never swung it before, and buried it so deeply in the giant's temple that only a little of the handle stuck out. "Can you feel that?" he roared.

Skrymir opened his eyes, and as they rested upon the angry god, asked sleepily: "Are there any birds on the tree above me? I thought some moss fell upon my forehead." Then opening his eyes wider, he added, "But it is morning, and we must start on."

When they were ready to go, the giant turned to Thor with an odd smile on his face, and said, "You evidently think me rather large, Asa-Thor; but when you reach Utgard, you will find larger men than I. Let me give you some advice: do not brag too much. Utgard-Loki, the lord of Utgard, and his big courtiers will not stand the boasting of little men like you. In fact, the best thing you can do is to turn back and give up visiting Utgard. Dangers that you little suspect may lie before you in that giant-land."

Thor tried to answer Skrymir, but he was so choked with rage that the words would not come out.

The giant continued, "If you are determined to go on, turn to the east, toward the mountains that you see yonder." And taking the provision sack, he disappeared in the woods.

Thor started after him with Mjöllnir; but he seemed to have changed suddenly into a large grey mountain on their right.

As the giant had carried off the food, they were forced to content themselves with the few berries and roots that they could find on their way; for there was no game in the woods.

About noon the forest ended abruptly, and they came into a large plain that extended on all sides like a grey sea. There were rocks here and there; but not a blade of grass, not a tree gladdened the eye as it roamed over the dreary waste. In the midst of the plain was a huge castle. Even at that distance they had to bend back their necks in order to see its turrets, half hidden by clouds. It looked as though carved roughly by giants out of a rocky mountain. Its rude walls bore the scars of time, and showed in places the fierce sport of the lightning.

Thor and his companions went towards the castle, clambering over the bowlders. It was farther off than they had thought: its great size made it seem near. When at last they stood before the high walls that surrounded it, night was beginning to fall. The great god Thor seemed but a child as he stretched up his hand to reach the lock of the ponderous gate. In vain: it was too high for him. Loki had already wriggled between the bars; and he now called to the others to follow him. Once inside the walls, they saw through the open door of the castle a hall larger than Thor's whole palace.

The gods and their companions walked in boldly and looked about. They could see clouds floating in and out through jagged openings in the vast heights above. In the centre of the hall was a table of rough granite which was supported by monsters whose wide-open jaws made huge caverns. At the upper end of the table was Utgard-Loki, the giant-king. He sat on a high seat, the back and arms of which were formed by the coils of the Midgard serpent sculptured in stone. The huge, horrid head of the monster stretched out over the king. The beard of Utgard-Loki was the colour of the grey rocks, and fell in masses to the ground. His motions were heavy and slow. When he reached his hand for the beer-mug which stood near him on the table, it was some time before it reached his lips; and after a long drink he would give a sigh of satisfaction that sounded like the roaring of the wind. His features were slow in changing their expression. His large round eyes were neither kind nor fierce; for they had no more human feeling in them than cold mountain lakes.

On each side of the table there were stone benches whose high backs made comfortable resting-places for the heads of the giants. These giants were nearly as large as Utgard-Loki, and all were drinking beer. Someone had evidently made a joke just before Thor and his companions entered; for a deep, slow "Ha! Ha!" came from one and then another of the giants, until the roar of their great guffaws filled the vast hall, and rolled out like thunder into the gathering night. The gods could examine everything at their leisure; for not one of the giants seemed aware of their presence.

Thor's blood began to boil as he looked at the dull, mountain-like creatures; and he longed to fling his hammer and change them into real mountains as they sat on their benches of stone; but he forbore, and going up to Utgard-Loki, placed himself directly in front of him. The king turned his expressionless eyes upon him, and after staring for several moments, burst into a loud laugh, showing his granite teeth.

"Why, what have I before me?" he roared. "This stripling must be Asa-Thor of whom I have often heard. I am surprised! But perhaps you are really bigger than you look!" Then in a moment he added: "What can you do? We always make our guests prove their strength or their skill before we invite them to eat and drink with us."

Loki was very hungry, and pushing himself in front of Thor, he cried eagerly, "I will wager that no one here can eat as fast as I can!" And he laughed to himself at the thought of contending with the slow, clumsy giants.

Then Utgard beckoned to a man that Loki had not noticed. He sat at the lower end of the table, and was small and agile compared with the giants. A trough full of meat was brought in.

"Logi," said the king, "show this little man that giants can be as quick as he."

They began to eat, seated at opposite ends of the trough. Loki ate ravenously; for pride and hunger both spurred him on. Neither stopped to look at the other, till at last they met in the very middle of the trough. Loki then saw, to his amazement, that while he had eaten all the meat on his side, Logi had consumed not only the meat but the bones, and even the trough itself. So there was no question as to who had won the victory. However, the fact that he had enjoyed a hearty meal consoled Loki in part for his defeat.

Utgard next turned his eyes to where Thialfi stood and, pointing at him with his huge forefinger, asked, "What can that young man do?"

Thialfi straightened up, and answered proudly: "I can run a race with anyone you may appoint. He must be swifter than the eagle if he can outrun me!" The king rose slowly from his seat and walked with a lumbering gait through the vast hall and out upon the plain surrounding the castle. A few giants followed, one after another, and seated themselves on the large boulders that lay around.

Utgard-Loki pointed out the course, and then called in a loud voice, "Hugi, come here!"

Quick as a flash appeared an agile little fellow, apparently more akin to the elves than to the giants. A peculiar, dull smile overspread the features of the king as he said, "We do not match you little people against our giants; that would be hardly fair; this is one of our dwarfs." And he and his courtiers laughed loud and long at the joke.

The course pointed out was a long one, but Thialfi started like a steed of high mettle eager for the race. He flew as the swallow flies. Yet Hugi was so much swifter that he touched the goal and met Thialfi on the return before the latter had finished the course.

Utgard-Loki laughed, saying, "You must ply your legs better, little Thialfi; though you are a very fair runner!"

They ran a second time; and when Hugi turned back from the goal, Thialfi was a good bow-shot from it.

"Well run, Thialfi!" cried the king of the giants. "No better runner has ever visited us; but, for once, you have evidently found your match. One more course shall decide the contest."

This time Thialfi sped as swiftly as the winds that rush over the open plain; one could hardly see him as he flew along. Yet still his rival outstripped him; and when they met, Thialfi was not half-way to the goal. Even Thor cried out that it was enough. And eager to show that he, at least, could outdo the giants, he demanded a trial of his powers.

"Let me show your courtiers how an Asa can drink!" he said. "I do not fear to contend with the mightiest of you!"

They returned to the hall; and Utgard-Loki, again seating himself on his high throne, called out to his cup-bearer, "Bring hither our ancient drinking-horn!" Then he explained to Thor that it was from this horn that his courtiers were obliged to drink when they had trespassed in any way against the established usage of the land.

When the cup-bearer brought the horn, Thor found that while it was not very large at the top, it was exceedingly long, winding in coil after coil, so that it was hard to distinguish the end. Indeed, it reached far across the hall, and was there lost in the shadows. Thor gazed at it with interest. He saw that strange sea-monsters were carved upon it, and that its coils were encrusted with shells and barnacles, and fringed with sea-mosses.

The god was very thirsty, and with an expression of satisfaction he raised the horn to his lips. Long and deep was his draught. As he drank, the sound was like that of water breaking upon a pebbly beach. Yet when he stopped, breathless, and looked to see how much beer was left in the horn, he found, to his surprise, that there was about as much as at first.

Raising the horn again, he drank as long as he could without taking breath, and then looked in. The liquor had sunk even less than before.

Utgard-Loki smiled broadly, and said, "How now, Thor! Have you not saved for the third draught more than you can make away with? You must not spare yourself too much in a test of this kind. If you wish to drain the horn, you must drink deep!"

Thor was in a towering passion as he raised the horn for the third time. It seemed as though he would never stop drinking. The noise he made was like the roar of the waves as they dash upon the rocks in a storm; and yet, when he stopped and looked at the horn, the liquor was so high that it could only just be carried without spilling.

Shame and anger were pictured on Thor's face as he gave back the horn to the cup-bearer. "I own myself beaten," he said; "but let me try something else: I know I can outdo you giants in something."

"There is a little game our children sometimes play," said the king; "supposing you try that. I would not propose a child's game to Thor, had he not shown himself much weaker than I thought him. See if you can lift my cat from the ground."

As he was speaking, a large grey cat ran across the hall. Thor sprang towards her, and putting his hand under her body, tried to lift her from the ground; but as he raised his hand, she curved her back, and with his utmost efforts he could only raise one foot from the floor.

"Just as I expected," said Utgard-Loki; "the cat is large, and Thor is small compared with our men."

"You call me small," cried Thor, thoroughly enraged; "but which of you dares wrestle with me now that I am angry? "and his eyes darted forth sparks, and from his beard shot flames of fire, lighting up the grey hall.

"I see no one here", said the king, looking around, "who would not think it beneath him to wrestle with a little man like you. But here comes my old nurse Elli; she has thrown to the ground many a man as strong and boastful as Thor."

An old woman, bent nearly double, came into the hall. She was toothless, and had scant, grey locks. Her thin form trembled as she raised her bleared and almost sightless eyes to Thor. He looked at her with disgust.

"Wrestle with him, mother," said Utgard-Loki.

Whereupon she wound her long, thin arms about Thor, and the more he tried to throw her, the more firmly did she stand. At last, worn out with the conflict, the god sank upon one knee.

The king then stepped forward and said it was enough. Then he added, "Although you little people have shown yourselves weak compared with us giants, still we admire your spirit, and we invite you to eat and drink with us."

Thor and his companions were by this time thoroughly vexed and humbled. They gave up the contest, and accepted the hospitality of Utgard-Loki.

Long was the feast, and strange and dull were the stories told by the giants as they nodded over the foaming beer. Thor, as he sat in the dreary stone hall, thought of the wit and gayety that reigned in Gladsheim. But the giants seemed to be enjoying themselves.

The gods awoke at daybreak, and Utgard-Loki went with them through the iron gate. When on the other side he said: "What do you think of your journey, Asa-Thor? Do you consider that you have met your match among the giants this time?"

"I own myself beaten," said Thor; "I am ashamed. It vexes me to think in what esteem you must hold me."

"Well, Asa-Thor," replied the giant, "since you are beyond my castle walls, I will tell you the truth, if it will be any comfort to you. And first, let me say, that never again shall you or any Asa enter within my walls!

"I have all along deceived you by enchantments. It was I who met you in the forest, and there I found out how strong you were. The provision sack which you tried in vain to untie was fastened with iron; that was why you could not open it. The blows of your hammer were so mighty that the first one would have killed me had I not, by magic, brought a mountain between us. On your return you will see a mountain with three square glens, each deeper than the one before it. Those are the marks left by your hammer.

"In the same way I deceived you in your contests with my courtiers. Loki ate like hunger itself; but Logi was wild-fire, and that consumes all that is set before it. Thialfi's running struck us all with amazement, for he outstripped the wind; but Hugi was my thought, and that can fly more swiftly than the lightning as it flashes from peak to peak. When you tried to empty our ancient horn, you performed a feat so marvellous that had I not seen it myself I should never have believed it. The end of the horn, which you could not see, reached to the ocean. You drank so deeply that you lowered the great river. When you reach it on your way home, you will see how the water has fallen. In Midgard they will henceforth call this the ebb. When you lifted from the ground one paw of my cat, you were in reality raising the great Midgard serpent that encircles the earth. And you lifted him so high that you nearly pulled his tail out of his mouth. We feared the foundations of Jötunheim would be shaken. But your wrestling with Elli was the most astonishing feat of all. She was no other than old age. And there never has been, and never will be, a man whom old age cannot lay low, if he abide her coming.

You are a mighty god, Asa-Thor, and I shall take good care that you never find my country again, however diligently you may seek for it. We giants, dull and heavy as we may seem, have the wisdom of the ages."

Thor raised his hammer, but Utgard-Loki had vanished. And turning his eyes to where the castle was, he saw nothing but a beautiful green plain, upon which the slow-moving clouds cast their shadows.

Thor returned to his home in Asgard; but the memory of his adventures in the castle of Utgard-Loki stung him continually; and he determined to revenge himself by attacking the Midgard serpent in his ocean home.

THOR'S JOURNEY TO GET THE KETTLE FOR ÆGIR

as told by Mary Litchfield

ÆGIR, the ruler of the stormy western sea, feasted all the gods at harvest time; but there was never quite enough beer to go round. This angered Thor, for it showed a lack of hospitality; and he told Ægir, very bluntly, what he thought of it.

Ægir appeared to feel hurt, and said: "Your words are rude and unkind, Asa-Thor; the reason why the beer does not hold out is that I have no kettle large enough for the brewing. It is no small matter to make beer for all the dwellers in Asgard."

Tyr, who stood near, turned to Thor, and said: "My father, the fierce giant Hymir, dwells near heaven's end. He owns a caldron a mile deep. I think we can manage in some way to get it from him. Ægir will then have the satisfaction of entertaining his friends in a manner befitting his generous nature."

"It is too bad to trouble you," said Ægir; "it is such a long journey, and you may not be able to get the caldron, after all."

"Oh, friend Ægir!" cried Thor. "We count nothing as trouble if it only obliges you. Come, Tyr, let us be off! My goats are ready, and I long to see Jötunheim again. If I can only meet the Midgard serpent on this journey, I will pay him well for deceiving me as he did at Utgard-Loki's – making me lift him for a cat!"

So the two gods started off together. Tyr was a more fit companion for Thor than Loki was. He was as fearless as the thunder-god himself, and one of the noblest of the Æsir.

Thor put up his goats at some distance from the giant's castle; for wherever he went in his great rumbling chariot he was known as the mighty god of thunder; and this time he wished to go quietly.

Night was coming on as they neared the dwelling of Hymir, which stood by the frozen shore, surrounded by rocks and icebergs. The sides of the huge castle glistened with frost, and from its projections hung long icicles. As they went in through the wide door, the first object to meet their eyes was a giantess with nine hundred heads. She was nodding sleepily with all her heads in a corner of the vast hall; and she did not notice them. This was Hymir's mother.

A great fire of pine and fir trees burned at one end of the room, and near it sat a lovely woman, the firelight shining on her golden-brown hair. She greeted her son and his friend joyfully, and brought beer to refresh them after their long journey. Then looking out into the night, she said: "My husband will soon be home from his fishing. But he is often in an ill-humour, and the sight of guests might put him in a rage. Fearless as you are, do as I bid you: hide under those kettles at the other end of the room. It is dark there, and he will not see you." They did as she bade them.

Before long there was a loud rushing and roaring sound; it was Hymir coming home from his fishing, wading through the sea. Great waves broke upon the rocks and icebergs; and the sound of the giant's breathing was like the roaring of winds. The earth trembled beneath his tread, and the walls of the castle were shaken. As he entered, the gods saw that his huge head glistened with ice and snow and that "the thicket on his cheeks was frozen". With a grunt of ill-humour he threw down his net in which were whales and other sea-monsters, not yet dead.

His wife rose up, trembling, to meet him, and spoke gently, saying: "You must be tired, my husband, after your hard day's fishing. You see I have a good fire, and supper will soon be ready. It is a fierce night. Even you must have found it hard coming through the sea." A rough growl was the only reply to her kind words.

After Hymir had sat by the fire some time, and had taken great draughts of hot beer, his wife spoke to him again, saying: "I have been thinking much of our son Tyr of late; and, strange to say, he came home today; and he brought his friend Thor with him – Thor, the great thunder-god. I know you will be glad to see them.

"Where are they?" roared Hymir; and he glanced toward the dark end of the hall, where the kettles hung. The huge wooden beam broke as his eyes rested upon it, and eight kettles fell, all breaking but one. That one was the largest of all, a hard-hammered cauldron. The gods then stood forth, their shapely forms in strange contrast with the huge, uncouth figure of the giant. When Hymir saw the flashing of Thor's eyes, he felt that it boded evil to him.

Three oxen were cooked for supper, and Thor ate two of them. The giant, thinking such a guest would soon make havoc in his larder, said gruffly, "We shall have to live on what we can catch in the sea, tomorrow!"

"Nothing would suit me better than to go fishing with you, giant Hymir," said Thor.

The next morning the giant got ready for the expedition. Being in a bad humour, he said, "Get your own bait if you are going with me! You can catch an ox for yourself."

Thor found the herd of the giant, and going up to a coal-black bull, the finest of all, wrung his head from his neck and took it for bait.

When Hymir saw the head of his best bull, he said, "I wish you had sat quiet, and had let me get the bait!"

They started out in Hymir's boat, both rowing. Thor's mighty strokes sent the boat scudding over the angry sea. When they were far out, the giant said: "This is my fishing ground. Here I catch whales. We will stop."

"It is child's play to fish so near the shore," said Thor, redoubling the might of his strokes.

The sea grew rougher, and great waves broke over the boat. When at last they were in the very middle of the ocean, Thor stopped rowing. The giant at once threw his line, and drew up two whales with one bait.

Then Thor took out a line, which although slender was of great strength. He fastened the gory head of the black ox firmly to the hook. Down, down went the bait, far below the rough waves; deeper than where the whales sported; down to the very bottom of the ocean. There lay the mighty earth-encircler, the giant serpent of the deep.[1] For years he had lain in the quiet of the deep sea, with his tail down his throat, waiting with slow-burning hatred for the time of vengeance, the Twilight of the Gods. The coils of his mighty body were fringed with sea-mosses, and covered with clinging shells. Tall sea-palms waved gently in the dim waters above his head. Never, in all the

---

1   See Oehlenschläger's poem, "Thor's Fishing", in Longfellow's *Poets and Poetry of Europe*. The same poem may be found in Frye's translation of Oehlenschläger's *Gods of the North*.

long years, had bait with hook come near his dull eyes.

Thor had secured a most tempting bait. The gory head of the ox came near the serpent's head, and then floated slowly away like a living thing. Then it came near again. A look of eagerness came into the serpent's cruel eyes, and he drew his tail slowly from his jaws. As it reached him the third time, he opened wide his jaws, snatched it, and swallowed head, hook and all. Then came the struggle.

Thor pulled with such strength that his feet broke through the bottom of the boat, and he stood on the floor of the sea. The serpent, hissing and lashing with pain, was drawn up through the vast depths of mid-ocean. The sea, away to the horizon, was covered with poisonous foam. High waves rose like tossing mountains over the vast expanse. Heavy clouds met the waters, and Thor's lightnings darted amid the seething billows. The horrid coils of the great serpent rose above the sea, glistening with venom, and his huge jaws gaped as he strove to seize his powerful enemy.

Thor grasped him in his arms, and the struggle grew fiercer still. Sheets of poisonous foam mixed with the clouds. The crashing of the thunder mingled with the loud hissing of the serpent; and except for the lightning, darkness covered the sea. Thor loosed his hold of the monster for an instant that he might hurl Mjöllnir at his head. Then the giant, who saw with fear and hatred the triumph of the god, cut the line; and with a long hiss of vengeful hate, the serpent sank back into the sea; there to await Ragnarök, the Twilight of the Gods.

Thor's rage and disappointment knew no bounds. He struck the giant a blow that sent him reeling from his boat into the boiling sea. Then he himself started on foot through the ocean, carrying the boat and all it contained. But Hymir recovered, and reached the shore soon after Thor.

They supped upon the two whales that the giant had caught. As soon as they had finished eating, Thor asked for the famous kettle, Mile-deep, hinting that Hymir might fear the consequences should he refuse to give it to him.

"Asa-Thor," said the giant, "you are asking a great favour, and you should give me one more proof of your strength before expecting me to do so much for you." Rising from his seat, he took from a shelf a huge drinking-cup and, handing it to Thor, said, "If you can break this cup, you shall have the kettle!"

Thor first threw the cup at an upright stone that served as a seat. The stone broke in two, but the cup remained whole. Then, with all his might, he flung it at one of the pillars of the hall. The column was shattered, but the cup was unhurt, showing not even a dent.

Then Tyr's mother whispered in Thor's ear, "Strike at the head of Hymir; that is harder than any cup."

Tightening his belt of strength, Thor again threw the cup, and this time full at Hymir"s forehead. The cup was shattered to atoms.

Then was Hymir astounded and troubled. "That was a good cup," he said. "Never again can I say, when the beer is handed to me, 'Beer, thou art too hot.'" And thinking it best to be rid of so dangerous a guest as soon as possible, he said to Thor, "Now 'tis to be seen whether you can carry Mile-deep out of our dwelling."

Tyr went up to the huge iron pot, and tried to lift it; but he could only tip it a little toward one side. Then Thor, with his iron gloves, grasped it by the brim, while his feet burst through the floor; and putting it upon his head, he started off, the rings jingling about his heels. Tyr followed him.

They had not gone far when they heard a loud noise behind them; and turning around they saw a mighty band of frost giants, with Hymir at their head. Some brandished great stone clubs, while others carried bowlders and blocks of ice to throw at the Æsir; they shouted and roared as they came on. Then Thor put down Mile-deep, and grasping Mjöllnir, hurled it at the savage crew. Instantly all was still; and in place of the noisy giants, a line of snowy mountains raised their heads to the sky.

Thor and Tyr soon reached the place where the goats were tied, and putting the kettle into the chariot, drove rapidly toward Ægir's halls. They were delayed a little because the goat whose thigh-bone had been injured fell down, and then went lame. But in spite of this, they were not long in reaching Ægir's palace. The sea-god welcomed them, but looked with dismay at Mile-deep, knowing how great a brewing there would have to be in the future, when he feasted the gods.

IN THE GIANT'S HOUSE

as told by Abbie Farewell Brown

ALTHOUGH Thor had slain Thiassi the giant builder, Thrym the thief, Hrungnir and Hymir, and had rid the world of whole families of wicked giants, there remained many others in Jötunheim to do their evil deeds and to plot mischief against both gods and men; and of these Geirröd was the fiercest and the wickedest. He and his two ugly daughters – Gialp of the red eyes, and Greip of the black teeth – lived in a large palace among the mountains, where Geirröd had his treasures of iron and copper, silver and gold; for, since the death of Thrym, Geirröd was the Lord of the Mines, and all the riches that came out of the earth-caverns belonged to him.

Thrym had been Geirröd's friend, and the tale of Thrym's death through the might of Thor and his hammer had made Geirröd very sad and angry. "If I could but catch Thor, now, without his weapons," he said to his daughters, "what a lesson I would give him! How I would punish him for his deeds against us giants!"

"Oh, what would you do, father?" cried Gialp, twinkling her cruel red eyes, and working her claw fingers as if she would like to fasten them in Thor's golden beard.

"Oh, what would you do, father?" cried Greip, smacking her lips and grinding her black teeth as if she would like a bite out of Thor's stout arm.

"Do to him!" growled Geirröd fiercely. "Do to him! Gr-r-r! I would chew him all up! I would break his bones into little bits! I would smash him into jelly!"

"Oh, good, good! Do it, father, and then give him to us to play with," cried Gialp and Greip, dancing up and down till the hills trembled and all the frightened sheep ran home to their folds thinking that there must be an earthquake; for Gialp was as tall as a pine tree and many times as thick, while Greip, her little sister, was as large around as a haystack and high as a flagstaff. They both hoped some day to be as huge as their father, whose legs were so long that he could step across the river valleys from one hilltop to another, just as we human folk cross a brook on stepping-stones; and his arms were so stout that he could lift a yoke of oxen in each fist, as if they were red-painted toys.

Geirröd shook his head at his two playful daughters and sighed. "We must catch Master Thor first, my girls, before we do these fine things to him. We must catch him without his mighty hammer that never fails him, and without his belt that doubles his strength whenever he puts it on, or even I cannot chew and break and smash him as he deserves; for with these his weapons he is the mightiest creature in the whole world, and I would rather meddle with thunder and lightning than with him. Let us wait, children."

Then Gialp and Greip pouted and sulked like two great babies who cannot have the new plaything which they want; and very ugly they were to see, with tears as big as oranges rolling down their cheeks.

Sooner than they expected they came very near to having their heart's desire fulfiled. And if it had happened as they wished, and if Asgard had lost its goodliest hero, its strongest defence, that would have been red Loki's fault, all Loki's evil planning; for you are now to hear of the wickedest thing that up to this time Loki had ever done. As you know, it was Loki who was Thor's bitterest enemy; and for many months he had been awaiting the chance to repay the Thunder Lord for the dole which Thor had brought upon him at the time of the dwarf's gifts to Asgard.

This is how it came about: Loki had long remembered the fun of skimming as a great bird in Freyja's falcon feathers. He had longed to borrow the wings once again and to fly away over the round world to see what he could see; for he thought that so he could learn many secrets which he was not meant to know, and plan wonderful mischief without being found out. But Freyja would not again loan her feather dress to Loki. She owed him a grudge for naming her as Thrym's bride; and besides, she remembered his treatment of Idunn, and she did not trust his oily tongue and fine promises. So Loki saw no way but to borrow the feathers without leave; and this he did one day when Freyja was gone to ride in her chariot drawn by white cats. Loki put on the feather dress, as he had done twice before – once when he went to Jötunheim to bring back stolen Idunn and her magic apples, once when he went to find out about Thor's hammer.

Away he flew from Asgard as birdlike as you please, chuckling to himself with wicked thoughts. It did not make any particular difference to him where he went. It was such fun to flap and fly, skim and wheel, looking and feeling for all the world like a big brown falcon. He swooped low, thinking, "I wonder what Freyja would say to see me now! Whee-e-e! How angry she would be!" Just then he spied the high wall of a palace on the mountains.

"Oho!" said Loki. "I never saw that place before. It may be a giant's dwelling. I think this must be Jötunheim, from the bigness of things. I must just peep to see." Loki was the most inquisitive of creatures, as wily-minded folk are apt to be.

Loki the falcon alighted and hopped to the wall, then giving a flap of his wings he flew up and up to the window ledge, where he perched and peered into the hall. And there within he saw the giant Geirröd with his daughters eating their dinner. They looked so ugly and so greedy, as they sat there gobbling their food in giant mouthfuls, that Loki on the window-sill could not help snickering to himself. Now at that sound Geirröd looked up and saw the big brown bird peeping in at the window.

"Heigha!" cried the giant to one of his servants. "Go you and fetch me the big brown bird up yonder in the window."

Then the servant ran to the wall and tried to climb up to get at Loki; but the window was so high that he could not reach. He jumped and slipped, scrambled and slipped, again and again, while Loki sat just above his clutching fingers, and chuckled so that he nearly fell from his perch. "Te-he! Te-he!" chattered Loki in the falcon tongue. It was such fun to see the fellow grow black in the face with trying to reach him that Loki thought he would wait until the giant's fingers almost touched him, before flying away.

But Loki waited too long. At last, with a quick spring, the giant gained a hold upon the window ledge, and Loki was within reach. When Loki flapped his wings to fly, he found that his feet were tangled in the vine that grew upon the wall. He struggled and twisted with all his might – but in vain. There he was, caught fast. Then the servant grasped him by the legs, and so brought him to Geirröd, where he sat at table. Now Loki in his feather dress looked exactly like a falcon – except for his eyes. There was no hiding the wise and crafty look of Loki's eyes. As soon as Geirröd looked at him, he suspected that this was no ordinary bird.

"You are no falcon, you!" he cried. "You are spying about my palace in disguise. Speak, and tell me who you are." Loki was afraid to tell, because he knew the giants were angry with him for his part in Thrym's death – small though his part had really been in that great deed. So he kept his beak closed tight, and refused to speak. The giant stormed and raged and threatened to kill him; but still Loki was silent.

Then Geirröd locked the falcon up in a chest for three long months without food or water, to see how that would suit his bird-ship. You can imagine how hungry and thirsty Loki was at the end of that time – ready to tell anything he knew, and more also, for the sake of a crumb of bread and a drop of water.

So then Geirröd called through the keyhole, "Well, Sir Falcon, now will you tell me who you are?" And this time Loki piped feebly, "I am Loki of Asgard; give me something to eat!"

"Oho!" quoth the giant fiercely. "You are that Loki who went with Thor to kill my brother Thrym! Oho! Well, you shall die for that, my feathered friend!"

"No, no!" screamed Loki. "Thor is no friend of mine. I love the giants far better! One of them is my wife!" – which was indeed true, as were few of Loki's words.

"Then if Thor is no friend of yours, to save your life will you bring him into my power?" asked Geirröd.

Loki's eyes gleamed wickedly among the feathers. Here all at once was his chance to be free, and to have his revenge upon Thor, his worst enemy. "Ay, that I will!" he cried eagerly. "I will bring Thor into your power."

So Geirröd made him give a solemn promise to do that wrong; and upon this he loosed Loki from the chest and gave him food. Then they formed the wicked plan together, while Gialp and Greip, the giant's ugly daughters, listened and smacked their lips.

Loki was to persuade Thor to come with him to Geirrödsgard. More: he must come without his mighty hammer, and without the iron gloves of power, and without the belt of strength; for so only could the giant have Thor at his mercy.

After their wicked plans were made, Loki bade a friendly farewell to Geirröd and his daughters and flew back to Asgard as quickly as he could. You may be sure he had a sound scolding from Freyja for stealing her feather dress and for keeping it so long. But he told such a pitiful story of being kept prisoner by a cruel giant, and he looked in truth so pale and thin from his long fast, that the gods were fain to pity him and to believe his story, in spite of the many times that he had deceived them. Indeed, most of his tale was true, but he told only half of the truth; for he spoke no word of his promise to the giant. This he kept hidden in his breast.

Now, one day not long after this, Loki invited Thor to go on a journey with him to visit a new friend who, he said, was anxious to know the Thunder Lord. Loki was so pleasant in his manner and seemed so frank in his speech that Thor, whose heart was simple and unsuspicious, never dreamed of any wrong, not even when Loki added, "And by the by, my Thor, you must leave behind your hammer, your belt and your gloves; for it would show little courtesy to wear such weapons in the home of a new friend."

Thor carelessly agreed; for he was pleased with the idea of a new adventure, and with the thought of making a new friend. Besides, on their last journey together, Loki had behaved so well that Thor believed him to have changed his evil ways and to have become his friend. So together they set off in Thor's goat chariot, without weapons of any kind except those which Loki secretly carried. Loki chuckled as they rattled over the clouds, and if Thor had seen the look in his eyes, he would have turned the chariot back to Asgard and to safety, where he had left gentle Sif his wife. But Thor did not notice, and so they rumbled on.

Soon they came to the gate of Giant Land. Thor thought this strange, for he knew they were like to find few friends of his dwelling among the Big Folk. For the first time he began to suspect Loki of some treacherous scheme. However, he said nothing, and pretended to be as gay and careless as before. But he thought of a plan to find out the truth.

Close by the entrance was the cave of Grid, a good giantess, who alone of all her race was a friend of Thor and of the folk in Asgard.

"I will alight here for a moment, Loki," said Thor carelessly. "I long for a draught of water. Hold you the goats tightly by the reins until I return."

So he went into the cave and got his draught of water. But while he was drinking, he questioned good mother Grid to some purpose.

"Who is this friend Geirröd whom I go to see?" he asked her.

"Geirröd your friend! You go to see Geirröd!" she exclaimed. "He is the wickedest giant of us all, and no friend to you. Why do you go, dear Thor?"

"H'm!" muttered Thor. "Red Loki's mischief again!" He told her of the visit that Loki had proposed, and how he had left at home the belt, the gloves and the hammer which made him stronger than any giant. Then Grid was frightened.

"Go not, go not, Thor!" she begged. "Geirröd will kill you, and those ugly girls, Gialp and Greip, will have the pleasure of crunching your bones. Oh, I know them well, the hussies!"

But Thor declared that he would go, whether or no. "I have promised Loki that I will go," he said, "and go I will; for I always keep my word."

"Then you shall have three little gifts of me," quoth she. "Here is my belt of power – for I also have one like your own." And she buckled about his waist a great belt, at whose touch he felt his strength redoubled. "This is my iron glove," she said, as she put one on his mighty hand, "and with it, as with your own, you can handle lightning and touch unharmed the hottest of red-hot metal. And here, last of all," she added, "is Gridarvöll, my good staff, which you may find useful. Take them, all three; and may Sif see you safe at home again by their aid."

Thor thanked her and went out once more to join Loki, who never suspected what had happened in the cave. For the belt and the glove were hidden under Thor's cloak. And as for the staff, it was quite ordinary looking, as if Thor might have picked it up anywhere along the road.

On they journeyed until they came to the river Vimer, the greatest of all rivers, which roared and tossed in a terrible way between them and the shore which they wanted to reach. It seemed impossible to cross. But Thor drew his belt a little tighter, and planting Grid's staff firmly on the bottom, stepped out into the stream. Loki clung behind to his cloak, frightened out of his wits. But Thor waded on bravely, his strength doubled by Grid's belt, and his steps supported by her magic staff. Higher and higher the waves washed over his knees, his waist, his shoulders, as if they were fierce to drown him. And Thor said:

"Ho there, river Vimer! Do not grow any larger, I pray. It is of no use. The more you crowd upon me, the mightier I grow with my belt and my staff!"

But lo! As he nearly reached the other side, Thor spied someone hiding close down by the bank of the river. It was Gialp of the red eyes, the big elder daughter of Geirröd. She was splashing the water upon Thor, making the great waves that rolled up and threatened to drown him.

"Oho!" cried he. "So it is you who are making the river rise, big little girl. We must see to that." And seizing a huge boulder, he hurled it at her. It hit her with a thud, for Thor's aim never missed. Giving a scream as loud as a steam-whistle, Gialp limped home as best she could to tell her father, and to prepare a warm reception for the stranger who bore Loki at his back.

When Thor had pulled himself out of the river by some bushes, he soon came to the palace which Loki had first sighted in his falcon dress. And there he found everything most courteously made ready for him. He and Loki were received like dear old friends, with shouts of rejoicing and ringing of bells. Geirröd himself came out to meet them, and would have embraced his new friend Thor; but the Thunder Lord merely seized him by the hand and gave him so hearty a squeeze with the iron glove that the giant howled with pain. Yet he could say nothing, for Thor looked pleased and gentle. And Geirröd said to himself, "Ho, ho, my fine little Thor! I will soon pay you for that handshake, and for many things beside."

All this time Gialp and Greip did not appear, and Loki also had taken himself away, to be out of danger when the hour of Thor's death should come. For he feared that dreadful things might happen before Thor died; and he did not want to be remembered by the big fist of the companion whom he had betrayed. Loki, having kept his promise to the giant, was even now far on the road back to Asgard, where he meant with a sad face to tell the gods that Thor had been slain by a horrible giant; but never to tell them how.

So Thor was all alone when the servants led him to the chamber which Geirröd had made ready for his dear friend. It was a wonderfully fine chamber, to be sure; but the strange thing about it was that among the furnishings there was but one chair, a giant chair, with a drapery all about the legs. Now Thor was very weary with his long journey, and he sat down in the chair to rest. Then – wonderful to tell! – if elevators had been invented in those days, he might have thought he was in one. For instantly the seat of the chair shot up towards the roof, and against this he was in danger of being crushed as Geirröd had longed to see him.

But quick as a flash Thor raised the staff which good old Grid had given him, and pushed it against the rafters with all his might to stop his upward journey. It was a tremendous push that he gave. Something cracked; something crashed; the chair fell to the ground as Thor leaped off the seat, and there were two terrible screams.

Then Thor found – what do you think? Why, that Gialp and Greip, the giant's daughters, had hidden under the seat of the chair, and had lifted it up on their backs to crush Thor against the roof! But instead of that, it was Thor who had broken their backs, so that they lay dead upon the floor like limp rag dolls.

Now this little exercise had only given Thor an excellent appetite for supper. So that when word came bidding him to the banquet, he was very glad.

"First", said big Geirröd, grinning horribly, for he did not know what had happened to his daughters, "first we will see some games, friend Thor."

Then Thor came into the hall, where fires were burning in great chimney places along the walls. "It is here that we play our little games," cried Geirröd. And on the moment, seizing a pair of tongs, he snatched a red-hot wedge of iron from one of the fires and hurled it straight at Thor's head. But Thor was quicker than he. Swift as a flash he caught the flying spark in his iron glove, and calling forth all the might of Grid's belt, he cast the wedge back at the giant. Geirröd dodged behind an iron pillar, but it was in vain. Thor's might was such as no iron could meet. Like a bolt of lightning the wedge passed through the pillar, through Geirröd himself, through the thick wall of the palace, and buried itself deep in the ground, where it lodges to this day, unless someone has dug it up to sell for old iron.

So perished Geirröd and his children, one of the wickedest families of giants that ever lived in Jötunheim. And so Thor escaped from the snares of Loki, who had never done deed worse than this.

When Thor returned home to Asgard, where from Loki's lying tale he found all the gods mourning him as dead, you can fancy what a joyful reception he had. But for Loki, the false-hearted, false-tongued traitor to them all, there was only hatred. He no longer had any friends among the good folk. The wicked giants and the monsters of Utgard were now his only friends, for he had grown to be like them, and even these did not trust him overmuch.

THOR'S DUEL

as told by Abbie Farewell Brown

IN the days that are past a wonderful race of horses pastured in the meadows of heaven, steeds more beautiful and more swift than any which the world knows today. There was Hrîmfaxi, the black, sleek horse who drew the chariot of Night across the sky and scattered the dew from his foaming bit. There was Glad, behind whose flying heels sped the swift chariot of Day. His mane was yellow with gold, and from it beamed light which made the whole world bright. Then there were the two shining horses of the sun, Arvakur the watchful and Alsvith the rapid; and the nine fierce battle-chargers of the nine Valkyries, who bore the bodies of fallen heroes from the field of fight to the blessedness of Valhalla. Each of the gods had his own glorious steed, with such pretty names as Gold-mane and Silver-top, Light-foot and Precious-stone; these galloped with their masters over clouds and through the blue air, blowing flame from their nostrils and glinting sparks from their fiery eyes. The Æsir would have been poor indeed without their faithful mounts, and few would be the stories to tell in which these noble creatures do not bear at least a part.

But best of all the horses of heaven was Sleipnir, the eight-legged steed of Father Odin, who because he was so well supplied with sturdy feet could gallop faster over land and sea than any horse which ever lived. Sleipnir was snow-white and beautiful to see, and Odin was very fond and proud of him, you may be sure. He loved to ride forth upon his good horse's back to meet whatever adventure might be upon the way, and sometimes they had wild times together.

One day Odin galloped off from Asgard upon Sleipnir straight towards Jötunheim and the Land of Giants, for it was long since All-Father had been to the cold country, and he wished to see how its mountains and ice-rivers looked. Now as he galloped along a wild road, he met a huge giant standing beside his giant steed.

"Who goes there?" cried the giant gruffly, blocking the way so that Odin could not pass. "You with the golden helmet, who are you, who ride so famously through air and water? For I have been watching you from this mountain-top. Truly, that is a fine horse which you bestride."

"There is no finer horse in all the world," boasted Odin. "Have you not heard of Sleipnir, the pride of Asgard? I will match him against any of your big, clumsy giant horses."

"Ho!" roared the giant angrily. "An excellent horse he is, your little Sleipnir. But I warrant he is no match for my Gullfaxi here. Come, let us try a race; and at its end I shall pay you for your insult to our horses of Jötunheim."

So saying, the giant, whose ugly name was Hrungnir, sprang upon his horse and spurred straight at Odin in the narrow way. Odin turned and galloped back towards Asgard with all his might; for not only must he prove his horse's speed, but he must save himself and Sleipnir from the anger of the giant, who was one of the fiercest and wickedest of all his fierce and wicked race.

How the eight slender legs of Sleipnir twinkled through the blue sky! How his nostrils quivered and shot forth fire and smoke! Like a flash of lightning he darted across the sky, and the giant horse rumbled and thumped along close behind like the thunder following the flash.

"Hi, hi!" yelled the giant. "After them, Gullfaxi! And when we have overtaken the two, we will crush their bones between us!"

"Speed, speed, my Sleipnir!" shouted Odin. "Speed, good horse, or you will never again feed in the dewy pastures of Asgard with the other horses. Speed, speed, and bring us safe within the gates!"

Well Sleipnir understood what his master said, and well he knew the way. Already the rainbow bridge was in sight, with Heimdal the watchman prepared to let them in. His sharp eyes had spied them afar, and had recognized the flash of Sleipnir's white body and of Odin's golden helmet. Gallop and thud! The twelve hoofs were upon the bridge, the giant horse close behind the other. At last Hrungnir knew where he was, and into what danger he was rushing. He pulled at the reins and tried to stop his great beast. But Gullfaxi was tearing along at too terrible a speed. He could not stop. Heimdal threw open the gates of Asgard, and in galloped Sleipnir with his precious burden, safe.

Close upon them bolted in Gullfaxi, bearing his giant master, puffing and purple in the face from hard riding and anger. Cling-clang! Heimdal had shut and barred the gates, and there was the giant prisoned in the castle of his enemies.

Now the Æsir were courteous folk, unlike the giants, and they were not anxious to take advantage of a single enemy thus thrown into their power. They invited him to enter Valhalla with them, to rest and sup before the long journey of his return. Thor was not present, so they filled for the giant the great cups which Thor was wont to drain, for they were nearest to the giant size. But you remember that Thor was famous for his power to drink deep. Hrungnir's head was not so steady: Thor's draught was too much for him. He soon lost his wits, of which he had but few; and a witless giant is a most dreadful creature. He raged like a madman, and threatened to pick up Valhalla like a toy house and carry it home with him to Jötunheim. He said he would pull Asgard to pieces and slay all the gods except Freyja the fair and Sif, the golden-haired wife of Thor, whom he would carry off like little dolls for his toy house.

The Æsir knew not what to do, for Thor and his hammer were not there to protect them, and Asgard seemed in danger with this enemy within its very walls. Hrungnir called for more and more mead, which Freyja alone dared to bring and set before him. And the more he drank the fiercer he became. At last the Æsir could bear no longer his insults and his violence. Besides, they feared that there would be no more mead left for their banquets if this unwelcome visitor should keep Freyja pouring out for him Thor's mighty goblets. They bade Heimdal blow his horn and summon Thor; and this Heimdal did in a trice.

Now rumbling and thundering in his chariot of goats came Thor. He dashed into the hall, hammer in hand, and stared in amazement at the unwieldy guest whom he found there. "A giant feasting in Asgard hall!" he roared. "This is a sight which I never saw before. Who gave the insolent fellow leave to sit in my place? And why does fair Freyja wait upon him as if he were some noble guest at a feast of the high gods? I will slay him at once!" And he raised the hammer to keep his word.

Thor's coming had sobered the giant somewhat, for he knew that this was no enemy to be trifled with. He looked at Thor sulkily and said: "I am Odin's guest. He invited me to this banquet, and therefore I am under his protection."

"You shall be sorry that you accepted the invitation," cried Thor, balancing his hammer and looking very fierce; for Sif had sobbed in his ear how the giant had threatened to carry her away. Hrungnir now rose to his feet and faced Thor boldly, for the sound of Thor's gruff voice had restored his scattered wits. "I am here alone and without weapons," he said. "You would do ill to slay me now. It would be little like the noble Thor, of whom we hear tales, to do such a thing. The world will count you braver if you let me go and meet me later in single combat, when we shall both be fairly armed."

Thor dropped the hammer to his side. "Your words are true," he said, for he was a just and honourable fellow.

"I was foolish to leave my shield and stone club at home," went on the giant. "If I had my arms with me, we would fight at this moment. But I name you a coward if you slay me now, an unarmed enemy."

"Your words are just," quoth Thor again. "I have never before been challenged by any foe. I will meet you, Hrungnir, at your Stone City, midway between heaven and earth. And there we will fight a duel to see which of us is the better fellow."

Hrungnir departed for Stone City in Jötunheim; and great was the excitement of the other giants when they heard of the duel which one of their number was to fight with Thor, the deadliest enemy of their race.

"We must be sure that Hrungnir wins the victory!" they cried. "It will never do to have Asgard victorious in the first duel that we have fought with her champion. We will make a second hero to aid Hrungnir."

All the giants set to work with a will. They brought great buckets of moist clay, and heaping them up into a huge mound, moulded the mass with their giant hands as a sculptor does his image, until they had made a man of clay, an immense dummy, nine miles high and three miles wide. "Now we must make him live; we must put a heart into him!" they cried. But they could find no heart big enough until they thought of taking that of a mare, and that fitted nicely. A mare's heart is the most cowardly one that beats.

Hrungnir's heart was a three-cornered piece of hard stone. His head also was of stone, and likewise the great shield which he held before him when he stood outside Stone City waiting for Thor to come to the duel. Over his shoulder he carried his club, and that also was of stone, the kind from which whetstones are made, hard and terrible.

By his side stood the huge clay man, Möckuralfi, and they were a dreadful sight to see, these two vast bodies whom Thor must encounter.

But at the very first sight of Thor, who came thundering to the place with swift Thialfi his servant, the timid mare's heart in the man of clay throbbed with fear; he trembled so that his knees knocked together, and his nine miles of height rocked unsteadily. Thialfi ran up to Hrungnir and began to mock him, saying, "You are careless, giant. I fear you do not know what a mighty enemy has come to fight you. You hold your shield in front of you; but that will serve you nothing. Thor has seen this. He has only to go down into the earth and he can attack you conveniently from beneath your very feet."

At this terrifying news Hrungnir hastened to throw his shield upon the ground and to stand upon it, so that he might be safe from Thor's under-stroke. He grasped his heavy club with both hands and waited. He had not long to wait. There came a blinding flash of lightning and a peal of crashing thunder. Thor had cast his hammer into space. Hrungnir raised his club with both hands and hurled it against the hammer which he saw flying towards him. The two mighty weapons met in the air with an earsplitting shock. Hard as was the stone of the giant's club, it was like glass against the power of Mjöllnir. The club was dashed into pieces; some fragments fell upon the earth; and these, they say, are the rocks from which whetstones are made unto this day. They are so hard that men use them to sharpen knives and axes and scythes. One splinter of the hard stone struck Thor himself in the forehead, with so fierce a blow that he fell forward upon the ground, and Thialfi feared that he was killed. But Mjöllnir, not even stopped in its course by meeting the giant's club, sped straight to Hrungnir and crushed his stony skull, so that he fell forward over Thor, and his foot lay on the fallen hero's neck. And that was the end of the giant whose head and heart were of stone.

Meanwhile Thialfi the swift had fought with the man of clay, and had found little trouble in toppling him to earth. For the mare's cowardly heart in his great body gave him little strength to meet Thor's faithful servant; and the trembling limbs of Möckuralfi soon yielded to Thialfi's hearty blows. He fell like an unsteady tower of blocks, and his brittle bulk shivered into a thousand fragments.

Thialfi ran to his master and tried to raise him. The giant's great foot still rested upon his neck, and all Thialfi's strength could not move it away. Swift as the wind he ran for the other Æsir, and when they heard that great Thor, their champion, had fallen and seemed like one dead, they came rushing to the spot in horror and confusion. Together they all attempted to raise Hrungnir's foot from Thor's neck that they might see whether their hero lived or no. But all their efforts were in vain. The foot was not to be lifted by Æsir-might.

At this moment a second hero appeared upon the scene. It was Magni, the son of Thor himself; Magni, who was but three days old, yet already in his babyhood he was almost as big as a giant and had nearly the strength of his father. This wonderful youngster came running to the place where his father lay surrounded by a group of sad-faced and despairing gods. When Magni saw what the matter was, he seized Hrungnir's enormous foot in both his hands, heaved his broad young shoulders, and in a moment Thor's neck was free of the weight which was crushing it.

Best of all, it proved that Thor was not dead, only stunned by the blow of the giant's club and by his fall. He stirred, sat up painfully, and looked around him at the group of eager friends. "Who lifted the weight from my neck?" he asked.

"It was I, father," answered Magni modestly. Thor clasped him in his arms and hugged him tight, beaming with pride and gratitude.

"Truly, you are a fine child!" he cried. "One to make glad your father's heart. Now as a reward for your first great deed you shall have a gift from me. The swift horse of Hrungnir shall be yours – that same Gullfaxi who was the beginning of all this trouble. You shall ride Gullfaxi; only a giant steed is strong enough to bear the weight of such an infant prodigy as you, my Magni."

Now this word did not wholly please Father Odin, for he thought that a horse so excellent ought to belong to him. He took Thor aside and argued that but for him there would have been no duel, no horse to win. Thor answered simply:

"True, Father Odin, you began this trouble. But I have fought your battle, destroyed your enemy, and suffered great pain for you. Surely, I have won the horse fairly and may give it to whom I choose. My son, who has saved me, deserves a horse as good as any. Yet, as you have proved, even Gullfaxi is scarce a match for your Sleipnir. Verily, Father Odin, you should be content with the best." Odin said no more.

Now Thor went home to his cloud-palace in Thrudvang. And there he was healed of all his hurts except that which the splinter of stone had made in his forehead. For the stone was embedded so fast that it could not be taken out, and Thor suffered sorely therefor. Sif, his yellow-haired wife, was in despair, knowing not what to do. At last she bethought her of the wise woman, Groa, who had skill in all manner of herbs and witch charms. Sif sent for Groa, who lived all alone and sad because her husband Örvandil had disappeared, she knew not whither. Groa came to Thor and, standing beside his bed while he slept, sang strange songs and gently waved her hands over him. Immediately the stone in his forehead began to loosen, and Thor opened his eyes.

"The stone is loosening, the stone is coming out!" he cried. "How can I reward you, gentle dame? Prithee, what is your name?"

"My name is Groa," answered the woman, weeping, "wife of Örvandil who is lost."

"Now, then, I can reward you, kind Groa!" cried Thor. "For I can bring you tidings of your husband. I met him in the cold country, in Jötunheim, the Land of Giants, which you know I sometimes visit for a bit of good hunting. It was by Elivâgar's icy river that I met Örvandil, and there was no way for him to cross. So I put him in an iron basket and myself bore him over the flood. Br-r-r! But that is a cold land! His feet stuck out through the meshes of the basket, and when we reached the other side one of his toes was frozen stiff. So I broke it off and tossed it up into the sky that it might become a star. To prove that what I relate is true, Groa, there is the new star shining over us at this very moment. Look! From this day it shall be known to men as Örvandil's Toe. Do not you weep any longer. After all, the loss of a toe is a little thing; and I promise that your husband shall soon return to you, safe and sound, but for that small token of his wanderings in the land where visitors are not welcome."

At these joyful tidings poor Groa was so overcome that she fainted. And that put an end to the charm which she was weaving to loosen the stone from Thor's forehead. The stone was not yet wholly free, and thenceforth it was in vain to attempt its removal; Thor must always wear the splinter in his forehead. Groa could never forgive herself for the carelessness which had thus made her skill vain to help one to whom she had reason to be so grateful.

Now because of the bit of whetstone in Thor's forehead, folk of olden times were very careful how they used a whetstone; and especially they knew that they must not throw or drop one on the floor. For when they did so, the splinter in Thor's forehead was jarred, and the good Asa suffered great pain.

Thor in the Land of Giants

THE BINDING OF THE WOLF

as told by Mary Litchfield

ODIN returned to Asgard after a long absence, and all noticed that he looked more grave and majestic than ever. He spoke to no one but Frigg,[1] his wife, of the wonderful things he had seen and heard. Frigg never revealed what was told her in confidence.

Loki was away when Odin returned; and the latter at once took steps to place the children of the treacherous god and the witch of the iron-wood where they could do no harm.

The children were worthy of their parents. One was a wolf, Fenrir, not yet fully grown; him Odin had brought to Asgard and given in charge of Tyr,[2] one of the strongest and bravest of the Æsir. Another was a dangerous serpent; and he was put into the river, Ocean, that surrounded Midgard, the world of men. As soon as he touched the bottom of the sea he began to grow, and grew so fast that before long he reached entirely around Midgard; and his tail, finding no other place, grew down his throat. He was called the Midgard serpent from that time forth. But more dreadful in appearance than either of these monsters was the third. She had the form of a woman, but the hard heart of her mother, the witch of the iron-wood; and half her body was of a deathly white colour, so that no one could bear to look upon her. Odin sent her to Urd, guardian of the fountain under the third root of the World Tree, and ruler of all the realms of the dead. She made this dreadful being queen of the world of torture under Niflheim.

Loki's last two children were well disposed of, for the present, at least; but the wolf, Fenrir, kept growing stronger and fiercer each day; and Tyr, powerful as he was, found it no easy matter to control him. After consulting together, the gods decided to bind him with an iron chain.

---

1 Frigg is the usual form, but Frigga is sometimes preferred.
2 Son of Odin – one-armed god of war.

There was a smithy in Asgard, with the best facilities for making all kinds of metal things, such as chains, swords, shields and axes. And in this smithy the gods forged a chain larger and stronger than any that had ever been seen in Asgard. They took it to Fenrir and asked him to amuse them by showing his strength.

Fenrir was very proud of his strength; and as soon as he saw the chain, he knew he could easily break it.

So he let them bind him, standing quietly as they did so. When they had finished, he stretched his limbs, and the chain instantly broke in several places. The gods pretended to consider it a good joke, and praised the wolf for his strength, saying they would try the game again some day.

They now realized that to make a chain strong enough to bind the wolf was likely to prove no easy task. This time the most skilful workers in metal were secured, and they did their best to make the second chain the strongest that could possibly be forged. When it was finished, all declared that nothing like it had ever been seen in all the nine worlds.

They went to Fenrir as before; but when he saw them bringing a chain so heavy that it took several gods merely to drag it along the ground, his suspicions were aroused. He refused to be bound. Then they appealed to his pride till his strength swelled within him; and, eager to show his power, he let them wind the chain around till his whole body was covered with iron links. Then he rolled on the ground, and stretched his huge limbs, and the bonds burst as though made of some brittle metal. The gods dissembled their feelings as best they could, and praised the strength and courage of the wolf more than ever.

Odin, with his great wisdom, realized how important it was that Fenrir should be bound. Finding that Asgard could not produce a chain strong enough for that purpose, he sent Skirnir to the home of the dark elves to get one. For great as were the gods, the elves and giants knew more about some things than they did.

And indeed, the dark elves must have been very wise and skilful to have made the chain which they gave Skirnir. How they managed to get the materials of which it was composed is a mystery; for it was made of six things seldom seen in Asgard or Midgard, – namely: the footfalls of a cat, the beard of a woman, the roots of a mountain, the sinews of a bear, the breath of a fish and the spittle of birds. One could believe almost anything of a chain made of such things. It is no wonder that it was as soft and smooth as a silken string, and that its strength was greater than that of any chain made since the nine worlds were formed.

Skirnir did his errand very quickly, considering the long distance he had to go; and happy were the gods when he returned with the delicate, silken string. They felt sure of success now; for things made by the dark elves always possessed wonderful properties.

In order to disarm the suspicions of Fenrir, the gods planned an excursion to a rocky island, pretending that the sole object of the trip was amusement. The amusement was to consist mainly in trials of strength. Fenrir went with them. Had he discovered any chain, he would have suspected foul play; but there was nothing of the kind to be seen.

As soon as they reached the island, the sports began. They ran races, leaped over barriers, shot with bows, wrestled and, in short, did all those things that test men's strength and skill. After the trials were ended and the victors had been crowned, they sat on the grass near Fenrir, talking and jesting.

One of the gods then drew from his bosom the magic chain, and handing it to his neighbour, said, "They say this cord is stronger than it looks. See if you can break it." The one to whom it was given tried in vain; and then with a jest he passed it to the god next him, and so it went the rounds.

When all had tried and failed, Skirnir said, as though struck by a sudden thought, "Let Fenrir try. He has strength in breaking chains, if he can do nothing else."

So one of the gods held up the cord, saying, "Would you like to try your strength on this little string, Fenrir? Perhaps you will scorn to be bound by so slight a thing; but it is too strong for our hands to break."

The wolf refused the trial, for he suspected treachery. Then they taunted him, saying that only a coward would refuse to be bound by such a cobweb. Their taunts stirred Fenrir's pride; and he finally agreed to let them bind the chain about him, if one of their number would put his right hand into his jaws while it was being done, as a pledge of their good faith.

Upon this the gods looked at one another in dismay. But after an instant's pause, Tyr, well knowing what the result would be, stepped up to the wolf, and thrust his right

Odin and Fenrir

hand into his jaws, saying, with a laugh, "You see it is only a joke, Fenrir!"

The wolf let them bind him; and when the magic cord was tightly around, the gods moved away, all but Tyr, for they knew the struggle would be terrible.

The monster now stretched his limbs; and finding that the more he struggled the tighter grew the string, he bit Tyr's hand off at the wrist and then rolled on the ground, rending the air with his howls of rage and despair. When he had worn himself out with his desperate struggles, the gods secured him and took him back to Asgard.

Odin had him carried to a dark cave, on a rocky island, in the regions of torture below Niflheim.[3] He was chained to a rock that was sunk far into the earth, and his jaws were kept open by a sword that was thrust into them so that the hilt stood in the lower jaw and the point in the roof of his mouth. From his jaws flowed a poisonous river. There he would remain chained until Ragnarök, the Twilight of the Gods, should come.

Brave Tyr, by his sacrifice, had saved Asgard from a dangerous foe.

---

3   Rydberg describes the regions of torture in his *Teutonic Mythology*.

THE DEATH OF BALDR

as told by Mary Litchfield

LOKI proposed one day that they should have some sports on the plains of Ida; and he named among other things the game of shooting at Baldr.

Toward sundown the Æsir went out upon the broad, green plain, and Baldr stood up in the midst of them. He stood there like a beautiful victim surrounded by his foes; but his face was peaceful, and he smiled to see how they enjoyed the strange sport.

At last, all had shot except Hodur. When his turn came, he had no weapon. Some say he was blind, and that was why he could not shoot. Just then Loki came up, and said, "Here is a little arrow I found the other day; perhaps this will do." And he gave Hodur a small, well-made arrow. Hodur took the arrow, fitted it to the string, and in an instant it was whizzing through the air. The next moment Baldr had fallen, pierced to the heart by the fatal weapon of mistletoe.

The gods were so astounded that at first no one moved. Then Thor sprang forward and lifted Baldr gently from the ground – but he was dead. All eyes were now turned towards Hodur; for the Æsir did not suspect that Loki was the real author of the deed.

Still, no one sought to avenge Baldr's death; for the laws of the peace-stead, where they were, permitted no violence.

Wailing and lamenting, they took up the body and went slowly toward the palace of Gladsheim. The birds stopped singing, and the flowers drooped as the dead god passed by. When Odin saw them coming, and knew that Baldr was killed, he bowed his head, and said, "My son is dead! The light is gone from Asgard!" Frigg clasped him in her arms and vainly begged him to come back. The sorrow of Nanna, Baldr's wife, was too deep for tears. She did not speak or cry; but the colour left her cheek, and her eye grew dim.

BALDR'S FUNERAL

as told by Mary Litchfield

BALDR'S body was placed in the great hall of his palace of "Broad-shining-splendour". He lay there as though asleep. His broad brow was peaceful, and his expression radiant and beautiful. Tall youths stood about him, clad in white and holding torches of sweet-smelling wood. Reverently they stood with bowed heads, while many came from distant places to look once more upon the purest of the gods. At intervals the youths chanted solemn hymns in a low tone; and at the end of each hymn came in the refrain, "Baldr the Beautiful is dead!"

News of his death soon reached the world of men, and great was the sorrow felt at his loss.

Men reverenced Odin for his wisdom and his might in battle; Baldr, they loved. Even the light-elves, always gay and merry, wept for Baldr; and the dwarfs, when they heard of his death, began to search for jewels to be burnt with him. The stony hearts of the giants were softened, and they came in troops to see him, bringing great trees, to be burned in the funeral pile.

Baldr's ship, *Ringhorn*, was the largest ship in the world, and on that was built the funeral pile. The huge trees brought by the giants were first laid on; then smaller trees; and finally branches of all sweet-smelling woods. Over the boughs were laid mantles, beautifully wrought. Baldr's horse, richly caparisoned, was next placed upon the pile. And last, all who wished to honour the dead god brought gifts to be burnt with him. Odin gave his ring made by Sindri; Thor, a finely tempered sword; many of the goddesses brought their necklaces and bracelets; the dwarfs gave precious jewels; and the light-elves, having no possessions, strewed the pile with flowers.

When all was ready, they went to Baldr's palace. The youths who had been watching there placed the body upon a golden litter, and bore it slowly towards the ship. Behind them walked Nanna, supported by her maidens. She was clothed in white, and her long hair floated over her shoulders. The others, however, displayed all their magnificence in honour of the dead god. Odin was there with his wolves and his ravens. Frigg wore her richest garments, although her heart was sad. Frey rode the boar with the golden bristles, and Freyja was in her chariot drawn by cats. Thor had his famous goats. Many gods rode steeds of great beauty. And even Heimdall had left his post at the northern end of Bifröst, and came mounted on Goldtop, whose mane shone like the sun.

A strange procession it was; gods, giants, elves and dwarfs, all uniting to honour the purest of the Æsir. And strange were the hymns they sang, as they slowly traversed the long road from Baldr's palace to the sea. The deep tones of the giants blended for once with the shrill, piping voices of the light-elves, as ancient battle-hymns and songs of peace rose upon the still air.

When they reached the ship, all stood silent, while Baldr's body was lifted upon the funeral pile. As the youths stepped down, they saw that Nanna had fallen, and her maidens were trying in vain to bring her back to life. Her heart had broken when she saw Baldr leaving her to go alone upon his last voyage. So they placed her beside him whom she had loved better than life itself.

Thor raised high his mighty hammer and consecrated the pile, while sharp lightnings flashed, and thunder sounded through the clear sky. The white sails were spread, the youths lighted the pile with their torches, and the ship *Ringhorn* left forever the shores of Asgard, and sailed towards the setting sun. As it sailed away, the smoke rose to heaven, and soon the whole ship was in flames; until at last it sank behind the western horizon in a blaze of glory.

HERMOD'S JOURNEY IN SEARCH OF BALDR

as told by Mary Litchfield

AFTER Baldr's death Frigg asked whether anyone would be willing to go to the lower world in search of him, while preparations for his funeral were going on in Asgard. Hermod, the messenger-god, offered to go, and started off at once, on Sleipnir, the swiftest of steeds.

The Æsir watched eagerly for his return, and loud shouts went up when he appeared. He entered the great hall of Gladsheim, where all were gathered, and approaching Odin, said: "I bring you hope! Baldr greets you, and sends again this ring made by the dwarfs, which he asks you to keep always in remembrance of him." Then turning to Frigg, he gave her a carpet and other gifts from Nanna; and to Fulla, one of her maidens, a finger-ring. After bestowing these gifts, and giving each one a message from Baldr, he said:

"I went, as you know, by the bridge Bifröst, whose northern end is near Niflheim. For nine nights Sleipnir bore me through valleys deep and dark, and at last I reached the river Gjöll, which is spanned by the Gjallar bridge, whose roof is of glittering gold. As Sleipnir stepped upon the bridge, the maid Modgud, who keeps it, asked me my name and my parentage, saying that the day before five bands of dead men had ridden over, and had not made as much noise as Sleipnir's hoofs made in just striking the bridge.

"'And', she added, 'it did not shake beneath them as it does beneath you.' Then she looked closely at me, and said: 'You have not the complexion of the dead; why do you ride here on your way to the realms of Urd?' I told her I came seeking Baldr, and I asked her whether he had passed that way. She said that he had ridden over the Gjallar bridge; and she then told me how to go, that I might find him.

"I went as she bade me, and came at last to that part of Mimir's realms where rules

Delling, the elf of the dawn. After going far into a thick forest I found the castle she had described. It was as magnificent as Gladsheim; indeed, I cannot begin to tell of its beauty and grandeur; but it was surrounded by a wall so high that no intruder could hope to get near. Fortunately, I rode Sleipnir; no other steed would have served me then. With one bound he cleared the high wall, and I found myself in a lovely garden. Before me was the castle. The door was open, so I stepped in; and the first person I saw was Baldr. He sat upon a kind of throne. Nanna was beside him. The castle was filled with beings who were evidently rejoicing at Baldr's coming. They did not seem to be gods, and yet were fairer and nobler than mortals.

"Baldr rose to greet me as I entered, and his face beamed with the same expression of peace and good-will that it wore when he was among us. And Nanna looked as happy as on the day when she first came to Asgard as Baldr's wife. I was filled with wonder.

"Baldr said kindly: 'Hermod, you are astonished at seeing us so well and so happy here in the lower world. We have been warmly welcomed by the people who live in this beautiful castle, and their golden mead has the virtues of Idunn's apples, and even more; for it has restored Nanna and myself to the fullest enjoyment of life.'

"'Who are these people, Baldr?' I inquired.

"'I may not tell you all about them,' Baldr replied; 'but they are my loyal subjects, and repay my love and care with the greatest devotion.'

"Then we talked of Asgard, and of you all, as we drank the golden mead. I asked Baldr whether he would return to us should the great goddess of the realms of death allow him to do so.

"He pondered deeply, and then replied, 'Yes, I would return were it allowed; not wholly for my own pleasure – for I already love my new subjects; but because you all grieve so for my loss in the upper worlds.' And he added with a smile, 'We are very happy here.'

"When I left the palace, he and Nanna put into my hands the gifts I have brought, and seemed loath to part with me.

"From there I went south, to the land of Urd, so well known to you all. I found the mighty goddess seated by her well, her two sisters near. When I begged her to allow Baldr to return to Asgard, she said, 'Is Baldr unhappy in the lower world?'

"'No,' I replied; 'but we grieve for him in Asgard. The sun itself seems to have lost its brightness since Baldr left us; and not the gods alone, all mankind, the dwarfs and the elves, and even the stony giants, long for Baldr's return.'

"'Are you sure that all mourn for Baldr?' said the dread goddess, in her deep, solemn voice.

"'Yes, all,' I replied.

"Then after a pause, she said slowly, 'Should every creature wish for his return, should each one weep for him, he might go back to Asgard; not otherwise. Remember, all must weep!'

"And so I bring you hope; for surely all will weep for Baldr; he was so loved by all."

Messengers were sent far and wide to bid all beings weep for Baldr; even the trees and stones. On swift steeds the heralds rushed along, crying, "Baldr the Beautiful is dead! Weep for him!" Over high mountains, through deep valleys, by the lonely shore, everywhere they went, crying, "Baldr the Beautiful is dead! Weep for him!" And as they heard the cry, all beings, even the rocks and the stones, wept for the god beloved of gods and men.

The messengers were going home, rejoicing in their success, when they met a giantess who called herself Thok. As she gazed at them with her cold, unfeeling eyes, they cried, "Baldr the Beautiful is dead! Weep for him!" But she answered,

> "Thok will weep
> With dry tears
> For Baldr's death;
> Neither in life nor in death
> Gave he me gladness.
> Let Hel keep what she has."

As she spoke these words, the giantess laughed a hard, mocking laugh, and disappeared; and the messengers went slowly back to Asgard. No one knew until afterwards that the giantess was really Loki in disguise.

Hermod bows to Hela

LOKI AT ÆGIR'S FEAST

as told by Mary Litchfield

**ÆGIR** had a palace at the bottom of the ocean, in the western part of the lower world. It was an enormous building, and its many peaks and towers seemed to undulate as they rose through the dim waters. Near it were forests of sea-trees that lifted their palm-like branches as high as the castle's loftiest pinnacles. Beside the pearl walls glowed corals, red or rose-coloured, and over them ran vines of delicate green.

Ægir had asked all the gods to a feast. The huge kettle procured by Thor and Tyr was to be used for the first time; so there would doubtless be mead enough to go round.

As they entered the deep-sea palace, the gods beheld a scene of rare beauty. The large hall rose to a great height, its roof supported by pillars of coral. From the roof hung golden lamps, flooding the hall with light. Sea-plants grew in all the recesses, and from shells hidden away came sounds of low, sweet music.

The feast was spread upon a shell-shaped table. In the centre of the table stood the giant-kettle, Mile-deep; but so transformed that Hymir himself would not have known it. Its pearly sides gleamed with the soft tints of the rainbow, and around the edge was a rim of gold. It had undergone a "sea-change", and was now, indeed, "something rich and strange". Sea-youths and sea-maidens, some of them Ægir's own children, walked or rather floated about the palace; for in the deep sea no one walked as he would on the land. The maidens wore robes of green, and looked like mermaids with their long hair and their crowns of gold.

The guests were seated, and the feasting began. Ægir sat at the head of the table, with Odin beside him; while Ran, his wife, sat next Frigg.

Loki had not been invited; for, although no one could say that he had killed Baldr, all the Æsir felt that he had planned to bring about his death; and they could no longer endure his presence. But, unbidden, he appeared while they were feasting; determined to spoil their pleasure if he might not share it. He stood near the great door, looking with eyes of hate upon the fair scene. When some of the gods praised Ægir's servants, his fierce jealousy was aroused; for he could not endure to hear anyone praised. And there in the presence of Ægir and the gods he slew one of the servants. Thereupon the Æsir shook their shields and drove him from the hall. He quickly disappeared in the forest of sea-trees.

They went back to their feasting; but it was not long before Loki returned. With a sneer on his lips and fierce hatred in his eyes, he asked for a drink of the mead and a seat at the table. Bragi had great cause for disliking Loki, because he had betrayed Idunn, his wife, into the hands of Thiassi; and he spoke first:

"A seat and place will the Æsir never find for you at their board!" Loki answered him with taunts and sneers. Then he turned to Odin and reminded him of the oath they had sworn when both were young; and he told how, in those days, Odin refused even to taste beer unless it were offered to him also.

Not wishing to have the feast disturbed, Odin spoke to Vidar, the silent, and said, "Rise, Vidar, and let the wolf's sire sit at our feast, that he may not utter insolent words in Ægir's hall."

So Vidar rose up and presented Loki with a cup of mead; but instead of drinking, the latter began to pour out abuse upon the gods. No one escaped his venomous tongue. And, unfortunately, many of the bitter things he said were only too true; for brave and beautiful as were the gods, few of them were pure and good like Baldr. The worst he could say of Heimdall was that he had to spend his life guarding the trembling bridge.

When he reviled Frigg, she said, "False Loki, had I a son like Baldr here, you would not go out unhurt. You would be assaulted."

Then, his rage and hatred making him forget caution, Loki replied, "Shall I tell you more of my wickedness, Frigg? I am the cause of Baldr's absence. Because of me you do not see him riding to these halls."

At these awful words the gods rose to their feet and grasped their weapons; but at a sign from Odin they restrained their wrath, and again seated themselves. No violence might be done in Ægir's halls.

Loki kept on cursing the gods until he came to Sif, Thor's wife. Thor was not there; he was far from Asgard when the Æsir were bidden to the feast. However, as Loki was abusing Sif, one of Freyja's maidens cried: "The floor of the sea trembles. I think Thor is coming from his home. He will silence this reviler of the gods!"

She was right. In a moment a noise like thunder was heard, and Thor appeared, bearing his mighty hammer. When he understood what was going on, he called out to Loki: "Silence, vile creature! My mighty hammer Mjöllnir shall stop your prating. I will strike your head from your neck: then your life will be ended."

Loki's fear of Thor did not prevent his uttering insulting words to him also.

Then, again, the fierce thunder-god cried in a loud voice: "Silence, vile creature! My mighty hammer Mjöllnir shall stop your prating. Up will I hurl you to the east region; and no one shall ever see you again!"

Still Loki would not be silenced. In a sneering tone, he said: "Of your eastern travels you had better say little. It was there you were doubled up in a glove-thumb. You, the great hero of the gods! You hardly thought then that you were Thor."

Thor spoke again: "Silence, wretch! With this right hand, I, the terror of the giants, will smite you so that every bone shall be broken!"

Loki laughed a loud, mocking laugh, and said: "'Tis my intention to live a long life, although you do threaten me with your hammer. Skrymir's thongs seemed hard to you when you could not get at the food – you, strong and healthy, dying of hunger!" "Silence, monster!" cried Thor again. "My mighty hammer Mjöllnir shall stop your prating! I, the foe of the giants, will cast you down to hell, beneath the gratings of the dead!"

Loki spoke: "I have said before the Æsir, and I have said before the Æsir's sons, whatever my mind suggested; but for you alone will I go out, because I know that you will fight!" Then, turning to Ægir, he said: "Never again shall you brew beer and hold a feast of the gods. Flames shall play over all your possessions, and you shall be burnt with them!"

With these words he darted swiftly from the hall, and they saw him no more.

THE CAPTURE OF LOKI

as told by Mary Litchfield

LOKI, after he had fled from Ægir's halls, hid among high mountains, and there built himself a house with four doors, which looked north, south, east and west. Near the house a stream rushed foaming over the rocks into the sea. Here he lived in constant fear of the gods; for he knew that since he had owned himself the real slayer of Baldr, they would show him no mercy. But although he had chosen the remotest and most secure hiding-place, Odin from his High Seat spied him out, and Thor and some of the other gods at once set out to capture him.

Loki knew that the gods were coming some time before they reached the house. And hastily casting a fishing-net that he was making into the fire, he changed himself into a salmon, and leaped into the neighbouring stream.

The gods entered the house, but there was no Loki. They searched, but could not find him. As they were looking carefully in every nook and corner, knowing that the crafty god possessed the power of changing himself into different shapes, one of their number noticed something peculiar in the ashes, and called the others to come and look. One said that it looked as though a device for catching fish had been recently thrust into the fire; and on pulling it out, they found that it was a half-burnt net. This suggested the idea that in order to elude them, Loki had changed himself into a fish, and had leaped into the stream nearby.

The gods at once set to work and wove a net after the pattern of the one found in the ashes; and when it was finished, they took it to the river. Putting it in, they let it sink to the bottom. And then Thor took one end, while the other gods took the other, and thus they drew it along the stream. The wily salmon, however, thrust himself between two stones and the net passed over him. So, when the gods drew it up, they found that although it had touched some living thing, there was no fish in it.

The next time they put great weights into the net, so that it raked the bed of the river. Loki, finding that he could not escape if he stayed at the bottom, and knowing that it was but a short distance to the sea, swam rapidly down the stream, and leaped over the net to where the river fell foaming over the rocks. The gods saw him as he rose above the water in his flying leap. The next time they divided themselves into two bands; and they dragged the net, while Thor followed, wading in the middle of the river. Loki must now do one of two things – leap again over the net, upstream, or swim rapidly out to sea. He chose the former course, and leaped high into the air. But Thor was ready, and with a quick motion caught him in his hand. The salmon was so slippery that he would have escaped had not Thor had a firm grip on his tail.[1] Loki was now forced to take his proper shape; and they bound him and carried him to the lower world.

In the great judgment hall near Urd's well, his doom was pronounced. All beings who had suffered through him or who knew of his crimes were called upon to testify. Frigg charged him with the death of Baldr; Bragi, with the betrayal of Idunn; and Skadi said that he had caused the death of her father, Thiassi. All – gods, elves, dwarfs and giants – witnessed to the harm they or their friends had suffered at the hands of the wicked god. When all the evidence was brought in, it seemed as though no punishment could be great enough for so cruel and treacherous a being.

Urd's servants took him, bound, to the dark cave near Mt Hvergelmir. And there the iron gates were opened, and they went down to the world of darkness. Torches shed their lurid light upon the awful scenes. Here were confined many horrible monsters – giants, witches and dragons – foes to gods and men.

After a long journey they reached the borders of a dark, sluggish sea. Taking a boat, they rowed out to a rocky island, rising in the midst of the sea. The island was full of caves in which monsters were confined; in one was the wolf, Fenrir. They placed Loki near his offspring, binding his feet and hands with strong chains, and fastening him firmly to the rocks. The rest of his punishment was too dreadful to be told; but dreadful as it was, Loki deserved it all.

Near the rocky island was moored an enormous ship, called *Nagelfar*; it was larger even than *Ringhorn*, Baldr's ship. When Ragnarök, the Twilight of the Gods, should

---

1   Ever since that time salmon have had very fine, thin tails.

Loki is punished

come, Loki would be freed from his fetters; and gathering the hosts of evil, would set sail upon this ship to fight against the gods. Then the fierce venom of his soul, nursed through long years, would flame out in deeds against his hated foes.

THE BEGINNING OF POETRY

as told by Sarah Powers Bradish

I. KVASIR

THE gods once had a great dispute with the *vana*s, the spirits of the sea and air. When peace was made, the gods created a wonderful being in honour of the event. They called him Kvasir.

Kvasir was very wise, almost as wise as Odin himself. He spent his time walking up and down the earth, answering the questions of men. He taught new and useful things. Men loved him because he was so good and kind.

The dwarfs were jealous of him, and sought to destroy him. One day two dwarfs, Fialar and Galar, came upon him as he lay asleep in the forest, and killed him. They found his charm and saved it. It was a liquid, which they mixed with honey, to make a kind of mead. They kept it in three vessels: the kettle Odhoerir (inspiration), the bowl Son (expiation) and the cup Boden (offering). They knew that whoever tasted this magic mead would instantly become a poet, a sweet singer or an orator. Still, none of the dwarfs ever touched the mead. They kept it hidden in a secret place.

One day the dwarfs found the giant, Gilling, asleep on a steep bank. They shoved him off into the water, and he was drowned. Then the wicked dwarfs rolled a millstone upon the roof of Gilling's house. Some of them went into the house and told the giantess that her husband was dead. Frantic with grief, she rushed out to find his body. Just as she left the door, the other dwarfs rolled the stone down upon her head, and crushed her.

The cruel dwarfs thought themselves safe, because Gilling had no children to avenge his death. But he had a brother, Suttung, who caught them, and placed them on a shoal, where the tide would be sure to carry them out to sea. They begged for their lives, but he was deaf to their entreaties, until they promised to give him their precious mead.

Then he took them back to the shore, and they brought him the kettle Odhoerir, the bowl Son and the cup Boden. He gave them to his daughter, Gunlod, at the same time forbidding her to give a taste to either gods or men.

Gunlod watched over her charge day and night. To guard it more securely, she carried it into a cave within a mountain. Even Odin would hardly have known where it was, but for his ever-watchful ravens, Hugin and Munin, who flew back to Asgard with the news as soon as Gunlod had found a place for her treasure.

II. ODIN WORKS ON A FARM

ODIN was very wise, because, ages before, he had exchanged one of his eyes for a drink from Mimir's well at the foot of the great world tree, Yggdrasil. He had also hung nine days and nine nights from the boughs of Yggdrasil, for the sake of mastering the magic runes. But he was not a poet, and he could not sing. He could not rest until he had tasted the mead of the dwarfs. He put on his cloud cloak and his broad-brimmed hat, and set out for the land of the giants.

On the way to the house of Suttung, he passed a meadow where nine thralls were mowing. Their scythes were very dull. He drew a whetstone from the folds of his cloak and offered to sharpen them. The thralls gladly accepted his service. He did the work so quickly and so well that they asked to be allowed to keep the whetstone. Odin tossed it up in the air toward them. In the scramble that followed, the thralls became entangled in their scythes in such a way that each one cut off his neighbour's head. Odin, not at all disturbed, went quietly on his way.

He soon came to the house of Baugi, a brother of Suttung. Baugi received him very kindly. During their conversation, the giant said he did not know how he was going to finish haying, because all his thralls had been killed.

Odin at once offered to do the work of the nine thralls, if, at the end of the season, Baugi would get for him one draught of Suttung's mead. This, Baugi agreed to do; and Odin, who had given his name as Bolwerk, went to work. The hay was secured, the grain harvested, and all the summer work of the farm finished before the autumn rains set in.

When the first days of winter came, Bolwerk went to his master to ask for the prompt payment of his wages. Baugi said he dared not ask his brother for the mead, but he would try to get a few drops of it as he had promised.

III. GUNLOD'S TREASURE

ODIN and Baugi went together to the mountain where Gunlod was hidden. They could find no entrance to her cave. Odin gave Baugi his auger, Roti, and told him to bore a hole, through which they could creep into the mountain.

Baugi worked for a few minutes, and said he had bored the hole. Odin, suspecting treachery, blew into the hole. Dust and chips flew back into his face, so that he knew the hole did not reach clear through the rock. He told Baugi to bore again. When he blew into the hole a second time, no dust came back; and he knew an opening had been made into the cave. He took the form of a worm and crawled through the hole. Treacherous Baugi thrust the auger in after him, hoping to crush him, but he had come out on the other side.

Odin at once resumed his own form, and asked Gunlod for a sip of the mead. Three days and three nights he begged, but Gunlod refused.

At last, she brought out the three vessels, and told him he might take a little from each. But Odin managed to get every drop of the precious mead. Then he became an eagle, and flew away over the mountain tops toward Asgard. His flight was slow, on account of the weight of the mead. He was still a long way from Asgard, when he found that he was pursued. Suttung had also put on eagle's plumage, and was fast overtaking him. But Odin strained every muscle, and reached the wall a little in advance of Suttung.

The gods had seen the race, and had gathered a pile of chips and shavings, which they set on fire, just as Suttung flew over the wall. The flames rose high in the air, and burned the wings of Suttung, who fell into the fire and was destroyed.

Odin flew to the urn, which had been prepared to receive the mead, and poured it out with such haste that a few drops fell on the earth. Men found it, and as many as possible tasted it. All who tasted were known as rhymesters and poetasters.

The gods carefully preserved the mead; and sometimes, at long intervals, they gave a little to some favoured man, whom they wished to become famous for poetry or eloquence.

But Odin sipped only a little of the mead. Most of it was kept for his son, Bragi, who was born about this time. Bragi became the god of poetry and music. The gods gave him a magic golden harp, and put him into a ship, and let him sail over the ocean.

As the ship floated along, Bragi took the harp, and sang the "Song of Life", the sound of which rose to Asgard, and fell to the abode of Hela. As he played and sang, the ship glided over the water, and touched the shore. The young god walked through the forest, playing and singing as he went. The trees budded and blossomed, and flowers sprang up in the grass along his path, within the sound of the music.

In the forest he met Idunn, the daughter of Ivald, the dwarf. Idunn became Bragi's wife and the goddess of flowers and of immortal youth.

THE JUDGMENT HALL OF THE DEAD

as told by Sarah Powers Bradish

EACH day Odin and the other gods rode over Bifröst, going towards the south, and went down to the lower world. Near the southern end of the celestial bridge was the well that watered the third root of Yggdrasil. An old book says that the waters of this well were so "holy that everything that is put in the well becomes as white as the membrane between the egg and the eggshell". The roots of Yggdrasil were continually sprinkled with its waters, and were as white as silver in consequence. Two swans of purest white, the parents of all the swans that ever have been, glided over its surface; and its edge, like that of Mimir's well, was thickly overlaid with gold.

Urd, the great norn who was queen of the world of the dead, dwelt near the well with her two sisters. Multitudes of messengers and attendants stood ready to do her bidding; for her realms were vast, her power extending even to the dark region under Niflheim. All beings who died in Midgard came first to the great judgment hall near her well. And it was to meet them there, and with Urd to pass judgment upon them, that the gods each day crossed the trembling bridge and came to the lower world. Thor, the thunder-god, could not pass over the bridge, because his heavy iron chariot would have injured it; so he was obliged to ford three rivers on his way.

The great judgment hall was a solemn place, and the decisions pronounced there, whether gentle or severe, were always just. Mortals who had been very wicked were sent to the world of torture. Those who had died on the field of battle were claimed by Odin, the All-Father, or by Freyja, a Van-goddess who lived in Asgard with the Æsir. Odin sent his maidens, the Valkyries, to choose the heroes on the battle-field, and to conduct them to Asgard. They went to his great palace of Valhalla; and there they feasted and fought each day, that they might be ready to do battle with the powers of evil when Ragnarök, the Twilight of the Gods, should come.[1] Freyja united again lovers who had been faithful unto death. Mortals whose lives had been peaceful and pure went to a home prepared for them by Urd, in a land where the fields stretched green and beautiful, and where it was always summer.

The Valkyries

---

1   Freyr's sister, a Van-goddess. Half of the slain in battle belonged to her.

THE TWILIGHT OF THE GODS

as told by Mary Litchfield

**WHEN** the gods returned to Asgard, it seemed to them that everything was changed. Baldr was gone forever, and Loki, once a gay, witty companion, and later a secret and dreaded foe, was securely bound in the world of darkness. As evening fell upon the city, Odin, surrounded by the greater gods, stood looking out upon the sea, over which the ship *Ringhorn* had borne the dead Baldr.

All were silent, until at last Odin spoke: "Baldr has gone, and Loki is punished. A new life begins; and it is right that you, the wisest and strongest of the Æsir, should know what lies before you, and before us all. You are strong, and can bear the truth, hard though it be. You have heard that a time is coming, called the Twilight of the Gods; it is of that I will now speak." Then silence reigned again, while Odin stood with bowed head.

At last he spoke, uttering this solemn prophecy, while his eyes seemed looking into the far, dim future:

"As the ages roll on, wickedness shall increase in Asgard, and in the world of men. Witches and monsters shall be bred up in the iron-wood, and shall sow the seeds of evil in the world. Brothers shall slay each other; cousins shall violate kinship; shields shall be cloven; no man will spare another. Hard shall it be in the world – an axe age, a sword age, a wind age, ere the world sinks.

"The great Fimbul winter shall come, when snow shall fall from the four corners of heaven; deadly will be the frosts, and piercing the winds, and the darkened sun will impart no gladness. Three such winters shall come, and no summer to gladden the heart with sunshine. Then shall follow more winters, when even greater discord shall prevail. Fierce wolves shall devour the sun and moon, and the stars shall fall from heaven. The earth shall tremble, the stony hills shall be dashed together, giants shall totter, and dwarfs groan before their stony doors. Men shall seek the paths leading to the realms of death; and earth, in flames, shall sink beneath the seething ocean.

"Then shall the aged World Tree tremble; and loudly shall bark the dog of hell. At that sound shall the fetters of Loki and the wolf be broken; and the Midgard serpent, with terrible lashing and struggling, shall forsake the sea. The ship *Nagelfar* shall be loosed from its moorings by the rocky isle; and all the hosts of evil shall go on board, while Loki steers them across the sluggish sea. Surt[1] shall leave his fiery dales, and join the hosts of evil, to fight against the gods.

"Loudly shall the ancient horn of Heimdall then resound throughout the nine worlds. And when they hear the sound, the hosts of Odin shall make ready; the gods and all the warriors of Valhalla shall buckle on their armour for the last great fight. Odin shall seek wisdom from Mimir, that he may know how best to meet his foes.

"Terrible will be the onset when on the great plain[2] the hosts of the sons of destruction meet the armies of the gods. Then will come the second grief to Frigg, when Odin goes to meet the wolf. For then will her beloved fall. But Vidar, the great son of Odin, shall pierce the heart of Loki's offspring, and avenge his father's death. Mighty Thor will meet the Midgard serpent, and in his rage will slay the worm. Back nine paces will he go, and then fall – he who feared no foe – slain by the venom of the deadly beast. Tyr shall meet the fierce dog of hell, and they shall slay each other. Freyr will meet his death at the hand of Surt, slain by Thiassi's fatal sword. Little shall the love of Gerd avail him on that day. Heimdall, the wise and pure, shall fall at the hand of Loki, the father of monsters, and shall in turn cause Loki's death. Few shall be left alive who meet in that great fight!"

He ceased, and there was silence, while the shadows deepened, and the sea grew dark.

Finally Tyr spoke: "And is there no hope, Odin? Does all end in darkness?" At these words Odin's face changed; a gleam of sunshine seemed to fall upon it, and he said: "I see arise, a second time, earth from ocean, beauteously green. I see waterfalls where leap

---

1 Surt was the father of Suttung, from whom Odin treacherously obtained the poetic mead – the mead that could make men poets.
2 This plain was a hundred miles square.

A giant with a flaming sword

the fish, and eagles flying over the hills. I see Baldr and Hodur, the rulers of a purer race of mortals – mortals who have long served Baldr in the lower world – and near them Vidar and the sons of Thor. They meet on Ida's plains, and call to memory the mighty deeds of the old gods, and their ancient lore. They speak of the serpent, the great earth-encircler, and of the deeds of Loki and of Thor. Unsown shall the fields bring forth, and all evil shall be done away with, when Baldr and Hodur reign."

He ceased, while his gaze seemed penetrating through the misty ages.

The silence was long; but finally one of the gods said: "And what of us, Odin? Is there no hope for the old gods?"

As he spoke, a look never before seen on his bold features overspread the face of Odin, and raising his eyes reverently, he said: "After the Twilight of the Gods shall come the Mighty One to judgment – He whom we dare not name, the powerful One from above, who rules over all. He shall dooms pronounce, and strifes allay, and holy peace establish, which shall be forevermore. I see a hall with gold bedecked, brighter than the sun, standing in the high heavens. There shall the righteous dwell forevermore, in peace and happiness."

As the vision faded, Odin looked upon the gods, who stood silent before him. "My children," said the All-Father, "let us be strong and valiant. Long will be the ages, hard will be the fighting, and many the woes that we must endure; but the brave heart loves danger, and the strong soul shrinks not from evil and sorrow. To do our best, knowing that we shall fail; to fight to the end, and then give place to those who are wholly pure and good – that is the fate of the old gods. He whom we may not name has so decreed it; and His decrees are ever just and right."

TALES FROM THE SAGAS

THE STORY OF VÖLUND

as told by Julia Goddard

 THERE was once a king of Finnland who had three sons, all eager lovers of hunting. The two elder were named Slagfin and Egil, the youngest was called Völund.

But Völund not only loved hunting like his brothers; he had a power which his brothers did not possess. He was a wonderful craftsman at the forge, and could make arrow-heads, spears and weapons of all kinds. Moreover, he could model shields with rare chasing, and sometimes would fashion chains and armlets of fine gold that the daintiest queen might be proud to wear.

So well he loved his work that he spent more than half his time at the forge, and never gave it up but for a day's hunting with his brothers. And more than once he even gave up the chase, for though he loved hunting well, he loved his anvil better. And his workshop was quite a sight to see with all the wonderful things that he had made hanging round.

At last Slagfin said to Egil, "Völund spends too much of his time at the forge, it is not work befitting a king's son. He will lose all interest in the chase, unless something is done to rouse him."

And Egil replied: "Thou hast spoken well, my brother, and a thought has come into my mind. I am growing tired of the hunting grounds near home; the sport is not so good as it used to be. But far away in Ulfdal, on the shores of Ulf lake, is a mighty forest. There we may chase the wolf and the wild boar, and in the lake we may catch more fish than we shall know what to do with. Let us go thither and take Völund with us. Then will he forget his forge and his bellows, and live as a king's son ought to live."

The idea pleased Slagfin greatly, and away he went to Völund to propose the plan. He found Völund at work upon slender spears of a new pattern. "Ha!" he said, as he took one of them up to look at. "We could make good use of this at Ulfdal. What do you say to going there with Egil and myself? We might build a hut on the borders of the lake, and live upon the game we kill. You have been toiling at your forge too long, the change will do you good."

"I must finish this spear first," returned Völund. "It is the best of the lot, and though it is so light, it is so strong that nothing can blunt its point or break it in twain."

"Work away, then," said Slagfin, "but be ready to start with Egil and me by tomorrow's dawn. You must bring your choicest weapons with you, for we expect rare sport."

"Take any you please," answered Völund, "for I have no time to choose for you. The spear I am working upon will suffice for me, I shall want no other weapon."

Then Slagfin chose arrows, and sharp spears, and hooks, and strong chains, long nails and a heavy hammer.

"We must build for ourselves," he said, "for no man dwells on the borders of Ulf lake."

"So much the better," responded Völund ; "I like the sound of my hammer, and the song of the birds, better than the voices of men."

And Slagfin went away well pleased that Völund was willing to go to Ulfdal. And early in the morning, just as the sun was rising over the low hills, the three brothers were seen loaded with their hunting gear, starting off for the wild forest that bordered the lake.

Völund was strong and mighty of limb; he had muscles almost as strong as those of Thor, his eyes were dark, and his black hair curled crisply round his brow. He was not so handsome as his fair-headed brothers, but he was taller and more like a king, and everyone said as he passed along, "There is no one in Finnland to equal Völund."

Further and further they left the city behind, wilder grew the country and the sun shone high above them.

"Shall we not rest?" asked Egil. "We have journeyed many a mile and my limbs are weary; besides, it will be pleasanter travelling when the sun goes down."

Then Völund smiled: "If you were accustomed as I am to the heat of the forge, you would not mind the sun's rays. Nevertheless, let it be as you please," he added, throwing himself down at the foot of a tall pine tree. "There is no hurry for getting to Ulfdal, the game will not chide our loitering, since it will give them longer life in the forest."

So the three brothers rested and after a while set out again on their march. There remained yet three days' journey to Ulfdal. But at length they reached it, and were repaid for their toil when they saw the tall pines shoot up their branches high into the air, and heard the low growl of the wolf not far off, and beheld the blue lake stretching out like a quiet sea with the wild swan sailing on its glassy waters and the water-fowl rustling among the reeds and rushes.

"This is a pleasant place," quoth Slagfin.

Then the brothers heaped together a pile of boughs and brushwood and made themselves a fire. And Egil fitted an arrow to his bow and shot the sea-fowl as they lazily fluttered by, whilst Slagfin cast a net into the lake and hauled up a plentiful supply of fish.

Meanwhile the strong Völund had cut down several pines and built up a hut so quickly that Slagfin and Egil thought it had been done by magic.

It was but a rude hovel for the sons of a king, but what did the princes care? The summer sun shone brightly and the nights were warm, and besides they loved hunting well enough to care little for all discomforts.

They spent their time in the forest, and many a wolf-skin would they have to carry back to Finnland. Many a wild boar fell under the spear of Völund, and there was great slaughter among the water-fowl and the wild deer.

Day after day went by, and Völund rejoiced so much in the great free forest that Slagfin and Egil hoped that he had forgotten his forge.

One morning when they went forth from the hut they marvelled at hearing voices in the distance; and not the voices of men, but low sweet tones and gentle laughter, such as they were accustomed to hear from the queen's ladies at court.

And lo, close by the water's edge there sat three fair maidens spinning flax. And as they span they sang a song that even to Völund sounded sweeter than the notes of the forest birds.

The brothers drew nearer, and never had they seen faces so fair as those of the three maidens, who were so busily engaged in their task that they did not see Völund and his brothers until they were close to them.

When however they did see them, they seemed in no whit abashed, but began to talk to them, and to tell them how they too had heard of the quiet Ulf lake and had determined to leave their own country and abide on the outskirts of the wild forest.

"So we put on our swan-coats and flew away," said the maidens, "and the king, our father, knows not what has become of us."

When Slagfin heard that the damsels were king's daughters he was very glad, for he had already fallen in love with one of them.

So also had Egil, and so even had Völund, and by good luck each had chosen a different princess. There was no need of quarrelling in the matter, and it was soon arranged that the three princes should marry the three princesses and that they should all remain in Ulfdal together.

For a long time everything went well, and they were all very happy, and Völund and his brothers would have been content to live for ever in the forest with their beautiful wives. They went out hunting together, and Völund had built up a forge and he made all sorts of ornaments for his wife and her sisters.

But it happened that the sisters grew tired of the life they were leading. Though Völund and his brothers did not know it, their wives were Valkyries, who loved war better than anything else, and so they became weary of the pleasures of hunting and longed to go to battle again. And one day when their husbands were absent they put on their swan-coats and flew away.

When the brothers came back and found that their wives had left them they were in great trouble, and Slagfin and Egil determined to stay no longer in Ulfdal, but to seek through the world for their lost princesses. But Völund resolved to stay where he was, hoping that perchance his wife might come back to him ; and he continued to make armlets and necklaces and delicate chains to please her when she should return. But alas, she never came back.

And after a time it came to pass that Nidad, King of Sweden, heard tell of Völund and how he could make all sorts of armour and weapons and trinkets. And Nidad sent a band of armed men to Ulfdal, who took Völund and brought him to Sweden.

There he was obliged to work at the forge for the king's pleasure, and to make swords of sharpness and shoes of swiftness, and other marvels for the king and his people. And Völund was very angry and several times sought to escape.

Then the queen counselled Nidad to cut the sinews of Völund's legs, so that he should be unable to walk and might remain with them always.

And when this was done Völund was put on the island of Sjoa-stad, where he was obliged to work day and night with scarcely any rest.

Völund was very wroth at being thus cruelly treated, and determined upon revenging himself; but it was a long time before he was able to do so. He was lame and could not move about, and he grew very weary and began to languish. At last two of the king's sons came to him, and with bitter taunts bade him make two swords, sharper than any he had yet made; and Völund's wrath was roused yet more, and he rose up and slew the two young men, and of their skulls he made drinking cups which he sent to the king, and of their teeth a breast jewel for the queen. And the king and queen admired them greatly, little knowing how they had been made.

Soon the king's sons were missed, and search was made for them, but they were not to be found.

Long mourned the king and the queen; but Völund kept his secret, and worked on at the forge.

One fine morning when he was toiling at a shield which the king had bidden him make, the king's only daughter came to ask him to make a ring and a chain of gold for her.

She was very fair, fairer even than his Valkyrie wife, and she spoke in a gentle tone to Völund, for she felt the more sorry that he had to work so hard, because she knew he was the son of a king.

And Völund gazed eagerly upon her, and her soft voice was like music to his heart. He promised to make a ring and a chain of gold more beautiful than any she had ever seen, and the princess went away well pleased, promising to come for them in two days.

The two days seemed very long to the princess, for she was eager to see what her ring would be like, and she wanted to see Völund again, for she pitied him greatly.

To Völund the time went more quickly, for he had work to do, and the chain and the ring were only just made when the princess came for them.

She was delighted when she saw them, for never had anything been so delicately wrought in Sweden.

And Völund threw the chain around her neck, and gently put the ring on her finger, and then he sighed.

"Why do you sigh?" asked the princess.

"For my sorrows," replied Völund.

"Ah, you wish to go back to your own land," said the princess; "I do not wonder at it, for it is sad to be a captive."

"Until two days since I wished to return," answered Völund, "but not now unless, indeed,' he added, "you would go with me and be Queen of Finnland."

The princess made no answer, but Völund knew that she was not angry, for there was a smile upon her lips.

And after she was gone, Völund began to work away at something that he had not thought of before, and that was not in the way of his trade. He made two coats of feathers, so light that they would rise into the air of themselves; and the next time that the princess came he asked again if she would fly away with him and be Queen of Finnland.

Still the princess made no answer, but she took a ring from her hand and gave it to Völund and then went away, and Völund knew that before long he should fly home to his own country.

Again came the princess and again Völund asked her if she would fly away with him and be Queen of Finnland.

And the princess took up one of the feather coats, and without saying a word drew it over her dress. Then Völund put on the other coat and they rose up high into the air.

King Nidad and his queen were sitting on the terrace in front of the palace when Völund and the beautiful princess floated by.

The king shouted loudly, "Ah, traitor! Thou art carrying away my daughter. Out, archers, out and shoot him."

And Völund answered: "I have revenged myself for thy cruelty to me. Thy sons have I slain, and from their skulls hast thou drunk the sparkling wine, and the queen wears their teeth in her shining breast jewel. And now do I take thy daughter from thee, since she loves me better than she loves thee."

Then higher, higher rose Völund and the princess into the air, and soon they were out of sight.

There were great rejoicings in Finnland when Völund alighted at the palace, for the old king was dead, and Slagfin and Egil had not yet come home from searching after their wives, and the people had no one to reign over them.

So Völund reigned over Finnland, and ruled his people wisely and well. Nevertheless he loved his forge better than ruling, and all his spare time he worked away at his smithy, and may be working there yet if one could only tell where to find him.

KING OLAF THE SAINT

as told by Julia Goddard

 HUNDREDS of years ago lived Olaf, a brave king, and his brother Harald Haardrade.

One day, when these brothers were talking together, they began to speak of old Norroway, the land of their birth.

"It is a land full of high hills," said one.

"It is a land full of fertile valleys," said the other, "where there is no lack of waving corn, fair pastures and summer flowers.'

"It is a land over which anyone might be content to reign," said Olaf; "a monarch might be justly proud of such a kingdom."

"Truly," replied Harald Haardrade; "better fortune could no man wish."

"Then," answered Olaf, "let us make a bargain. Our ships are in the harbour; they are well matched. Let us sail forth, and he who reaches first our native land shall be king of old Norroway."

"I am quite willing," said Harald Haardrade; "yet there is one condition I should like to make. Thou hast said that our ships are equally matched; nevertheless, I take thine to be the fastest sailer. Art thou willing to change vessels with me? So will we run the race."

"I am willing," said Olaf. "If thou thinkest my vessel to be the fleeter, take her, and welcome, and I will take thine. Is this a fair bargain?"

"Perfectly fair," answered Harald Haardrade, well satisfied that he should have his brother's ship.

Now the vessel belonging to Olaf was called the *Dragon*. Lightly she danced over the waves, and a child could have turned her north, south, east or west, by just one touch to the rudder. Harald Haardrade's ship, the *Ox*, was heavier built, and not so easy to manage; nevertheless, there was no fault to be found with her.

However, Olaf thought one vessel as good as the other, and, therefore, said nought against his brother's proposal; perhaps, too, he felt himself to be the better seaman. However this may have been, the story does not say; but there is reason to think that something in his heart told Olaf that the change of ships would make no difference to their captains.

So the brothers parted, and Olaf, having made all things ready, went to the church to pray for a blessing upon his work, "For", said he, "how can I expect to prosper unless I have the blessing of heaven?"

And as he passed along the aisle of the stately building, with his beautiful hair flowing over his shoulders, the people wished him success, and prayed that good King Olaf might win the race. As he moved along in solemn mood, a messenger came in hot haste, and stopped him, saying, "Why dost thou waste time, King Olaf? Thy brother is sailing away in the *Dragon*. Far ahead of thee will he be, if thou dost not turn thy steps aside from the altar, and follow him without delay."

But King Olaf answered the messenger, "Let those sail who choose to sail; I will not depart without the blessing of heaven."

And so he waited quietly until the mass was over, and then went calmly down to the seashore. The great white-crested waves were dashing on the strand, and the *Ox* rocked heavily at her moorings, and over the wide sweep of blue sea there was no sign of the *Dragon*. Away, far away, had the *Dragon* sped; the wind was in her favour, and she had weighed anchor, and set her sails, and danced gallantly away till there were now many miles between her and the shore. Olaf strained his eyes, and saw a speck of white that fluttered for a moment and then vanished. Perchance it might be the *Dragon*.

However, Olaf did not despair. He had asked the blessing of heaven upon his undertaking, and although the beginning seemed bad, yet he said in his heart, "Who can see so far as the end? I will not be dismayed."

Strong in the might of his faith, he bade the sailors get ready, and when all was done he stepped on board his vessel. The anchor was raised; a gentle breeze stirred the sails; the helmsman guided the ship seaward; and as King Olaf stood at the prow, he said reverently, "O *Ox, Ox*, speed thee on in the Name of the Lord."

Then he leaned forward, and taking hold of one of the white horns of the *Ox*, as though it had been a living creature, he said, "Now speed thee, O thou patient *Ox*, even as though thou wert going to pasture in fragrant clover fields."

And as if in answer to his words, the heavy vessel gave a leap, and gallantly ploughed the wild waves. And the white spray rose even until it frosted over the king's beautiful locks, and he shouted to the watcher on the topmost mast, "Ho, lad! Ho! Canst thou see aught of the fleet-sailing *Dragon*?"

And the lad answered, "I see naught upon the sea. There is not even a fishing-boat out upon the broad waters."

And on they sailed in silence. After a while, King Olaf called to the lad again, "Ho, lad! Ho! Canst thou see aught of the good ship *Dragon*?" Then the lad answered, "Nigh the land of Norroway I espy the silken sails of a vessel. The sun shines upon them, and they glitter as though they were bordered with gold."

And King Olaf knew that it was his own brave ship, and again they sailed on in silence. After awhile he called yet again to the lad, "Ho, lad! Ho! Canst thou see aught of the *Dragon*?" And the lad made answer, "Nigh the shores of old Norroway, under the shade of the purple mountains, I see a vessel riding full sail before the wind, and I know that it is the good ship *Dragon*."

Then King Olaf struck the *Ox* upon the ribs, and cried, "Faster, faster, thou *Ox*, faster. There is no time to lose."

And again he struck the *Ox* upon the eye, and shouted, "Faster, faster, faster, if thou wouldst have me win the haven."

And suddenly it seemed as though the *Ox* had started into life, and was putting forth all its new-gained powers, for forward bounded the vessel with a sudden leap. Swiftly, swiftly, swiftly, no one had ever known such sailing. Swifter than a bird on the wing, swifter than an arrow through the air. So sped the *Ox* through the foaming sea. The sailors could not climb the rigging; indeed, it was more than they could do to stand firmly upon the deck; so King Olaf lashed them firmly to the masts, though the steersman asked him who was going to guide the ship. "I will see to that myself," answered King Olaf; "not one of you shall be lost through me. I will guide the ship straight on like a line of light." And King Olaf stood by the helm, and he steered neither to the right nor to the left, but on, straight on, and his eye was fixed upon the goal.

"So must I run," he said, "if I would win the race."

What mattered it to King Olaf though rocks and mountains stood in the way? His faith was stronger than the rocks. Right onward he went, and the valleys filled with water, and the mountains disappeared, the blue waves rolled over them, and the *Ox* went triumphantly on its way. Out came running the little elves, for the sudden rising of the floods had disturbed them. "Who art thou, bold mariner, who sailest over our homes? Behold the mountains shake with fury. Tell us what is thy name?"

"Quiet ye, quiet ye, little people," answered King Olaf. "I am Saint Olaf; turn ye into stones until I come this way again."

So the little elves turned into stones, and rolled down the mountain sides, and the good ship went on her way. She had not gone far before out came an old Carline, and said, "Saint Olaf, I know you, with your beard shining like red gold. Wherefore do you bring with you the waters to mock us in our dwellings? Your ship has burst through the wall of my chamber. Evil luck be with you."

Then Saint Olaf, for he was a saint as well as a king, fixed his glance witheringly upon the old Carline.

"Be thou turned into a flint rock," said he, "and so remain for ever and ever."

And the Carline was turned into a rock, and Saint Olaf and his crew sailed on and on. So fleetly flew the good ship Ox, that anyone must have had good eyes to see her as she flashed past, for so she sped on that if Saint Olaf drew his bow and shot an arrow forward, it fell far behind in the wake of the vessel.

This was fast sailing indeed, and with such speed it is not wonderful that though Harald Haardrade had had the start of his brother, yet Saint Olaf reached home three days before him. Harald Haardrade was wild with rage when he came those three days later and found Saint Olaf king of Norroway. And he raged and raged until at length he became a dragon. And this is the last that we hear of Harald Haardrade.

Now, as Saint Olaf had prayed for the blessing of heaven before he set out on his voyage, it was natural that his first act upon landing should be to go to the nearest church to return thanks for having so mightily prospered. And as he walked up the crowded nave, a golden glory beamed from his fair hair, and the people of Norroway learned a great lesson from the faith of King Olaf the Saint.

SIGNY

as told by Sarah Powers Bradish

I. THE BETROTHAL

VÖLSUNG'S daughter, Signy, had many lovers, but she was so happy with her brothers, under the protecting boughs of the Branstock, that she did not wish to leave her father's house. One day an earl came from Siggeir, king of the Goths. He brought presents of gold and jewels, and offered the Völsungs his master's friendship, and aid in battle; but he wanted, in return, the promise that Signy would become his master's wife. Völsung and his sons were pleased at the prospect of an alliance with a great king, and urged Signy to accept this offer. She trembled, and hesitated, because she did not like the earl who had brought the presents and the message, and she dreaded the great king.

Völsung tried to calm her fears, and said, "You will bring honour to our family and kingdom." At last, to please her father, she promised to become Siggeir's wife.

The next day the earl departed, taking with him gifts of gold from King Völsung; and Signy began to prepare for her wedding.

II. THE WEDDING DAY

ON Midsummer eve, Siggeir came to the land of the Völsungs. The wedding guests had assembled beneath the Branstock, and Völsung and his sons went out to meet the bridegroom, who stood by King Völsung, "as the bramble by the oak". The top of his helmet did not reach the shoulder of the smallest of the Völsungs. But they paid him the honour due a great king and Signy's promised husband.

The next day, Signy sat beside Siggeir at the banquet. She was young and fair; he was old and wrinkled. She was tall and straight; he was short and bent. She was calm and silent; he was the noisiest of the guests. Sigmund, the youngest of Völsung's sons, watched the ill-mated pair, and understood his sister's unhappiness. He longed to send the bridegroom away, but dared not break the Völsung word. Siggeir understood how he was esteemed by this young brother; but the father was blind to everything but the coming glory of the Völsung race.

They were feasting under the Branstock; stories had been told about gods and heroes; and an old sea king was playing on a harp of gold, and singing of the lighting of the stars and the creation of the world. All were intent upon the music, when a clap of thunder shook the hall, and a man entered the door. He was very old, and had but one eye; yet his presence was commanding. He wore a broad-brimmed hat of blue, and a cloud-grey cloak. He carried on his shoulder a heavy spear that glittered in the sunlight. Völsung knew that this man was Odin, King Sigi's father, the ruler of the world. Odin went straight to the Branstock, without speaking a word. He drew a sword from the folds of his cloud cloak, and struck it deep into the heart of the oak. Then he turned and addressed the Goths and the Völsungs.

"There, in the Branstock, is a blade of great worth," he said, "which is my gift to the man who can pluck it out. It will never fail him, so long as his own heart is brave and true." Then he withdrew as quickly and as quietly as he had come in.

III. THE TAKING OF THE SWORD

THE wedding guests sat in silence, gazing at the jewelled hilt of the sword, which they knew was intended for the most worthy man among them.

Völsung was first to speak. "Why are you so silent?" he said. "Do you think it an evil omen that the father of the Völsungs has appeared among us? Do not fear to try the sword."

Siggeir asked to be allowed to try first, because he feared that another might take the sword that was designed for him.

Völsung smiled as he said: "We ask you, as our honoured guest, to open the contest. But, in this case, the first has no advantage over the last; for Odin knows to whom the sword will be given."

Siggeir went to the tree, and pulled with all his might at the sword; but, try as he would, he could not loosen it. Flushed with anger, he resumed his seat at Signy's side, and she blushed with shame at the unbecoming conduct of her lord.

Völsung said: "The greatest of all kings comes back empty-handed, and we might suppose that there is small hope for the rest. But each man knows best what he can do. Perhaps today an unknown warrior may begin a glorious course that will lead him beyond the attainments of kings. So let no one fear the trial; but our guests, the earls of Gothland, shall make the first attempt."

The earls of Siggeir tried the sword; but it remained as fast as ever in the heart of the oak.

Then came the Völsungs' vassals, shepherds, oarsmen and soldiers. They could not move the sword; but they went back to their places with shouts of laughter, while Siggeir sat in angry silence.

Then they called on Völsung, who rose from his seat and said that he would put his hand to the hilt, though he liked his own sword best, and he lifted the golden sheath, to show the peace strings as he said: "This was my first sword, and it will go with me to the grave. I shall bear in my hand this blade, unsheathed and without peace strings, when I stand, with the hosts of Odin, at the Twilight of the Gods."

He went to the Branstock, and grasped the hilt of the sword. He pulled long and hard, but he could not move the blade. He again took his place on the high-seat, and bade his sons take their turns.

The eldest went first, and the others followed, until nine of Völsung's stalwart sons had failed to draw the sword. Now it was Sigmund's turn; and his brothers smiled to think that a slender stripling should be called to take the sword after warriors had failed. But, at his father's bidding, Sigmund laid his hand upon the hilt. A shout filled the air; for the sword blazed in the hand of the youth, as he waved it over his head. He had drawn it from the oak, as if it had lain loose in the heart of the Branstock; and he knew that Odin had chosen him to do some glorious deed. But he thought, as he stood with his ruddy cheeks and golden hair shining in the light of the sword, that he might be called to defend the Branstock alone, after his father and brothers had gone to live in Valhalla; and, with downcast eyes, he took his place at his father's side.

IV. SIGGEIR TRIES TO BUY THE SWORD

SIGMUND looked up, to find Siggeir smiling upon him; and then the old king spoke flattering words in the ear of the youth. He said: "I am glad of your success; but you do not need this sword. Its coming to you shows that you are already the best of the Völsungs. You need not gild fine gold, or colour a red rose; so let me have this sword that came to you on your sister's wedding day."

Then he offered Sigmund gold, silver, amber and purple from over the seas. But Sigmund refused all the gifts, and kept the sword of Odin. He said:

"Came the sword to thy wedding, Goth king;

To thy hand it never came;

And thence is thine envy whetted,

To deal me this word of shame."

Siggeir was very angry; but he smiled, and told Sigmund how much he admired and loved him; and he invited Völsung and all his sons to spend the winter with him in Gothland.

Völsung thanked Siggeir. He said that they would accept his invitation at the end of two months; and asked Siggeir to stay with them until that time.

But Siggeir said that the sea would be too rough for Signy, who must have a smooth and easy voyage; and that he would go the next day, to prepare for their visit.

Sigmund heard these words with a sinking heart; for he read in the face of Signy that she feared the evil of the coming days.

V. THE DEPARTURE OF THE GOTHS

EARLY in the morning, before any of the household were awake, Signy stole to her father's bedside to beg him not to accept Siggeir's hospitality.

"My child," said Völsung, "my word is given. I must go; but your brothers I will leave behind."

"No, father," said Signy, "if you must come, bring your sons with you, and a great army also."

"I must go as a guest, as I have promised," answered Völsung.

"The decrees of the Norns are hard," Signy replied; "when I see you again, you will stand in a hopeless battle."

Signy went back to her couch, and Völsung fell asleep. When he awoke, the household was gathering in the hall, to drink the parting cup. Signy, dressed for the voyage, stood by the Branstock, and looked so rosy and happy that her father could hardly believe that her visit had not been a dream. The horses were brought, and the Völsungs rode with the Goths to the seashore. The ships were already prepared; and Signy kissed her brothers good-bye; but she hung upon her father's neck, and whispered in his ear. Siggeir blessed them all; and, drawing Signy into the ship, gave the order to sail.

VI. THE VISIT TO THE GOTHS

WHEN two months had passed, Völsung called his sons together, and told them of Signy's warning, and of her last words when she bade them farewell. He admitted that Siggeir was not the noble man that he had supposed the king of the Goths must be; and that he had faith in the words of Signy, because she had always been wise. "Still," he said, "Signy may have been too anxious, and perhaps her grief, at leaving home, made her suspicious. Perhaps, after all, Siggeir intends to do me honour. I will go alone; for, if I fall, I shall only go to Odin's halls a little sooner. But you must stay at home, and attend to the wants of the people; for if the sons of Völsung perish, the loss to the world will be great."

But they all said that they would go with him, if he must go. Still Völsung urged that he be allowed to go alone, in the ship of some merchant; but they insisted on going with him, in their own ships. So they sailed together in three ships, and arrived in Gothland, where they found Signy on the shore to meet them.

"How glad I am to see you," she said; "but the time is short for the work you have to do. You remember the warning I gave you? My fears have all proved true; and now Siggeir's men lie in ambush for you. But you still have time to escape; for you have come sooner than you were expected. Turn back, I pray you, and take me with you."

But Völsung kissed her tenderly, and said that he had never turned back from sword or fire, and his sons were as brave as he.

Signy wept, and entreated them to let her stay and share their fate. But Völsung said that she was the wife of a king, and must not shrink from her duty. So she went back; and, that evening, she sat as usual by her husband on his high-seat.

The Völsungs landed, the next morning, and took the road that led to Siggeir's dwelling. When they reached the top of the hill, they saw a great army in the valley. They tore the peace strings from their swords, and stood still till Siggeir's men came up.

There was no hope for the Völsungs; but they fought bravely until their father fell; when the brothers, weakened by many wounds, were captured by the enemy.

Siggeir sat on his throne, waiting for tidings from the unequal battle. An earl announced King Völsung's death, and Siggeir asked, "Where are the sons?"

"Fettered in the courtyard," answered the earl; "and it seems to me that it would be a noble deed to break their bonds and send them back to their own country."

"Fool!" said Siggeir. "Do you not know the saying: 'Slay the wolf by the house door, lest he slay thee in the wood'?"

VII. THE WOOD LAWN

SIGNY stood by the door; and as the earl passed out, she hastened to the high-seat, and said to the king, "Now, while you are happy in the downfall of my kinsmen, I pray you to grant me one request: Let a day or two pass before my brothers go the way of death."

Siggeir answered, "You are not asking a kindness for your kinsmen; but, since you have asked it, a place shall be prepared for them on the wood lawn."

Then he gave orders that Signy should be kept under guard in her chambers, and that her brothers should be chained to heavy logs on the lawn in the wood.

Every morning, he sent a man to see how his prisoners fared; and, every morning, the man returned saying that two of the brothers had been devoured by wild beasts during the night.

At last on a certain day he said, "The beasts have devoured them all."

Siggeir had expected this, and had sent for Signy, to sit with him on his throne. When she heard the dreadful words of the king's messenger, she uttered a piercing shriek, and ran from the king's presence. No one tried to hinder her; for all thought that the last of the Völsungs had perished. She had no need of a guide to the place where her brothers had lain; for the path to the wood had been well worn by the feet of the messenger.

VIII. SIGNY FINDS SIGMUND

WHEN she reached the lawn, she saw a man digging the turf with a piece of wood, which he had torn from a tree.

"Sigmund! Sigmund!" she cried. "Speak to me, and tell me what you are doing here!"

Sigmund turned and said, "My sister, Signy, I have looked for you before. But what could one woman do alone? I am weak from wounds and hunger. Come and help me bury our brothers' bones."

Signy did as she was asked, and their work was finished at sunset; but Signy lingered to learn how Sigmund had escaped.

He said that a grey wolf had come to him; that he had seized her with his teeth, and held her, and that, in the struggle, his fetters had broken; and he had killed her with the broken irons. Then he lamented the fall of his father's house, and the prosperity of Siggeir.

But Signy told him that Siggeir would surely suffer for his cruel deeds, and that they both would live to see it. She said that Sigmund would be a great king, and that the time would come when he would understand the things that now seemed unjust; but he must live, for a time, in the forest; and she should see him again. Then she kissed him, and went back to the king's palace.

IX. SIGGEIR'S SON

SIGGEIR thought that he was now the greatest king in the world; for he had Sigmund's sword, his army had taken possession of the land of the Völsungs, and Signy was his obedient handmaid, as well as his wife.

  179

Signy went again to the forest, and found Sigmund living in a cave. When she saw him, she said that she had once more seen a man. She wept, and left him, and took her place in Siggeir's palace. She never wept again. She was as beautiful as ever, and men said that she was unchanged; but her face expressed neither hope nor fear; and, while she never wept, she never laughed.

Sigmund lived alone in his cave, and followed the trade of a smith. Sometimes a hunter saw the light of his forge, and woodmen said that a king of the giants had come to live in the cave that the dwarfs had deserted. One morning, when he was forging a sword, he looked up, and saw a woman standing on the opposite bank of the river, holding a little lad by the hand. The woman returned his greeting and said, "Oh, forest dweller, do us no harm; for we have come at Signy's command. She says, if this boy proves to be good and brave, he may help you in your work."

She left the child, and disappeared among the trees. Sigmund crossed the river, and bade the boy hold his sword, while he took him on his shoulder, and waded back to his cave. The child did not fear the swift current of the river; but prattled merrily, and asked questions as the dark water rose about them. Sigmund thought him brave enough, but he mistrusted the lad because he had his father's dark hair and eyes.

They had lived together three months, when Sigmund said to the boy, "I am going into the forest to hunt deer, but you must stay here to bake our bread."

At noon Sigmund came home, and asked whether the morning's work were done. The boy did not answer, but was pale and trembling.

"Tell me," said Sigmund, "are you afraid to bake bread?"

"I went to the meal sack," answered the lad, "and something moved in the meal. I thought it was the serpent that we saw last night, and I dared not touch it."

Sigmund laughed and said, "I did not suppose that the son of a king could be scared from his bread by all the serpents in the world." He opened the meal sack, and took out a grey adder, which he set down in the grass, and said, as he drew his sword from its sheath, "Do you fear this, that men call the serpent of death?"

The boy replied, "I am too young for war, but I shall carry a sword like that before I am many years older."

Sigmund went into the forest and leaned upon his sword for a long time, thinking of Signy's message. When the moon rose, he returned to the cave and called to Siggeir's son, "Come out, and go with me, for I can keep you no longer."

The boy rose at once, and Sigmund led him through the forest, until, at early dawn, they came to the lawn in the wood. "Stay here", said Sigmund, "until the sun has risen, and then go home to your father's palace, and say to your mother, Signy, that Sigmund lives alone, and will not have a foster child."

The lad obeyed Sigmund, and told only his mother what he had seen and heard in the forest, for he was indeed a noble prince, although he was Siggeir's son.

X. SINFIOTLI COMES TO THE FOREST

TEN years passed, and Sigmund still lived alone in the forest, and worked at his forge. One morning, when he was making a golden helmet, he looked up, and saw a boy standing on the opposite bank of the river. This boy had a broad white brow, and rosy cheeks, and fair hair that looked golden in the sunlight; and he cried out to Sigmund: "You are the master smith of whom my mother told me. I will corrie to you." And he plunged into the river. The water came up to his chin, but he showed no fear, and struggled with the current until his feet touched the bank near Sigmund.

"Here are the cave and the river, the forge and all the things my mother told me about; but you cannot be the master smith, because my mother said that no one could look upon his face and not tremble with fear, and I feel no fear when I look into your face. I must go on until I find my foster father; but I wish he might be a man like you."

"Stay with me," said Sigmund, "for you have found the foster father to whom your mother sent you. You have looked into the face of Völsung's son, and smiled. Tell me your name and the message that Signy sends."

"My name is Sinfiotli," answered the child. "I am ten years old. My mother, Signy, said only this: that she sends you a man to help you in your work; and that whether he be of the kings or of the gods, you will find out in your time of need."

Sigmund looked upon the lad, and said to himself, "Shall I cherish another son of

Siggeir?" But the boy looked up with the blue eyes of the Völsungs, and Sigmund took him to his heart.

Sigmund gave his foster son heavy tasks to perform, and sent him on dangerous errands. But Sinfiotli never complained, or showed any sign of fear. When they had lived together a year, Sigmund said: "I am going to get venison for our dinner, but you must stay at home and bake bread, to eat with our meat."

In the evening Sigmund came home with a deer on his shoulder. Sinfiotli went out to meet him, as he always did, and said with a smile, "You have brought the meat, and the bread is ready for our dinner."

"Indeed," said Sigmund, "did you knead the meal that was in yonder sack?"

"I had no other," said the lad; "but there was something strange about it; for, when I took up the bag, something moved within it. It looked like an ashen stick; but it seemed to be alive. I knew we must have bread for our dinner; so I kneaded it all together; and now the squirming thing is baked in the bread."

Sigmund laughed as he answered, "You have kneaded into the bread a deadly adder; so, tonight, do not eat of the bread; for, I fear, harm may come to you." Sigmund could handle venomous serpents, or taste poison in his food, and escape unharmed; but he was afraid to give his sister's son too severe a test.

After this trial of Sinfiotli's courage, Sigmund looked upon him as Signy's son only. He thought no more of Siggeir's treachery, which he had feared might appear in the youth; and he taught him the use of the sword, and the arts of war.

XI. THE WEREWOLVES

ON one of their journeys through the forest, Sigmund and Sinfiotli came to a hut, and knocked at the door. No one answered, and they entered, unbidden. The walls of the hut were hung with gold, and two men lay asleep on benches. They wore the dress of the Southern people, and had heavy gold bracelets on their arms. Over the head of each hung a grey wolfskin. Sigmund gazed long at one of the wolfskins, and remembered the words he had spoken when he lay chained to the log on the wood lawn: that, at the last great battle, the gods would miss a man, and find a wolf instead.

He took down the wolfskin and put it on. Sinfiotli took the other wolfskin and did as his foster father had done. They both became wolves, and ran through the forest, howling and doing wolfish things. The men in the hut were sons of kings, and were the victims of enchantment, which compelled them to rove as wolves, nine days out of ten; and, on the tenth day, when they were allowed to take their own forms, they lay exhausted.

Sigmund and Sinfiotli still had kings' hearts under their wolfish dress; and their kings' hearts told them to go back to their cave, and wait until they could be changed to men again. But their wolfish bodies drove them through the forest to the homes of men, and made them prey upon sheep and other domestic animals. A band of hunters saw them, and attacked them with spears; but, after a short struggle, every man was killed, and the wolves went on their way.

They met a score of traders from over the sea, whom Sinfiotli wanted to attack. But visions of the gold in their cave, and a desire to return to it, floated through Sigmund's dulled brain; and he tried to restrain his companion. But Sinfiotli broke through the thicket, and rushed out at the men; who, raising their axes and drawing their swords, almost killed the werewolves; though, at the end of the fight, not a man was left.

Sinfiotli lay fainting on the grass, and Sigmund was howling over the slain; when, somehow, the thought of the ruin they had wrought entered his wolfish head; and he turned on Sinfiotli, who had caused their latest trouble, and tore him, as one wolf tears another.

Two weasels came past, and one bit the other, until she fell down dead, and then he seemed to regret his rash act. In an instant, he ran into the thicket, came back with a leaf in his mouth, and laid it on his dead mate. She sprang up perfectly well, and the two happy little creatures ran away together.

Sigmund was wondering where he could find a leaf from the same herb, when a raven flew over his head with one in his beak. He dropped it, and Sigmund picked it up, and laid it on Sinfiotli's wounds, which were healed at once. They were both tired of the wolfskins, and of the work of the witches, so they went home and waited in the cave until the rest of the nine days were past, when they could again take their own forms, and speak in the language of men.

Sinfiotli spoke first, and said: "When I left the palace of kings, I had many lessons to learn. You have taught me many things, but the gods have taught me more, and, in bringing us to the hut in the wilderness, they have humbled us both, to make us willing to do whatever work comes to our hands. Now how long must I wait, before I shall be able to do some great deed? You are a master; make me a master too."

Sigmund's face was sad, but a strange light shone in his eyes. "This is the great deed that lies before us," he said. "We must slay my father's foe, and what if that foe be your father?" For he did not yet know that Sinfiotli was of the race of the gods. Then he told Sinfiotli of Siggeir's treachery, and said, "Now think well of this: can you endure it, if, all your life, men say, 'He slew his father, and amended wrong with wrong'?"

"What father have I," said Sinfiotli, "except him who saved my life? I remember that Signy is my mother, and, for her sake, I will avenge the wrong."

"The gods have sent you," said Sigmund, "for you neither start nor turn pale, and I dare not refuse what they have put in my hands, to avenge the death of Völsung."

"Strike what blow you will," said Sinfiotli. "Take me as the sword of the gods, and keep your hand on the hilt."

XII. THE DEATH OF SIGGEIR AND SIGNY

ONE winter afternoon Sigmund and Sinfiotli went to the palace of King Siggeir. Unobserved, they entered the hall at dusk, and hid behind the great wine tuns, near enough to the banquet hall to see the lights and hear the voices. No one came near them except the cup bearer, who drew wine for the king, and the king's two little children, who were trundling golden hoops about the hall. A ring, from one of their toys, rolled away, and they followed it to Sigmund's feet. They ran out into the hall, crying: "We have seen two men among the wine. We know them by their wide white hats."

The earls from the banquet hall rushed out with drawn swords. But the two men fought bravely, until Sinfiotli slipped and fell, when they were both taken and bound.

The next morning, Siggeir ordered his men to build a double tomb, divided by a stone partition. The two prisoners were cast into these stone chambers; but, before the roof was laid over Sinfiotli's tomb, Signy came and threw a bundle of straw at his feet. The labourers thought she had given him a package of food, which would only prolong the time of his suffering, so they finished their work, and went away.

Sinfiotli cried out, "Best unto babe is mother," for he thought that Signy had thrown him a piece of boar's flesh, wrapped in straw. Then he was silent, and Sigmund asked: "What is the matter? Is there an adder in the meat?"

"Yes," answered Sinfiotli, "the serpent of the Branstock, which Siggeir took from you."

He struck the wall, and the sword point pierced the stone. Sigmund seized it in his hands, and together they sawed down the wall, cut away the rafters, and leaped out. They went to Siggeir's palace, piled wood against the doors, and set it on fire. Siggeir, roused from sleep, thought he was besieged by robbers, and called to ask what price they wanted, whether half of his kingdom or all his treasure. Sigmund answered: "We have not come to rob you; we have gold and purple, and care not for your kingdom or your treasure. We remember our father, Völsung, and our kin. This deed is done by Sigmund, the Völsung, and Sinfiotli, Signy's son."

Then he called to Signy to come out. She came, with her women, but when she had seen her attendants safely sheltered, she bade her brother and son farewell, and went back to her husband in the burning building. The flames reached the roof as she entered the hall, the walls fell in, and the palace of King Siggeir was only a blackened ruin.

KING SIGMUND

as told by Sarah Powers Bradish

I. HELGI

SIGMUND gathered an army, and all embarked on ships, to go back to his native land. Sinfiotli was his constant assistant and adviser. When they arrived at the land of the Völsungs, the people received them gladly, and proclaimed Sigmund king.

When he sat once more beneath the Branstock, he thought of Signy, and how she had given herself to save her father's family; and he remembered her wedding day, when he had drawn the sword of Odin from the oak; and how he had thought, that day, that he might be left to defend the Branstock, after his father and brothers had ascended to the halls of Odin.

He married a princess, whose name was Borghild.

They had two sons, named Hamond and Helgi. When Helgi lay in the cradle, the Norns entered the room, and blessed the newborn babe. They called him "Sunlit Hill", "Sharp Sword" and "Lord of Rings"; and promised him a glorious career. He was brought up in the house of Hagal, a wise teacher.

At the age of fifteen, he had grown so tall, and had become so brave, that he ventured alone into the house of Hunding, his father's enemy. The family did not recognize the young prince; and he passed through without exciting much attention. But he left an insolent message, which made Hunding so angry that he started in pursuit of the bold young fellow. Hunding followed him to Hagal's house, and went in after him; but found no one, except a maid, who was grinding corn. Hunding was surprised that a maid should be so tall, and have such brawny arms; but he did not suspect that she was Helgi, in disguise, as she really was.

After this, Helgi was considered proficient enough, in courage and cunning, to join the army. He marched, with Sinfiotli, against the Hundings, and fought a great battle. The Valkyries were hovering near, waiting to choose the slain for Odin's halls, when their attention was called to the great courage of Helgi. One of their number, named Gudrun, admired him so much that she came to him and offered to be his wife. They were married at once.

After the battle, only one of the Hunding family remained alive; and he was allowed to go free, after he had promised not to avenge the death of his father; but he borrowed Odin's spear, and killed Helgi. Helgi's wife was heartbroken at the death of her husband. She wept constantly, until she learned that, every day, Helgi's voice called to her from his tomb. That night, she entered the tomb, and asked why Helgi called her, and why his wounds still bled. Helgi's voice answered, "I cannot be happy while you weep; and, for every tear you shed, a drop of my blood must flow."

Gudrun wept no more; but Odin soon called her, to cross the rainbow bridge. Helgi had been made leader of the heroes in Valhalla; and Gudrun, again a Valkyr, came to earth, to choose the slain heroes, who should fight under Helgi's command at the last great battle.

II. SINFIOTLI AND GUDROD

AFTER the death of Helgi, Sinfiotli returned to Sigmund's palace, where he was held in high esteem. But he soon became weary of continual feasting and song, and longed for an active life. In the spring, he joined his forces to those of Gudrod, Borghild's brother, and sailed over the sea, to gain new victories.

They conquered a rich nation, and took much spoil. Gudrod was brave in battle, but he had a greedy heart. He wanted to divide the spoil at once; but Sinfiotli said it was not becoming, in two kings of war, to dispute over booty, as pirates might do; and that he would come back at night, and take what Gudrod thought best to give him. He went to his warship, to rest until evening.

Gudrod worked all day; and, when Sinfiotli returned at night, he found the spoil divided into two parts, and Sinfiotli's share was larger than Gudrod's. But the things of value were all in Gudrod's part. Sinfiotli was indignant; and the men of his command were very angry. Gudrod, seeing this discontent, called on his own men to slay the "wood abider"; but the soldiers stood still, and no sword was unsheathed.

Then Sinfiotli challenged Gudrod to single combat, and they met the next morning. Gudrod fought bravely, but fell mortally wounded.

Sinfiotli returned to the land of the Völsungs, with the army. Sigmund made a feast in his honour, and was listening to the story of the war, when Borghild entered and asked why her brother had not come back from the sea. Sinfiotli answered:

"The white swords met in the island; bright there did the war shields shine. And there thy brother abideth; for his hand was worse than mine."

Borghild called on Sigmund to drive this "wolf of the kingfolk" out of the land of the Völsungs.

Sigmund answered that, when she had heard the story of the war, she would know that her brother had not kept his word. But, even if he had stood by his agreement, Sinfiotli could not be punished, because Gudrod had perished in a fair fight. Still he said that he would pay gold for her brother's death, because he loved her.

Borghild went to her own apartments, where she lay silent for a long time.

III. THE DEATH OF SINFIOTLI

THE next day Borghild went to Sigmund to say that she was no longer angry, and that she would take his gold. She kissed him and Sinfiotli also, and sat down on the high-seat. She asked her husband to make a funeral feast for her brother, Gudrod. This he was willing to do, and one autumn evening all the princes and earls assembled in the great hall under the Branstock to do honour to Gudrod's memory. Borghild was there, and pouring wine for Sinfiotli, said, "Drink now of the cup from my hand, and let us bury hate that is dead."

Sinfiotli took the cup, but did not drink.

Sigmund asked why he sat so silent and sorrowful in the midst of the feast.

Sinfiotli said that he saw hate in the cup.

"Give it to me," answered Sigmund, and taking the cup, he drank the wine.

Borghild gave Sinfiotli another cup, which he passed to Sigmund, who drank as before.

When she brought the third cup, she taunted Sinfiotli with cowardice and fear of death. He took the cup from her hand, but did not drink. Sigmund again asked why he took no part in the feast, and he said, "Because there is death in the cup."

The old king did not take the wine this time, and Sinfiotli thought that he wished him to drink it. So he raised it to his lips, and drained the cup, and fell back dead.

Sigmund raised the body of his foster son. His grief was so great that no one dared look upon it, or listen to the words he spoke. He bore the body in his arms out into the darkness. The wind shrieked through the Branstock, and blew black clouds across the face of the moon. Sigmund went away from the dwellings of men to the forest at the foot of the mountains. A wide river stopped his progress. He followed along its bank until he came to the sea. An ancient, one-eyed boatman hailed him, and asked where he was going. He answered that he wished to cross the sea, because the light of his life had gone out.

"I have come", said the boatman, "to convey a great king across the water."

So Sigmund laid the body in the bottom of the boat; but before he could himself step in, the boat and the boatman had vanished. Then he knew that the boatman was Odin, and that he had taken Sinfiotli to the home of the heroes.

IV. THE DEATH OF SIGMUND

SIGMUND went back to his father's throne, and attended to the business of the kingdom. He went to war and conquered his enemies; but he cared little for glory, now that Sinfiotli and Helgi were gone. He had sent Borghild away after Sinfiotli's death, and he was left alone in the great house of the Völsungs.

He heard that a distant king had a daughter who was beautiful, good and wise; and he sent an earl laden with gold and gifts, to ask her to be his queen. The king's name was Eylimi, and his daughter's name was Hiordis.

On the very day of the earl's arrival at Eylimi's court, a messenger came from King Lygni to ask the hand of Hiordis. Lygni's kingdom was near Eylimi's, and Sigmund's was far away. Lygni was young, and Sigmund was old. Both were rich and powerful kings.

Eylimi listened to both messages, but had no word to say. He asked both earls to wait, and while they were entertained in the banquet hall, he sought his daughter and told her of her suitors. She chose the Völsung king.

The old king went out with a sad heart, for he thought that the young king Lygni would make a more suitable husband for Hiordis. But he had said that she should have her way, and he could not change her choice. So he sent rich gifts to Lygni, with the word that his daughter was betrothed to another king; and King Sigmund's earl received the welcome news, that in two months' time his royal master might come for his bride. "But", said Eylimi, "bid him come with sword and ships of war, for I fear that he may be attacked."

But Sigmund remembered his father, and scorned to take an army to a wedding. Still he prepared ten long ships, and filled them with the best of his men. They arrived at Eylimi's kingdom without accident, and received a warm welcome.

White-haired Sigmund and fair Hiordis were greatly pleased with each other, and the wedding feasts were joyful. Eylimi loved Sigmund for his goodness, and admired him for his wisdom and dignity. He no longer feared for the happiness of Hiordis because she had chosen an old king for her husband. But one day, sails were seen approaching the island. Lygni was angry at the refusal of Hiordis, and said that he would have the princess as well as the gifts. He came, with a fleet and army, on the day that Sigmund and Hiordis had intended to sail for the land of the Völsungs.

Sorrow and dread filled the heart of Eylimi; but Sigmund bade him be of good cheer, for he said that, even if he had not come, Hiordis could never have been persuaded to marry Lygni. He cut the peace strings from his sword, and set his little army in battle array.

It is said that the number of Sigmund's and Eylimi's men was to the hosts of Lygni as the brown pips are to an apple when it is cut through the core. But the little army marched out bravely, and Hiordis, with her maid, followed at a distance.

Sigmund stood like an image of gold, in the front of the battle, with the sword of the Branstock unsheathed. As the hosts of Lygni advanced, it seemed as if the whole world were moving. But the flashing sword of Odin hewed down all that came within its reach, as Sigmund wielded it with more than youthful vigour. He was no longer worn and old; the hope and eagerness of youth had come back in the excitement of the battle, and he said to himself, "A few more strokes of the sword, and I shall have conquered the world."

But an old, one-eyed man, wearing a broad-brimmed hat and a cloud-grey cloak, made his way across the battle-field. He carried a heavy spear, with which he struck the sword of the Branstock, and the sword fell in pieces at Sigmund's feet. The old man vanished; and the advancing army of Lygni struck down Sigmund. His warriors fell like grass before the scythe, and the only ones left standing were Lygni's men.

"Who will now oppose King Lygni's wooing?" cried the king; and he led the way to Eylimi's palace.

When the last warrior had left the battle-field, Hiordis came out from the thicket, to look for her husband. She found him wounded, but still alive. He opened his eyes as she bent over him, and she cried out with delight. But he said: "I cannot live; this day my eyes have seen Odin, and I must do his will. Take the pieces of my sword, the sword of the Branstock, and keep them as your choicest treasure. If the gods give you a son, he will be a greater hero than the Völsung race has yet known. Give the broken sword to him when he has grown to manhood, and the new-welded blade will be invincible. Put away your sorrow, for, even now, I see the light, and hear the music, in the great banquet hall of Odin's heroes."

V. THE BURIAL OF SIGMUND

HIORDIS lingered beside her dead until day began to dawn. As she looked toward the sea, she saw a warship approaching the shore. She returned to the thicket, where her maid was waiting, and told her of the death of Sigmund, and of the ship that she had seen. "Now," she said, "give me your dress of blue, and take my purple and gold. And, when the men ask our names, say that you are Hiordis, the wife of King Völsung, and that I am your handmaid."

When the ship's company landed, they were led by a king, Elf, the son of the Helper. He had just come from war, and had turned his ship toward the island, in the hope of finding water. As they drew near the shore, they saw that there had been a great battle; and they noticed that a woman, dressed like a queen and wearing a gold crown, sat among the slain. She ran into a thicket; and they lost sight of her.

They went directly to the battle-field, and at once recognized the body of Sigmund as that of a great king. "Come," said King Elf, "and look upon his face. Few such are left on earth. Then let us go to the thicket, where the queen is hidden; and learn from her the story of the mighty dead."

They found the women, and greeted them kindly. To their questions, the one in the queen's dress answered: "I am Hiordis, the queen. The slain lord in yonder field was my husband, Sigmund, the Völsung."

"And who is this blue-clad one?" asked King Elf. "She is my waiting maid, who weeps for her lover, killed in the battle," answered the queen.

The king looked again at the maid's sorrowful face, but said no more. He went, with the women, to the battle-field, and built a mound for Sigmund, the Völsung. The walls were made of the broken shields of his foes, and hung with their banners. His sword could not be found; and the maid explained that her royal master had commanded that the pieces of his broken sword be taken by the queen.

After Sigmund's body had been laid in the mound, King Elf asked the women where they would go, since the island was in the hands of Lygni. Hiordis asked that they might go, with him, to his home. The king gladly gave them passage in his warship; and they sailed to the happy land of King Elf and his father, the Helper.

THE HOUSE OF THE HELPER

as told by Sarah Powers Bradish

I. KING ELF FINDS OUT THE QUEEN

THE Helper and his wife gave their unexpected guests a cordial welcome; and Hiordis was comforted by the kindness of her new friends.

One morning Elf's mother said to her son, "I have observed these women carefully, and I should like to know why the inferior woman is the better dressed."

Elf said, "She is Hiordis, wife of Sigmund, the Völsung."

The old queen laughed aloud, and said: "It is not so, my son. Have you not noticed that the handmaid speaks whenever any matter of importance is to be decided? "

"Yes," he said, "and she is both wise and gracious, and very dear to me."

"Follow my advice," said the wise queen mother, "and, when you have won your queen, see if they do not again change raiment."

One day Elf said to the woman in purple and gold, "How do you know, in the dark winter mornings, when it is time to rise?"

She answered: "When I lived in my father's house, the folks must be astir, whether the fields were light or dark. I rose early to go to the meadows, and drank milk before I left the house; and now I am always thirsty when it is time to rise."

Elf laughed, and said: "That was a strange custom that required a king's daughter to go to the fields before light. And now, fair maid with eyes of grey, how can you tell that morning has come, when the heavens are as dark as midnight?"

She said: "My father gave me this gold ring, which has this strange property: it grows cold upon my finger when day comes. So when my ring grows cold, I know it is time to rise."

Elf laughed again. "Indeed," he said, "there was gold in your father's house. Come

193

now, tell me that you are Hiordis, wife of Sigmund, the Völsung; and I will make you queen of my people."

"Give me a year to mourn for Sigmund, and then I will be your queen," she said.

II. THE BIRTH OF SIGURD, THE VÖLSUNG

THERE was peace in the land of the Helper, and joy in King Elf's home, for a beautiful babe lay in the arms of Hiordis. His eyes were so bright that the women shrank from their gaze, and so strong that they could look at the sun. Hiordis held him close, while she told him the story of Sigmund, and then gave him to the women to show to the kings.

The Helper and his son were sitting on their high-seat, when they heard the sound of music, and four women, dressed in white, entered the hall.

"O daughters of earls," said the Helper, "what tidings do you bring?"

The women talked of grief, wonder, fear and joy, until King Elf grew impatient and cried out, "Yet you come rejoicing; what have you to tell?" Then they advanced to the high-seat; and, drawing away the purple covering, presented the child, and said, "Queen Hiordis sends you this; and she says that he shall be called by the name that you shall give him."

King Elf took the child in his arms, and held him a long time, while he thought of all that Hiordis had told him, of the might of the Völsungs, and the battle by the sea. Then he said, "His name shall be Sigurd, the Völsung," and sprinkled water upon the head of the young prince.

Men heard the name, and echoed it through hall and courtyard and market place. Hiordis heard it in her chamber; and, when the women returned with the baby, before they could speak, she greeted him as Sigurd, the Völsung.

Sigurd grew in beauty and wisdom; and, after a time, his mother Hiordis was married to King Elf. Peace and plenty blessed the land.

III. GREYFELL

TWO ancient men lived in the country of the Helper. One was related to the giants, and the other to the dwarfs. Gripir was tall and stately, with hair and beard of snowy white. He knew all things, from the beginning of the world; and he knew many things that were to be.

Regin was beardless, crooked and short. His face was pinched and wan. He was so old that no one knew how long he had lived in the land of the Helper. He was skilled in everything except the arts of war. He was eloquent, and men believed every word he spoke. He sang and played the harp most beautifully. He could read the clouds and the winds, and still the sea. He could bind up wounds, and heal the sick. He taught men how to sow and reap; how to spin and weave. He was master of all work in metals. He loved young Sigurd, and asked to be his teacher.

The Helper said: "You taught me, and you taught my son. We know you are the master of masters. Three times man's lifetime would not be long enough to learn your wisdom. Yet your heart is cold. We love young Sigurd, and would not have you make him grim and ill-tempered."

Regin laughed as he answered, "I taught you cunning by measure; but I shall measure nothing to him; I shall not make him cold-hearted or ill-natured."

So Regin took Sigurd to his house in the forest, where he taught the young prince all things, except the art of war. He taught him to make swords, and all kinds of weapons and armour. He also taught him many languages, how to carve runes, and how to play the harp and to sing. He taught him the haunts of wild animals, the names and uses of flowers and plants; how to ply the oar and spread the sails on the sea.

One day, as they sat by the forge, Regin told tales of ancient kings and heroes, until Sigurd's heart swelled within him, and his longing to do noble things gave a new light to his eyes.

Regin said, "You will go out into the world, to do greater and braver deeds than your fathers ever did."

But the boy shook his head, and said, "I love the Helper and King Elf; their land is fair and good."

"Yet do as I bid you," said Regin. "Ask for a war horse."

The lad was angry, as he replied: "I have all the horses I need, and everything I want. Why would you have me ask for more?"

"The Völsungs were a noble race," said Regin. "They were not satisfied with good, but demanded the best." Then he took his harp, and sang of the deeds of the heroes and of the rides of the Valkyries, until Sigurd forgot his anger. He left the forge, with the song ringing in his ears; and that night he asked the kings to give him such a horse as he might choose.

"The stables are open to you," answered King Elf.

But Sigurd begged a token for Gripir, who had charge of all the horses; so that he might take the best of the strong and the swift. "But," he added, "if I ask too great a gift, I pray you, forget what I have said."

King Elf smiled, and said: "You will take a long ride. You will see war and sorrow, and death at last; but you will win praise and honour. So have your way, for we can no more hold you than we can hold back the rising sun."

Sigurd thanked the kings; and, early next morning, went to Gripir. The wise old man lived in a house on a mountain crag. Eagles flew about it; and winds from the heart of the mountains blew through every room. Few men dared step across the threshold. Sigurd entered the hall, and found Gripir seated in a chair made from a sea serpent's tooth. His beard almost swept the sea-green floor. His robe was made of gold, and his staff had a knob of crystal.

Gripir knew Sigurd, and said: "Hail, king with the bright eyes! You need no token, nor need you tell your errand. The wind brought me word that you were coming to choose a war horse from my meadows. Now go, and take the best; but come back when you have your sword."

Sigurd ran down the mountain side, and was on his way to the meadows, when he met a man wearing a broad-brimmed hat, and a cloud-grey cloak. He had but one eye, and he seemed very old. He spoke to Sigurd, and said, "Let me tell you how to choose your horse."

"Are you Gripir's horseherd?" asked Sigurd; and he had begun to ask the old man whether he would take gold for his advice, when he noticed his noble bearing, and said, "Your face is like that of the heroes, my master, Regin, tells me about; and your cloud-grey garment I have seen in my dreams."

"There is one horse in the meadow, better than all the rest," said the stranger; "and if

Sigurd takes advice from a wise old man

you would have him for your own, follow my directions." Sigurd said, "What shall I do?"

"Drive all the horses into the river," said the old man; "and wait, to see what happens."

Sigurd drove them into the water; but the current was so strong that it carried many fine horses out to sea. Some turned and swam back to the bank; others were caught in the eddies and drowned. But one swam across the river, climbed the opposite bank, and galloped over the meadows on the other side. Then he wheeled, leaped into the river, and swam back. He shook the water from his mane, and stood neighing at Sigurd's side.

"Listen, Sigurd," said the old man. "I gave your father a gift which you will yet hold dear; and I now give you this horse. Do not fear to go where he may carry you, for your fathers are now in my house, enjoying the rewards of their valour. Like all your noble race, live so that you will not care when death may come."

Then Sigurd knew that Odin had come to him, and would have asked about many things, but Odin faded away, and only Greyfell stood beside his master on the river bank.

REGIN'S STORY

as told by Sarah Powers Bradish

I. REIDMAR AND HIS SONS

ONE day when Sigurd was sitting with Regin, the dwarf told stories of kings who had won their crowns by many hard-fought battles. At last he said: "You are Sigmund's son; will you wait till these peaceful kings of this little kingdom are dead, and then will you serve their sons? Will you spend your life in idle waiting for the time when their war banners shall float in the breeze?"

Sigurd answered: "You taunt me too much. I love these peaceful kings; their land is good. Perhaps the time may come when I shall be called to do some daring deed. When the call is heard, and the deed is ready, the man will not be wanting."

Regin replied: "The deed is ready, but you love this land, and why should he who can feast be content to eat rye bread? They say that you are Sigmund's son, but you need not be a warrior, for Sigmund lies quiet in his mound by the sea."

Sigurd's eyes flashed as he said, "Mock not the son of Sigmund, but tell the deed that waits."

The cunning master answered, "The deed is the righting of wrong, and the winning of great treasure."

Sigurd asked: "How long have you known of this? And what is the treasure to you?"

"I have known of the wrong", said Regin, "for hundreds of years. And the treasure is mine, but it is beyond my reach; for I know nothing of the art of war. I came to this land to seek a hero to undo the wrong, and bring back my treasure; but generations passed, and the end seemed no nearer, until I saw your eyes in the cradle."

Sigurd was silent, but at last he said: "I will do the deed, and you shall have your treasure, and the curse also (if a curse rests upon the gold); but I will surely do the deed. Tell me where the treasure lies."

Regin answered, "I must first tell you the story of my life; so keep your seat and listen to a tale of things that happened before kings were born.

"I belong to the race of the dwarfs. We knew no right nor wrong; we had no love; we made and unmade, and felt no sorrow. We were wise and powerful, and our day is not wholly past. Trust not your life in my hands when I dream of my kindred, and when I seem most like the dwarfs of long ago.

"After a time the gods came among us, and we learned to love, and hope, and fear. We lived in the depths of the earth, and learned to work in metals. We knew of poisons and medicines; we made the spear and bow; we built ships to sail on the sea.

"Reidmar was my father. He was old and wise. To my brother, Fafnir, he gave a soul that knew no fear, a brow like hardened iron, a hand that never failed, an ear that could not listen to a sorrowful tale and a heart as greedy as a king's. To my brother, Otter, he gave a snare and a longing to search the forests and streams until nothing was left alive. To me, the youngest, he gave memory of the past, fear of the future, a hammer, an anvil and coals of fire burning in the forge.

"Now we were but little better than men; but we still had the power to change our shape, and appear in whatever form we would. Fafnir went abroad and became the terror of the world. Otter lived with the animals that he hunted, and so often took their forms that he seemed to be the king of the forest. I toiled to build my father's house, and, as the walls rose bright with gold, my hands became soiled and misshapen, and I looked upon the sun and the wind and all things in nature as only the tools of my smithy.

II. THE THREE TRAVELLERS

"AFTER a time, three travellers came from Asgard to look over their work. They were Odin, Hoenir and Loki. They passed through a forest and came to a river where they found an otter eating a fish. Loki picked up a stone and threw it at the otter, which fell dead. Loki took both the otter and the fish and went on with his companions. They soon came to a house at the foot of a mountain. They were tired and hungry, and, as the sun was setting, Odin said to his brothers, 'Let us seek shelter for the night in this house.'

"They found the master of the house seated in a golden hall, on a chair made from a whale's tooth. His robe was purple, and he wore a crown of gold.

He had no sword, and received his guests kindly. He ordered a feast spread before them; and sweet music played while they ate. But, in the midst of the feast, they felt they were under a spell, so they could not throw off the semblance of men. Besides, they were unarmed, and Odin had foolishly lent his spear, Gungnir. Their host taunted them with their helplessness.

"Loki had thrown down the dead otter when he entered the hall. Fafnir and I recognized our brother Otter; and we knew that our father, Reidmar, would demand satisfaction for his death. When his guests were completely under his control, Reidmar told them that they had killed his son, Otter, and that they were his prisoners until they could atone for the offence.

"Then Odin said: 'We have indeed done you a grievous wrong; but we will do what we can to compensate you for the injury. You love gold; we will give you gold. It is for you to say how much.'

"Then Reidmar, Fafnir and I cried out with one voice, 'You shall die, and we will rule the world.'

"Odin answered with calm and awful voice, 'Be just, O Reidmar! How much gold do you require?'

"Then covetous Reidmar forgot his anger and his wisdom; his greed alone spoke out, 'Give me the Flame of the Waters and the Gold of the Sea, which Andvari hides beneath a mountain, until every hair of this dead otter is covered.'

"'Let Loki fetch it,' said Odin; and I released the mischief maker from his bonds.

"In the most distant part of the world there is a place called the Desert of Dread. A great river falls over a terrible precipice; and that waterfall is called the force of Andvari. Andvari was a dark elf who lived alone in the land of cloudy waste. Long years ago, he knew of the sun and stars, the sea and land; but he forgot them all in his love of gold. He knew nothing of men or gods; he heeded neither cold nor heat; he knew not night from day; he had forgotten even his name. He took no rest, but toiled constantly, always gathering gold, gold, nothing but gold.

"Loki found the desert and the waterfall, but he saw nothing of the elf. At last he remembered that Andvari took the gold from the water. So he went to the river; and, looking down into the water, saw a salmon, which he thought must be Andvari, who had taken fright at the sound of footsteps. The salmon was too wary to be taken with a hook; so Loki went to borrow a net from Ran, who, at that time, had the only net in the world. She was very careful of it; but after much trouble, Loki induced her to lend it to him, to catch the owner of the Flame of the Sea.

"Loki stretched the net across the river, and took Andvari in its meshes. When the elf felt the tightening of the cords, he remembered gods and men and his own name; and when Loki lifted him from the water, he took his own form, and said, 'You know that I am Andvari, and you have come to take my gold.'

"He led Loki into his storehouse and gave him all his gold, even the hauberk of gold, and the Helmet of Dread. When the last piece had been delivered, Andvari turned away, and Loki saw something glitter on his finger, which he made the elf give to him.

"As Andvari drew the ring from his finger, he said: 'I can spare all the rest better than this; for this is the seed of the gold; and with it I can make more gold. But take that, if you will. My curse shall go with it; and, to whomever it is given, he shall have the curse.'

"Loki placed the ring on his finger, and brought the gold to my father's house. When all that golden treasure was heaped upon our floor, it seemed as if the sun itself were shining within our walls.

"Then Odin said to Reidmar, 'The ransom is paid.' But Reidmar said, 'We do not know whether the gold will cover the body of the otter.' So Fafnir and I brought in the otter, and piled the gold around it, until it was all covered, as we thought; but we had taken every piece of the gold. Then Reidmar caught the gleam of the ring, and, at the same time, discovered a hair near the otter's mouth; and he said, 'You shall be my slaves till you give me that ring, the seed of gold and grief, to cover this one hair.'

"Then Odin took the ring from Loki's finger and threw it upon the heap, saying, 'I am glad you have it all, even the curse of the elf king.'

"Reidmar laughed, as he answered: 'Who shall do me harm? My sword is Fafnir, and my shield is Regin, the smith.'

"I struck the shackles from the gods, and they went out into the night; but, at the door, Odin turned and warned us of the danger of the love of gold. Then they went away; and the gold was ours.

III. THE CURSE OF THE RING

"I **LOOKED** upon the gold, and loved it, as it shone upon our faces like the sun. I longed for it, but smiled and begged my father to keep the greater part, but to give Fafnir a share, and me a little handful, for my skill as a smith, and for my help that day. But I might have asked for much or little; for he made no answer. He sat on his ivory throne, and stared at the gold. Fafnir did not speak, but looked at the gold and our father.

"We watched the gold till morning; when Fafnir took his sword, and I, my hammer; and we went out into the world. I came back at night; and, while I longed to see the gold, I dared not go into the hall where it lay. As I lay in my bed, I thought I heard the clink of the gold, and saw the light. I slept, and dreamed, and woke with a cry. I sprang from my bed, and ran to the hall. Fafnir stood by the gold: at his feet lay our father, whose body was covered with gold, and whose face became white, in death, as I looked. Fafnir wore the Helmet of Dread; and he held his bare sword in his hand.

"'I shall keep the gold,' he said, 'and shall live alone, to guard the gold and take its curse. Will you leave me, or stay until I shed your blood?'

"I fled from the house with neither gold nor tools. I had only my remembering heart and my skilful hands. I came to this land, and taught men to sow and reap; and men said that Freyr had taught them husbandry.

"I taught them to work in metals, to sail on the sea, and to tame and use horses; and they said that Thor had taught them all these things. I gave the shuttle to maidens, and taught them to weave; and the needle, and taught them to sew; and, when they were old, they said that they had learned these things from Freyja.

"I taught them poetry and music; and they said that Bragi was their teacher, while I was a wandering *skald*. Still I became a master of masters. But I shall meet my fate by a sword in the hand of a stripling.

"I became wise; but I longed for my brother's gold; and I envied him, when kings gave me golden gifts to pay for my skill. Once I went back to my native land, and found the fields lying waste and desolate. The house was falling; the roof was gone. I looked into the hall, and saw the gold and a great dragon coiled about it. I fled again; and, many years after, I heard men tell of the treasure of gold, that lay on the Glittering Heath, guarded by a dreadful serpent.

"Then I knew the Völsung race; and, at last, I saw you in the house of the Helper. I dreamed dreams, saw your glory, and knew that your sword would win my treasure.

"I think that Fafnir was wiser than I, because he did not waste his treasure on men. But I shall have it all, some day; and then I shall be king of men."

Then he slept, and Sigurd rose, and cried "Awake, O master."

Regin opened his eyes, and said: "Have you listened, Sigurd? Will you avenge the wrong, and win the treasure?"

And Sigurd, looking at him with clear eyes, said, "You shall have the treasure and the curse."

THE FORGING OF THE SWORD

as told by Sarah Powers Bradish

I. REGIN'S FAILURES

SIGURD came to Regin again, and said, "I ask a gift at your hands."

Regin answered, "I would reach to the end of the world, to find the gift you need."

"But the gift I require lies near you," said Sigurd; "I want you to forge me a sword."

"Here is your sword," said Regin, "wrought with many charms. I began it when the waning moon was new."

Sigurd took the sword, and looked at the jewelled hilt, and the runes engraved upon the blade, while Regin waited for a word of approval. Sigurd turned and struck the anvil with it; the sword fell in pieces on the earth. Then he went out into the forest.

When two moons had waxed and waned, Sigurd came again to ask about his sword; and Regin said, "I have worked day and night, and my hand has surely lost its cunning, if this fails to satisfy you."

Sigurd struck with it the anvil again; and again the pieces of the sword were shattered.

The next day Sigurd said to his mother, "Where are the pieces of the sword of the Branstock, mother?"

"Are you angry, my son?" she asked.

"No, mother; but the time for deeds has come."

She took his hand, and led him to her treasure chamber; and, unrolling bands of silk, showed him the pieces of his father's sword, which gleamed as white as silver; and the jewels in the hilt shone with as bright a light as when Sigmund plucked it from the oak.

Sigurd smiled, and said: "You have kept your charge well; but your watch is over now. These pieces shall be welded to shine again in the rain of Odin."

She gave him the sacred steel that she had guarded so faithfully. He kissed her gently, and left her standing alone. She did not speak; but, with eager eyes, she watched her godlike son, who had grown so tall and fair and glorious.

II. THE WRATH OF SIGURD

SIGURD went swiftly to Regin's smithy, and gave him the pieces of the broken sword.

"Will nothing else satisfy you?" asked Regin. "This sword, that I fashioned long ago, brought death to your father's father, and to all his sons."

"With this sword I shall slay the serpent and win the gold," said Sigurd. "It is too late to turn back from the path you bade me take."

When the moon of May was full, Sigurd again sought Regin at midnight. The dwarf was worn and pale, but he said, "I have done as you wished," and gave Sigurd the welded sword.

Sigurd raised it high above his head, as his father raised it, when he drew it from the Branstock. Then, as he struck a fearful blow upon the anvil, he shouted for joy; for he held the sword, unhurt in his hand, while the anvil was cut in two.

Then Regin took his harp, and sang about making the sword, which he called the Wrath of Sigurd. He sang of how he had forged it long ago, and how he had welded and wrought it again.

Sigurd listened to the song, and said: "I will avenge your wrong, for you have failed me in nothing. The sword is all I could ask."

"Come," said Regin, "let us try the sword in another way."

They went out to the river, and Regin threw a lock of wool into the stream, and held the sword in the water until the current brought it against the blade, which cut the wool in two.

Then they placed the Wrath of Sigurd in a golden sheath, and tied the peace strings.

THE PROPHECY OF GRIPIR

as told by Sarah Powers Bradish

 THE next morning Sigurd mounted Greyfell, and rode again to Gripir's house. He entered the hall, and stood leaning on his sword, while he saluted the ancient king.

Gripir said, "Hail, Sigurd!" and welcomed him to his home.

Sigurd said: "Hail, father! I have my new sword, and have come for your parting word."

"What would you hear?" asked Gripir.

"Your word and the Norns'."

"What sight would you see?"

"I would see as the gods see; though the sight be dreadful."

"What hope would you hope?"

"Your hope and the gods'."

The ancient king was silent as he looked at Sigurd, and thought of the future of the youth. Then he spoke of that future, and told Sigurd that he would do valiant deeds, win great wealth, and live with the Cloudy People; but his glorious day would be short.

Then he called Sigurd to sit beside him on his throne, and told him of mighty deeds, of distant lands, of the sea and heavens.

Then Sigurd said that he must not linger, for a war horse as swift as the wind, and his father's sword, had been given him; that he must obey the voice that called him to ride to the Glittering Heath.

So the old king bade the young warrior farewell, and Sigurd returned to Regin when the sun was sinking in the west.

THE GLITTERING HEATH

as told by Sarah Powers Bradish

I. ODIN DIRECTS SIGURD

THE next morning Sigurd rode away with Regin for guide. They soon left the pleasant land of the Helper, and came to the hill country. All day they climbed higher and higher, and at night they slept upon a mountain top. In the morning they looked back to the beautiful country where Sigurd had spent his boyhood, and forward to the range of mountains that rose like a wall before them. For three days they rode over mountains and across deserts. The fourth day they came to a desolate region that was as brass under Greyfell's hoofs. This was the entrance to the Glittering Heath. Sigurd dismounted, and walked carefully in the thick fog to meet the terrible dragon.

Regin had fallen back, but Sigurd hardly missed him, he was so intent on finding the guardian of the treasure. Suddenly a man appeared in his path, one-eyed and old, wrapped in a cloud-grey cloak, and wearing a broad-brimmed hat.

"Hail, Sigurd!" he said.

"Hail! I greet you, my friend and my father's friend," answered Sigurd.

Odin asked where Sigurd was going. Sigurd answered that he was going to slay the dragon that guarded the golden treasure.

"Then let me tell you what to do," said Odin. "You will find a slot worn in the stone. It is the path worn by the dragon in his daily journey after water. Dig a pit in this path, and lie in it with your naked sword in your hand."

Sigurd worked all night; and at daybreak the pit was dug. He lay in it, with his sword in his hand. The light was growing brighter, when he heard a noise like the trampling of many feet, and the tinkle and clatter of gold dragged over the earth. The sounds came nearer, and the light was shut off. It seemed to Sigurd that an inky river rolled over the

pit, and the air was heavy with the poisonous breath of the serpent; when Sigurd made an upward thrust with his sword, and pierced the heart of the dragon. Then he leaped out; and, as he stood with uplifted sword by the side of the dead monster, seven eagles settled on a mountain peak, and uttered hoarse cries.

Sigurd was still standing by the dragon, when Regin came up and reproached him with the murder of his brother.

"I have done your deed," said Sigurd; "and now we must part."

"You have slain my brother," said Regin; "what atonement can you make?"

"Take the gold," said Sigurd, "as a ransom for my head."

"You have slain my brother," repeated Regin. Then he drew his sword, and cut a piece of the dragons flesh, which he ordered Sigurd to cook for him, while he lay down and slept.

Sigurd found waste wood in the heath, with which he made a fire. He fixed the piece of flesh on a spit, and held it to roast. The eagles flew down, and sat near him, while he cooked. He put out his hand, to see whether the meat were done; and some of the juice of the dripping meat fell on it, and burned his finger. He unconsciously put his finger into his mouth, and tasted the meat juice. Then he understood what the eagles were saying.

II. THE EAGLES' COUNSEL

THE first eagle asked why he waited so long to roast the meat.

The second said, "Go, for the king's feast awaits you."

The third said, "How great is the feast of him who feeds on wisdom."

The fourth said, "Will you let Regin live, to spread waste and ruin over the world?"

The fifth said, "Regin knew that a youth would slay him; but he intends to slay the youth."

The sixth said, "He has lost all sense of truth, in his greed for gold."

The seventh said, "Hasten, Sigurd! Strike while he dreams."

Then Sigurd, for the second time, lifted his sword; and Regin lay dead beside the dragon, slain by the stripling for whom he had forged the sword, and whom he had planned to kill.

III. SIGURD TAKES THE TREASURE AND THE CURSE

SIGURD sheathed his sword, and mounted Greyfell. The eagles flew about his head, as he rode along the path of the serpent, to the ruins of the golden house, of which Regin had told him. The hoard of gold lay in heaps upon the floor. There were coins from ancient cities, golden armour, magic rings and bracelets, and blocks of gold, just as the elfin miners had cut them from the rock. The hauberk of gold and the Helmet of Dread lay with the rest. Brighter than all gleamed Andvari's ring; the ring that Loki had taken, that Odin had asked for, and that Reidmar had demanded to cover the last hair of the otter; the ring that bore the curse.

Sigurd put on the hauberk of gold, the Helmet of Dread, and the fatal ring. Then he carried out the gold, while the eagles screamed, "Bind the red rings, O Sigurd."

He worked all night; and, in the morning, took Greyfell by the bridle, to lead him from the Glittering Heath, because he thought that the weight of the gold was enough for the horse to carry. But Greyfell refused to stir, until Sigurd, clad in all his armour, vaulted into the saddle; when he bore his royal master across the desolate waste, to the green world beyond.

BRYNHILD

as told by Sarah Powers Bradish

I. THE SLEEPING MAIDEN

DAY after day, Sigurd rode, always rising higher and higher, until he came to a lofty mountain. Its peak was capped with clouds, through which fire seemed ready to burst. Sigurd thought that, from the top of this mountain, he could get a view of the country he was about to cross; so he began the ascent. The fire burned brighter and brighter, until flames appeared above the clouds. Then the clouds thickened, and hid the mountain. Night fell around them; but Sigurd encouraged Greyfell; and they went on in the darkness.

As they climbed up a great rock, the whole summit appeared as a mass of flame. At dawn they came to a plain, from which they could see the topmost peak, surrounded by a circle of fire. But neither horse nor rider hesitated.

As they approached the flaming wall, Sigurd bent low over the horse's neck, and spoke kindly to him. Then he tightened the saddle girth, grasped the reins firmly, and, with his sword unsheathed in his right hand, urged Greyfell to make the daring leap.

Greyfell plunged into the flames, which had blazed more fiercely as horse and rider approached the circle. As they dashed through it, the fire leaped up as if to grasp them both, and then died away, leaving a ring of white ashes.

A castle stood before them. Sigurd entered the open gate and passed through the hall. He came to a mound, on which lay a warrior clad in armour. Sigurd unclasped the warrior's helmet, and beheld the face of a sleeping woman. He cut the rings of her armour with his sword; and she still lay asleep, dressed in fine white linen, with her golden hair covering her breast. Sigurd knelt beside her and woke her with a kiss.

II. THE MAIDEN TELLS HER NAME

"WHAT is your name, O fairest of the earth?" he said. "I am Sigurd, son of Völsung. I have slain the terrible dragon and taken the hoard of gold."

She answered: "My name is Brynhild. I was one of the daughters of earth, but the All-Father took me, and made me a Shield maiden. I was one of the band of Valkyries, who hovered over battle-fields, to decide victories, and to bear the slain to Odin's halls. Once he sent me to attend a single combat, and bade me give the victory to an ancient robber king. I knew the story of the quarrel which led to this fight; and I loved the fair maiden who must wed the victor. So I pricked the robber with the point of my sword, and carried him to Valhalla; and left the handsome young lover to take his bride.

"For my disobedience, Odin said that I must again become a woman, and also a wife. I begged that my husband might be a hero, who knew no fear. Odin said, 'That request I will grant, but you will have long to wait for that hero.'

"He brought me to the top of this mountain, Hindfell, and pricked me with a sleep thorn; and, striking the rocks with his spear, made the ring of flickering flame, through which you rode. I knew no more until you woke me just now."

Then she talked with Sigurd; and her words showed that she was the wisest as well as the most beautiful of women.

III. THE BETROTHAL

BRYNHILD was satisfied that Sigurd was a fearless hero; so it was settled that they should be married at her sister's home in Lymdale, where she would go at once.

Sigurd said:

"O Brynhild, now hearken while I swear,

That the sun shall die in the heavens, and the day no more be fair,

If I seek not love in Lymdale, and the house that fostered thee.

And the land where thou awakest 'twixt the woodland and the sea!"

Brynhild answered:

"O Sigurd, Sigurd, now hearken while I swear,

That the day shall die forever, and the sun to blackness wear.

Ere I forget thee, Sigurd, as I lie 'twixt wood and sea,

In the little land of Lymdale, and the house that fostered me."

Then Sigurd, forgetting the curse, placed on her finger the ring of Andvari. After this he remounted Greyfell and rode onward over the mountain. But Brynhild hastened to the house of her sister in Lymdale.

GUDRUN'S DREAMS

as told by Sarah Powers Bradish

I. WHY THE PRINCESS WAS SAD

IN the Land of Cloudy Mists lived a people known as the Niblungs. They were brave and warlike, and had never known defeat in battle. Their king and queen were Giuki and Grimhild, who had three sons and one daughter. The eldest son, Gunnar, was tall and fair; the second, Hogni, was very wise; the third, Guttorm, was a great warrior; and their daughter, Gudrun, was very beautiful.

One morning Gudrun, who was as charming in manner as she was pleasing in person, passed down the garden walk, without speaking to any of her attendants. Her nurse came to ask her why she had left unnoticed the things of which she was so fond; why she did not speak to her maidens, or go to her embroidery, or join in the chase.

"Tomorrow I shall do as I have always done," she answered; "today I am sad, because I cannot forget the dream that came to me last night."

"Tell me your dream," said the nurse; "for dreams often indicate only the weather."

Gudrun said: "I thought I sat by the door of my father's hall, and saw a falcon come from the north. His feathers were golden, and his eyes were as bright as crystal in the sunshine. Men feared him, but I felt no fear. My heart was light with hope. He hovered over the Niblung palace, and then flew down to my knees. He cried out to me, and I clasped him in my arms."

"This falcon is a king's son," said the nurse, "who has won honour for his noble deeds, and will come to ask you to be his bride."

"You give good interpretations to my dreams, because you love me," said Gudrun. "My mother, Grimhild, is also wise; but she turns my dreams to evil."

"Your dream is easy to read, and its meaning is good," said the nurse; "but, if you are in doubt, let us go to Lymdale, to consult Brynhild, who is skilful in all such matters. She will give the same meaning that I have given; but your confidence in her will give you peace."

"Let us go to Brynhild," said Gudrun.

II. THE VISIT TO BRYNHILD

SO the wagons were prepared, the maidens dressed for travel, and Gudrun hastened to Lymdale. When they arrived at the white castle by the sea, Brynhild's maidens came out to meet them, and lead them into the hall.

Brynhild had been sitting at her embroidery, and she led Gudrun to the frames, on which she was working pictures of great deeds. For a while, they asked and answered questions about each other's friends; then the maidens brought a dainty repast, and talked of kings and heroes, and asked who was the greatest hero. Brynhild spoke of kings of distant lands, and Gudrun said, "Why do you not name my brothers, who are called the greatest men of our time?"

"Your brothers are great kings," answered Brynhild, "but I have seen one greater than they. His name is Sigurd the Völsung, son of King Sigmund."

Gudrun trembled and turned pale, but asked, "How do you know that Sigurd is the greatest king?"

"His mother went to the battle-field," said Brynhild, "and found King Sigmund lying among the slain. He was mortally wounded, but still alive. He told her that her son would be a greater king than he, and he had been greater than any king who ever lived.

"Young Sigurd was brought up in the house of the Helper, and every day he did some wonderful thing. He has already killed the terrible dragon that guarded the golden treasure, and he will soon come to us across the mountains."

Gudrun was silent, then rose and said: "It is late; the guard of the Niblung gate looks in vain for the light dust of our golden wagons. Come with your maidens to my fathers house, and we will welcome you, as you have welcomed us today."

Brynhild thanked her for her kind and cheerful words, but looked into her sad eyes, and said, "Stay with your friends, who wish you only happiness."

Then Gudrun said: "I came to tell you my dreams, for I knew you were wise and true. I dare not tell my mother, and I fear the mocking laughter of the wise women, when they hear a maiden's dream."

"I shall not mock," said Brynhild, "but I may not be able to give you the help you need."

"This was my dream," said Gudrun: "I thought I was sitting at the door one morning, when a falcon came out of the north. He flew over the kingdoms of men, and filled their hearts with fear. Then he circled about the Niblung castle, and my heart beat high with hope.

"He was a beautiful creature; his feathers were like gold, and his eyes flashed like crystal in the sunshine. He flew down to my knees, and I took him in my arms."

"That is indeed a good dream," said Brynhild. "A great king will make you his queen."

"I have not told you all," said Gudrun. "With joy I clasped him to my breast, and it was stained with purple blood. My heart grew cold and heavy as lead. I laid my hand upon it, and my falcon was gone."

Now Brynhild was pale, but she said: "Fear not, O daughter of Niblungs. The king will come and wed you, and you will be happy. Do not think it strange that changes should come to a great and warlike race. Your husband will fall dead beside you, but that is not the worst that could befall you. Do not think of his death, but of his glorious career."

"After this dream, I dreamed again," said Gudrun. "I thought I sat in the garden, and a hart came out of the forest. His hair was golden, and his antlers glittered in the sun. He was the noblest deer ever seen. He came to me and laid his head upon my arm. Then a fair queen came and sat beside me. The heavens grew black, and in the gathering darkness I saw a hand and arm, with the jewels and rings of the queen. There was a sudden sword thrust, and my beautiful hart lay dead at my feet.

"I cried out in anguish. I was no longer in the garden, but in the depths of the forest. Wild wolves howled around me, and I called them my friends. I spoke in strange language, and my hands were wet with blood."

For a long time Brynhild was silent. At last she said: "This dream is the same as the other. The hart from the forest is a great king from a foreign land. He shall be slain at your feet; but be comforted, for you have had the spring of life, and the summer draws near. The daughter of a conquering race would not desire constant peace. You will have joy and sorrow. You may understand the howling wolves, and your right hand may be wet with blood, but rejoice in the love that you have, and in that which shall come. And come again to Lymdale, to bless the friends who love you."

They drank the parting cup. The Niblung maidens put on their dark blue cloaks, and the golden wains were driven slowly homeward, under the light of the moon.

SIGURD AT LYMDALE

as told by Sarah Powers Bradish

I. HIS ARRIVAL

HEIMIR, king of Lymdale, whose wife was the sister of Brynhild, had brave sons and fair daughters. He was a valiant king, and often led his warriors in battle, but in time of peace he taught them to cultivate the rich fields of Lymdale, and to look after their sheep and cattle.

One spring morning, King Heimir and his princes and earls were about to mount their horses for the chase, when they saw a warrior approaching. He rode a grey horse, and his armour was all of gold. His fair hair waved in the breeze, and his bright eyes won the hearts of all who looked upon him.

Heimir, putting away his spear, saluted the stranger, whom he begged to stay with his people for a little time, and, offering him the hospitality of his home, asked whence he came.

The horseman answered: "I am the son of a king, but I alone am left of all my kin. I am of the Völsung race, and they were the sons of Odin.

"I am young, but I have sought wisdom. I have no army, but I, alone, have slain the dragon, and taken his treasure. My name is Sigurd, and I was brought up in the land of the Helper. I am grateful for your welcome, and tonight I will stay in your palace, but tomorrow I must go to Lymdale."

As Sigurd leaped from the saddle, Heimir said:

"You have already come to Lymdale. I am King Heimir, and am better skilled in the touch of the harp than in the arts of war."

The princes and earls, who had heard of Sigurd's exploits, looked with admiration on his bright face. They gave up the hunt, and went with him into Heimir's hall, where they spent the day in feasting and song. They talked of the dragon and the

Glittering Heath. Four strong men brought in the treasure, and the earls gazed, with ever-increasing wonder, at the shining armour, the cunningly wrought rings and the blocks of gold.

II. SIGURD FINDS BRYNHILD

THE next day they went out to hunt. Sigurd was riding alone; the hounds had gone on, and his hawk was sitting on his hand. He was thinking of Brynhild, when he saw a white house among the trees, on the roof of which many doves were sitting in the sun. The hawk flew straight as an arrow toward the house. Sigurd expected to see him attack the doves; but he flew to a window in the tower, and looked within. Then he cried out, as the ravens of Odin cry when they see the morning sun, and flew in at the casement.

"Here is the dwelling of an earl," thought Sigurd, "or perhaps of a prince, of whom they have not told me. I will go in to claim my hawk, and find a friend."

No servant answered his call, so he entered the open door. He saw a staircase, and followed the stairway, which led to a chamber in the tower. His hawk was perched in a window, and on a raised seat sat a beautiful woman, clothed in white, with gold bracelets on her arms. Her embroidery frames stood before her, and in a golden web she was working scenes from the lives of the Völsungs, such as the taking of the sword from the Branstock, the death of Sigmund, Queen Hiordis in the house of the Helper, the beautiful babe named by the Helper and his son, the child in the smithy of the dwarf, the youth taking Greyfell, the forging of the sword, the dragon on his bed of gold, the eagles on the Glittering Heath, the death of the dragon and the dwarf, the journey across the desert, the flaming mountain top, Greyfell and his rider dashing through the fire, the sleeping maiden, forests, meadows, cities and seas, and Sigurd in them all.

With wonder Sigurd saw all this, as he stood in the doorway, and when the woman raised her head, he looked into the eyes of Brynhild. Both were silent. Sigurd was the first to speak, "Hail, lady and queen! Hail, fairest of the earth!"

Brynhild answered him kindly, as she rose, and led him to a seat beside her. They talked of their separation, and of the joy of meeting again.

Brynhild said:

"I bid thee remember the word that I have sworn,

How the sun shall turn to blackness, and the last day be outworn,

Ere I forget thee, Sigurd, and the kindness of thy face."

Sigurd answered:

"O Brynhild, remember how I swore,

That the sun should die in the heavens, and day come back no more,

Ere I forget thy wisdom, and thine heart of inmost love."

Then they talked of the days to come, when they should sit on the throne together.

And they saw their crowned children, and the kindred of the kings,

And deeds in the world arising, and the day of better things,

All the earthly exaltation, till their pomp of life should be passed,

And soft on the bosom of God their love should be laid at the last.

SIGURD AT THE PALACE OF THE NIBLUNGS

as told by Sarah Powers Bradish

I. GIUKI'S WELCOME TO SIGURD

THE household of Heimir had risen early; the great hall was filled with earls, and shepherds thronged at the gates. Even the housewives had left their baking and brewing, and the maidens had forgotten the bright colours of their weaving and embroidery. But it was impossible to tell whether the people were moved so strangely by sorrow or by joy. Suddenly their voices were hushed, and their heads were bowed, for Heimir's hand swept the harp strings, and he sang a farewell song to the guest who had grown so dear. Then a shout went up, as the gates were opened and the earls came out. The people fell back to make way for Sigurd, who, clad in golden armour, and mounted on Greyfell, rode out to bid them all good-bye. Another shout arose, though many were silent from grief at parting with their royal guest. They watched until Greyfell disappeared in a turn of the road, then each went back to his work, sorry that Sigurd had gone.

Sigurd rode westward from Lymdale, over plains and across mountains, through valleys and along river banks, until he came to a great stone gateway. There was no sentinel to stop him, and he rode through a long passage, which brought him to a palace courtyard. The beautiful horse, golden armour, and more than all the magnificent form and dignified bearing of the rider, attracted the attention of the earls, so that they sent to tell the king.

Before the king came, Sigurd had ridden to the entrance and asked to what country he had come, and who lived in the palace.

"You have come to the land of the Niblungs, and this is the home of King Giuki," answered one of the earls.

Then King Giuki came, and asked, "Who is this who rides into my castle without permission?"

"I am Sigurd, the Völsung, son of Sigmund," was the answer; and Giuki, who had heard of Sigurd's daring, welcomed him most kindly.

Sigurd had already made friends of the king's retainers, who rejoiced when Giuki led him into the hall and presented him to Queen Grimhild, and to his sons, Gunnar, Hogni, and Guttorm, and to his daughter, Gudrun.

Grimhild and the young kings greeted him kindly; Gudrun alone was silent and at last she said, as she offered him a cup:

"Hail, Sigurd the Völsung! May I see thy joy increase.

Thy shielded sons beside thee, and thy days grown old in peace."

He took the cup and thanked her but his thoughts were with Brynhild.

King Giuki ordered a feast, and the kings and nobles passed the night in feasting and drinking and happy conversation.

II. SIGURD LEADS THE NIBLUNGS TO WAR

SIGURD stayed in the house of Giuki week after week. When he spoke of going away, a hunting party was planned, or someone remembered that a festival must be kept, or games of skill and strength were proposed.

At midwinter, news came that an enemy was about to attack the Niblungs. Sigurd offered to assist his new friends in the war, and one winter's morning, long before dawn, the army of the Niblungs marched eastward, with three young kings at its head. Sigurd was chief in command, Gunnar rode on his right, and Hogni on his left. All men loved Sigurd, and it was easy to distinguish him by his hauberk of gold, his Helmet of Dread, and his fair hair.

The enemy melted like wax before the fire under the stroke of Sigurd's sword. Before spring the last foe was gone, and minstrels sang the praise of Sigurd in the Niblung hall. This was a part of their song:

"When the sun of summer shall come aback to the land,
It shall shine on the fields of the tiller that fears no heavy hand,
That the sheaf shall be for the plower, and the loaf for him that sowed,
Through every furrowed acre, where the son of Sigmund rode."

Sigurd was dear to rich and poor alike. Little children crowded about the gate to catch a glimpse of his golden armour when he went in or out, and mothers brought their babes, that the glance of his bright eyes might rest upon them for an instant.

Gudrun stood in the hall and filled the cups of the victorious kings while the earls brought in the spoil. There were jewelled swords, crowns of kings, shields and spears, rings and silken garments, which they gave to Giuki, saying, "Sigurd won our battles and led us to all these things."

Sigurd came in, and kissed the hands of Giuki and Grimhild, who loved him as they loved their own sons, to whom he was both friend and leader. But he was dearer to Gudrun than to all the rest, although the name of Brynhild was ever on his lips.

His fame spread over the seas; and merchants told the story of his prowess in all the kingdoms of the world. Wise men came to visit him; and poets sang of his glory. Still he lingered in the house of the Niblungs.

III. THE CUP OF FORGETFULNESS

IN early summer, an enemy from the north came to make war on the Niblungs. Again Sigurd went with the three young kings, and led them to victory. As he stood among the dark-haired Niblung warriors, he longed to leave all, and return to Lymdale, to seek the fair maiden who was waiting for him, in the white castle. But he went back with the victors to Giuki's palace, and sat on the high-seat at the feast, though his thoughts went over the mountains to Brynhild.

The sound of the revels grew louder; but Sigurd remained silent, until Giuki asked him to sing of the gods and heroes. They brought a harp, and Sigurd sang of Odin, Rerir, Völsung, Signy and Sigmund. The people listened attentively; and, as the song went on, they seemed to see the Branstock and all the brave deeds of Sigmund; and they loved Sigurd more than ever.

Grimhild rose and stood by Sigurd, and said, as she gave him a cup: "None of these ancient kings did deeds as "great as yours. You have sung of your fathers, but men shall sing of you, and remember the house of the Niblungs, in their songs. Drink of this cup; for my love is mixed with the wine."

Sigurd took the drinking horn from her hand, and held it, while he noticed the exquisite carving; and smiled upon Grimhild as he drank the wine. He did not know that she had given him a magic potion. As soon as he had sipped the wine, a change came over him; and the people who loved him felt a chill. A shadow settled upon his face; the hall grew dark.

Grimhild alone was happy; for she saw, from Sigurd's eyes, that she had conquered a brave warrior, and filled a faithful heart with deceit. She bade Sigurd be merry, although his kin had passed away; because he had found a new mother in her love, a new father in Giuki, and brothers in their sons, Gunnar, Hogni and Guttorm. Then she told him of the glory that would come to the Niblung house through his valiant deeds.

As Sigurd listened, the magic potion worked; and he forgot Brynhild. The people sat silent, as if the breath of a coming frost had swept over the summer land, and the earls looked in sorrow upon the dimmed eyes of Sigurd.

In Lymdale, as Brynhild was sitting at her embroidery, a sudden fear smote her heart, and a circle of flame sprang up around her dwelling.

The Niblung minstrels tried to sing; but their notes were discordant and died away; no sound was heard except the cries of the eagles and the sighing of the wind. One by one the people passed out, until Sigurd was left alone. He went to the stables and saddled a horse, but not Greyfell; he had forgotten Greyfell. He rode to Brynhild's house; but he had forgotten Brynhild. His horse dared not approach the flickering flames. Sigurd turned and rode away, without knowing where he was, until he heard the shout of the Niblung earls, who welcomed him home again.

Sigurd asked what deeds there were for his sword. Grimhild came to lead him to his place, and the three young kings greeted him with loving words. Sigurd could not understand his own sorrow; but he knew that the Niblungs were all very kind to him, and said, "I will try to do as I have always done, and perhaps the cloud will clear away." So he took his seat beside the kings, and spoke to the people. Their fear vanished at the sound of his voice, and all things went on as before, though Sigurd never smiled.

Then Grimhild mixed another potion in a golden goblet, and bade Gudrun take it to Sigurd, who forgot his own trouble in pity for the sad-eyed girl. He tried to cheer her, and said: "The people about us are glad, and we alone are silent and sorrowful. Now if we might comfort each other:

"Then belike were we gladdest of all; for I love thee more than these
The cup of goodwill that thou bearest, and the greetings thou wouldst say,
Turn thee to the cup of thy love, and the words of the troth-plighting day."

The next morning Sigurd dimly remembered the words that he had spoken to Gudrun. So he rose quickly and sought her in the garden, and said to her:

"O Gudrun, now hearken while I swear.
That the sun shall die forever, and the day no more be fair,
If I forget thy pity and thine inmost heart of love!"

And she answered:

"Herewith I swear, O Sigurd, that the earth shall hate the sun,
And the year desire but darkness, and the blossoms shrink from day,
Ere my love shall fail, beloved, or my longing pass away!"

Then they went into the hall. Giuki, Grimhild and their sons greeted them kindly; and Sigurd said to Giuki:

"Stretch forth thy hands to thy son; for I bid thy daughter to wife,
And her life shall withhold my death day, and her death shall stay my life."

Giuki replied:

"Hail, Sigurd, son of mine eld!
And I bless the gods for the day that mine ancient eyes here beheld.
Now let me depart in peace, since I know for very sooth.
That waxen e'en as the Godfolk shall the Niblungs blossom in youth.
Come, take thy mother's greeting, and let thy brethren say
How well they love thee, Sigurd, and how fair they deem the day."

IV. THE WEDDING OF SIGURD AND GUDRUN

THE wedding day dawned fair and bright. People thronged to the Niblung castle from

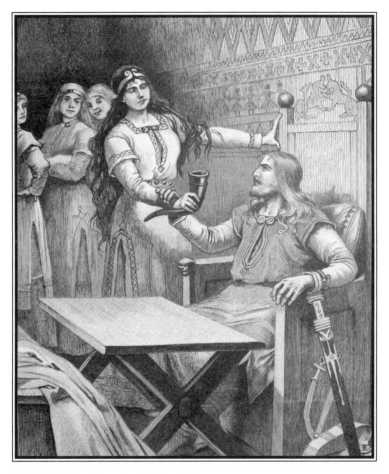

Grimhild gives Sigurd a drink of wine

fields and forests. The earls were there, and kings came dressed in purple. The benches in the hall were covered with cloths embroidered in gold, and strewn with flowers. The name of Sigurd, the Völsung, was heard on every hand.

For men drink the bridal of Sigurd and the white-armed Niblung maid.

In the midst of the feasting and laughter all voices were hushed, and the glitter of swords appeared in the doorway, while warriors, clad in armour, brought in the cup of promise and the roasted head of the sacred boar. Sigurd rose; and, unfastening the peace strings from his sword, he laid it on the boar's head while he spoke the words of the ancient oath:

> "By the Earth that growth and giveth, and by all the Earth's increase,
> That is spent for gods and man folk; by the sun that shines on these;
> By the Salt-Sea Flood that beareth the life and death of men;
> By the Heavens and Stars that change not, though earth die out again;
> By the wild things of the mountains, and the houseless waste and lone,
> By the prey of the Goths in the thicket, and the holy Beast of Son,
> I hallow me to Odin, for a leader of his host,
> To do the deeds of the highest, and never count the cost;
> And I swear that whatso great one shall show the day and the deed,
> I shall not ask why nor wherefore; but the sword's desire shall speed.
> And I swear to seek no quarrel, nor to swerve aside for aught,
> Though the right and the left be blooming, and the straight way wend to naught;
> And I swear to abide and hearken the prayer of any thrall.
> Though the war torch be on the threshold, and the foe man's feet in the hall;
> And I swear to sit on my throne, in the guise of the kings of the earth,
> Though the anguish past amending, and the unheard woe have birth;
> And I swear to wend in my sorrow, that none shall curse mine eyes.
> For the scowl that quelleth beseeching, and the hate that scorneth the wise.
> So help me, Earth and Heavens, and the Under-sky and Seas,
> And the Stars in their ordered courses, and the Norns that order these."

Then he drank the cup of promise. The daughters of earls refilled the cup, as Gunnar advanced with the unsheathed sword of the Niblungs in his hand. He also laid the edge of the sword upon the boar's head, while he took the oath, and drank the cup of promise.

The maidens again filled the cup; and Hogni took the oath, with his naked sword lying on the boars head. Then it was Guttorm's turn; but his place was empty, for he had grown tired of peace, and had gone to seek glory on the eastern seas.

Giuki blessed his sons, and Sigurd took his place by Gudrun. But his heart was filled with fear, and she trembled as she remembered her dreams.

THE WOOING OF BRYNHILD

as told by Sarah Powers Bradish

I. THE OATH OF BROTHERHOOD

SOON after the wedding, Sigurd went to the Doom Ring with Gunnar and Hogni. They cut a piece of turf, and turned it back, so as to leave the earth exposed. With the point of his sword, each opened a vein in his arm; and they let the blood trickle down into the earth. Then they knelt, with their hands upon the spot that had received the blood, and took the oath of brotherhood:

Each man, at his brother's bidding, to come with the blade in his hand,
Though the fire and the flood should sunder, and the very gods withstand.
Each man to love and cherish his brother's hope and will;
Each man to avenge his brother, when the Norns his fate fulfil.

Sigurd took part in all the work of the kings, and often sat in the Doom Ring, to decide the disputes of the people. The poor were glad to see him there, because he always saw that justice was done; and it is said that the sorrowful loved him best.

II. GRIMHILD URGES GUNNAR TO WED

THE old king, Giuki, died; and Gunnar succeeded him on the throne.

One day, Grimhild came to him, and said: "You have been a good son, a brave warrior and a wise ruler; but the reign of the Niblungs will end with you, unless you take a wife from among the kings' daughters."

Gunnar answered: "You are not speaking hastily, mother? You must have found the king's daughter whom you would have me choose."

Grimhild said: "In the land of Lymdale is a golden-roofed castle, around which fierce fires burn continually. Within the castle dwells the wisest of maidens, who is as beautiful as she is wise, and as brave as she is beautiful. Yet the sons of the kings pass by, because they are afraid of the flickering flame. She has said that she will wed the man who knows no fear; but he must prove his courage by riding through the circle of fire."

Then she appealed to Sigurd, to urge Gunnar to win this maiden for his bride. And Sigurd answered that, of all the sons of men, it was most fitting that Gunnar should wed this peerless maiden.

Gunnar said: "I am contented with my kingdom, and satisfied with the companionship of my brothers; but, in obedience to my mother's wish, I will try to win this princess."

"Not yet, my son," said Grimhild; "we must know the will of the Norns."

Then Grimhild shut herself up alone, and mixed a magic drink, which she gave to her three sons, to make them do her bidding. She told Gunnar many tales, which made him think of the maiden by day, and dream of her by night.

III. SIGURD WINS BRYNHILD FOR GUNNAR

ONE morning in May, Gunnar rose early and called his brothers, Sigurd and Hogni, to go with him to seek the maiden. They had put on their armour, and their war steeds were ready, when Grimhild came out to give them her blessing and wish them success. Then they rode away to Lymdale.

Toward evening, they came in sight of the fire; and, as night came on, they rode in silence, with drawn swords in hand. The Wrath of Sigurd sent out red gleams, and the Helmet of Dread shone red as blood, in the light of the fire.

Gunnar rode up to the circle of fire; but his war horse, for the first time, refused to obey his command and, instead of entering the flames, wheeled and carried his rider to the place where the two kings were standing.

Hogni said: "Take Sigurd's horse." So Sigurd gave Greyfell to Gunnar, and offered him his armour. But Hogni thought that Gunnar had better keep his own armour.

Sigurd and Gunnar at the fire

Gunnar thanked Sigurd; and, springing into the saddle, gathered the reins in his hand; but Greyfell refused to stir. Gunnar cried out in anger that Sigurd was mocking him; but Hogni said, "Come, Gunnar, stand by Sigurd, take his hand in yours, and look into his face."

Gunnar took Sigurd's hand, while Hogni repeated his mother's magic words, which made them exchange forms, so that Sigurd looked like Gunnar, and Gunnar looked like Sigurd.

Sigurd, in the shape of Gunnar, leaped into the saddle; and Greyfell bore him safely through the circle of fire, which died away, leaving a ring of white ashes, after the horse and rider had passed.

Sigurd entered the hall, and found Brynhild sitting upon the throne, with a gold crown on her head, and a sword in her hand. Her face was stern and sorrowful; for she had been confident that none but Sigurd would ride through the flickering flame; and now she saw the steel-blue armour and long black hair of the Niblung king.

They gazed at each other in silence until Brynhild said:

"King, King, who art thou that cometh, thou lord of the cloudy gear?"

Sigurd answered, with Gunnar's voice, that he was Gunnar, King of the Niblungs. Then he reminded her of her promise to wed the man who should ride through the fire; and he claimed her as the Queen of the Niblungs.

Brynhild was silent for a time. At last she called him to the high-seat, and said that she would be Gunnar's wife. He drew his sword, and they sat with the naked blade between them while they talked. When it was time for him to go back to the brothers, he gave Brynhild a gold ring; and she drew from her finger the ring of Andvari, and gave it to him, saying, "It was my dearest treasure." Sigurd put the ring on his finger; but it brought no memory of the past. He strode out of the hall, mounted Greyfell, and rode away, with downcast eyes.

Hogni spoke to him; and, looking up, he saw a man in golden armour, sitting on a horse. Sigurd did not speak, but stretched out his hand to Gunnar: and they looked into each other's eyes, until the charm of Grimhild's words, uttered by Hogni, changed them into their own forms again. Then Sigurd said to Gunnar, "Brynhild will be your wife, and will come to the Niblung palace within ten days."

The three kings returned to the Niblung hall, and told Grimhild how Sigurd had won a bride for Gunnar; and she made a feast in honour of his success. After the feast, Gudrun asked Sigurd how it was that he wore a different ring on his finger. He told her that Brynhild had given it to him, thinking that he was Gunnar; and that Brynhild then had the ring that he was accustomed to wear. Then, with loving words, he took the ring from his finger and put it on Gudrun's.

IV. THE WEDDING OF BRYNHILD AND GUNNAR

EARLY on the morning of the tenth day, the watchman on the tower called out that many people were coming over the mountains. Then the kings rode out to meet Brynhild and her attendants.

Brynhild rode alone in a golden wagon drawn by snow-white oxen. She sat on a carved-ivory seat, covered with dark blue bench cloths. She saluted the Niblungs, and they rode together to the king's house. When they arrived at the gate, she stood up and blessed the house of Gunnar. The tall war chiefs came out to meet her, and, in the doorway, she saw one in cloudy garments whom she recognized as Gunnar from his ruddy cheeks and long black hair; and she blessed him as the hero of the flickering flame.

Then she received the war duke's greeting; and Gunnar presented his brother, Hogni, but he said that his youngest brother, Guttorm, had gone to the eastern wars; and she asked, "Who is the fourth king? I thought there were but three."

Gunnar answered that the fourth king was not of their blood, but that he had been their most welcome guest, and was now their brother, and that his name was Sigurd the Völsung.

She knew the name, but she turned, unmoved, to receive the homage of the Niblung people, and the greeting of Grimhild. Sigurd looked down from the high-seat where he sat by Gudrun's side. Grimhild's spell was broken, and he remembered the sleeping maiden and the words they had spoken on Hindfeirs top.

He led Gudrun down to Brynhild, who greeted him very kindly, though she had no word for Gudrun. The music sounded in the hall; the eagles screamed above the roof; and the wedding feast began.

THE QUARREL OF THE QUEENS

as told by Sarah Powers Bradish

I. THE MORNING BATH

GUTTORM returned from the wars, and took his former place in the hearts of the Niblungs, although he had learned to love fighting above all things.

Brynhild was Queen of the Niblungs, and no one guessed that she was unhappy. She often talked with Gudrun, and boasted of her husband, Gunnar, who rode through the fire to win her. But Gudrun said nothing in reply, though she well knew the story of that ride.

Hogni, the wise, grew wiser every day. He alone understood the scheming of his mother, Grimhild; and saw that her feet were going down a path from which they could never return.

Gunnar lived quietly with his wife, though he listened to his mother, who talked constantly of the "hoard of gold", "supplanters of kings" and "leaders of war". He said it was nothing; but, in the long hours of the night, he turned his mother's words in his mind, and wondered whether Sigurd were a "supplanter of kings".

One morning, Brynhild rose early to go to the baths in the river. She had hardly passed the screen of rose and hawthorn, when she saw Gudrun, and bade her go into the water first, because she was the sister of Gunnar.

Gudrun said that a wife was more than a sister, and that if Sigurd's sister were there, she would not give place to her sister-in-law. But, since Sigurd was the greater king, she would accept Brynhild's courtesy; and she stepped into the water.

Brynhild then waded far out into the stream, and Gudrun asked why she went so far away. She replied that they must always be far apart, because she was the wife of a great king, who rode through the flickering flame to win her, while Sigurd stood waiting at the door like a servant; besides, Sigurd was only a vassal of the Helper.

Gudrun waded up the stream to Brynhild; and holding out her hand on which sparkled the ring of Andvari, said, "You may know by this, whether the greatest of kings and the bravest of men is your husband."

Brynhild grew white, as she asked, "By all you love, where did you get that ring?"

Gudrun laughed and said, "Do you think that my brother Gunnar gave this ring to me?" And then she told Brynhild that Sigurd had given it to her, on his return from Lymdale where, in the form of Gunnar, he had ridden through the flickering flame, and secured her promise to be the wife of Gunnar and the Queen of the Niblungs.

Then Brynhild, pale as death, sprang upon the bank, threw her robe about her, and ran across the fields. But Gudrun came slowly from the water with triumph in her face.

II. GUDRUN'S REPENTANCE

AS Gudrun walked home, she remembered that Sigurd had charged her to say nothing about the ride through the flickering flame, or the ring of Andvari; and she was sorry that she had spoken so hastily. In the evening, she went to Brynhild, to ask her to forgive the words spoken in the morning.

Brynhild said that she regretted her own thoughtless words, and that she would forget it all, if Gudrun would only say that her brother Gunnar had given her the ring. But Gudrun said, "Shall I tell a lie to hide the shame of Gunnar?" and she showed the ring again, and repeated the story she had told in the morning.

Brynhild turned and cursed the house that she had blessed on her wedding day. Then, overcome with chagrin, she lay ill upon her bed. Gunnar came to comfort her, and to beg her to tell him of her trouble.

She said, "Tell me, Gunnar, that you gave Andvari's ring to Gudrun."

Gunnar left the room, without speaking.

Gudrun sent her maidens to Brynhild; but they came back, saying they dared not enter her chamber. She sought her brother, Gunnar, whom she found sitting alone, with his drawn sword lying across his knees; and she said: "O Gunnar, go to her and say that my heart is grieved with her grief, and I mourn for her evil day." But Gunnar said he could not undo the work of a traitor.

She hastened to Hogni, who sat with his armour on, and his naked sword lying across his knees; and entreated him to convey her message to Brynhild.

But he said: "I will not go to Brynhild, lest I make the matter worse; there are words that cut deeper than the sharpest sword. The Norns have ordered, and we must submit."

Then she found Sigurd wearing his hauberk of gold, and his Helmet of Dread, with his sword lying across his knees. She asked him to go to Brynhild; and he consented.

When he entered the open door of Brynhild's room, she asked why he had deceived her; for she knew nothing about the cup of forgetfulness that Grimhild had given him. They talked a long time, and he tried to comfort her. At last, he offered to put away Gudrun; but she would not consent to that, and he went out. She sent for Gunnar, and asked him to slay Sigurd before the sun rose again.

III. THE DEATH OF SIGURD

GUNNAR tore the peace strings from his sword, and went to Grimhild and Hogni. He threw the sword between them, as they were sitting together.

"For whom are the peace strings rent?" asked Grimhild; and he told her that he must take the life of Sigurd. Hogni reminded him of the oath of brotherhood; but Grimhild asked for Guttorm, who was not included in the oath of brotherhood.

As they spoke, Guttorm entered the room. Grimhild rose and gave him a cup which she had prepared. Guttorm drank, and cried, "Where is the foe?"

His mother gave him the cup again, and he asked for his sword. He drank the third time, and put on the armour that his mother brought.

At dawn, he went to Sigurd's room, but shrank from the glance of Sigurd's eyes; and went back to his brothers with his sword unstained.

He went again, and again the bright eyes of Sigurd drove him back. Then footsteps were heard in the hall, and Brynhild stood among them. The third time Guttorm went to the bed of Sigurd, and this time thrust him through with the sword. Then he turned to go away, but fell dead in the doorway, pierced by the Wrath of Sigurd, which the dying Völsung had hurled at him.

Gudrun cried out in grief and terror, "Awake, O House of the Niblungs, for slain is Sigurd the King!"

IV. GUDRUN'S MOURNING

THE people wept for Sigurd, but Gudrun shed no tears. The women wailed, but Gudrun did not sigh. The earls came to her, and ancient men, great warriors, and sweet singers came to comfort her.

But no tears and no lamenting in Gudrun's heart would strive,

With the deadly chill of sorrow, that none may bear and live.

The daughters of kings and earls told her of their sorrows. Her fathers sister said that her king was slain beside her, and then death claimed her sister, all her brothers and both her children; and yet she was living a useful and contented life.

Queen Horberg said that her husband and seven sons fell in one war; her father, mother, and four brothers were lost at sea; and she herself was captured by pirates, and made to serve a robber king.

Then a Niblung maid, named Gullrond, drew away the linen from Sigurd's face, which she turned toward Gudrun. When Gudrun saw it, she bowed her head upon it and wept. Then, with a bitter cry, she left the high-seat and fled from the house.

V. THE DEATH OF BRYNHILD

BRYNHILD stood by a pillar and gazed long at the wounds of Sigurd. Then she went to her room and lay upon her couch. Gunnar came to her, but could speak no word of cheer.

She bade her maidens bring her finest linen, her best robes, and all her jewels. When they were spread before her, she rose and dressed herself in them. "Now," she said, "bring the sword that I carried when I chose the slain."

They brought it, and she laid it unsheathed across her knees, and bade the maidens take whatever they might choose from the store of gold and jewels that her father had given her; but the weeping maidens touched none of her gifts. She stood up, and the point of the sword pierced her heart.

They were laying her on the bed when Gunnar entered, and she opened her eyes and asked that she might be laid on Sigurd's funeral pyre with the Wrath of Sigurd between them.

The maidens wept, and Gunnar said:

> "Wail on; but, amid your weeping, lay hand to the glorious dead
> That not alone, for an hour, may lie Queen Brynhild's head;
> For there have been heavy tidings, and the mightiest under shield
> Is laid on the bale high builded in the Niblungs' hallowed field.
> Fare forth! For he abideth, and we do All-Father wrong,
> If the shining Valhal's pavement await their feet o'erlong."

They carried Brynhild out to the mound on which Sigurd lay with his shield, his hauberk of gold, and Helmet of Dread, and his sword, the Wrath of Sigurd. An old man ascended the pyre, and held the sword unsheathed until Brynhild's body had been placed on the bed that had been prepared for it. Then he laid the sword between them, and the earls applied the torches.

> They are gone: the lovely, the mighty, the hope of the ancient earth!
> It shall labour and bear the burden, as before the day of their birth;
> It shall groan, in its blind abiding, for the day that Sigurd hath sped,
> And the hour that Brynhild hath hastened, and the dawn that waketh the dead;
> It shall yearn and be ofttimes holpen, and forget their deeds no more,
> Till the new sun beams on Baldr, and the happy sealess shore.

THE END OF THE TREASURE

as told by Sarah Powers Bradish

WHEN Gudrun fled from the Niblung palace, she went into the forest, where the wolves howled night and day. She did not fear them, for she did not care to live after Sigurd was gone; but they did not hurt her. She went on until she came to a pleasant land, where the people were kind and good. It was the land of the Helper: and King Elf gave her a home in his own house, where she lived with Queen Thora, whom King Elf had married after the death of Hiordis. Gudrun spent the time in teaching the peasant girls to weave and embroider, and herself embroidered many scenes from the life of Sigurd. She never smiled, but was contented; and, as the years passed, became happy in her work.

At the end of seven years, King Atli, Brynhild's brother, sent an earl to the Niblung court, to ask the hand of Gudrun. Atli was old and ugly, but rich and powerful; and Grimhild said that Gudrun must be his wife. "But", she said to her sons, "Gudrun will never listen to you; I must go with you; and we must take her a present of gold, to atone for the murder of her husband." This they could afford to do, since they had kept the golden treasure which Sigurd had taken from the Glittering Heath.

So the two kings and their mother set out on the journey to the land of the Helper, where they found Gudrun in the house of Queen Thora. They told her why they had come; and she said, "I will not go with you; I will not be King Atli's wife."

But Grimhild coaxed and flattered, and finally told her how much trouble her wilful daughter had made. Then Gudrun faltered, and, at last, took the cup her mother offered, and drank the wine. It was the cup of forgetfulness; and she forgot everything, except her love for Sigurd; but she said that, if it would please her mother and brothers, she would become King Atli's queen. Then they rode away together; and, soon after. King Atli claimed his bride.

After a few years, a messenger came from Atli, to say that Gudrun longed to see her brothers. He brought a gold ring, tied with wolf's hair, and engraved with runes.

Gudrun had written the runes, to warn her brothers of Atli's treachery; but the messenger had changed some of the letters, to make an invitation, instead of a warning, to the Niblung kings. Hogni suspected that something was wrong, because the ring was tied with wolf's hair, and said, "By this hair Gudrun means to say, 'Atli is a wolf; beware!'"

Hogni's wife, Kostbera, examined the ring, and found that something had been written over the runes to give them a different meaning. She was greatly alarmed, and told her fears to Glaumvor, Gunnar's wife. That night, they both dreamed of flood, fire and destruction; and both waked their husbands, to beg them not to go to Atli's court.

Gunnar thought that these fears were groundless, and after drinking wine at a banquet, he promised that both he and his brother would visit King Atli and their sister. Hogni said that, the royal promise having been given, it would be cowardly to break it; and they began to prepare for the journey. But the next morning, before it was light, Hogni called his wife's two brothers and asked them to help him dispose of the golden treasure, because it had already made trouble enough.

They went to the treasure house, brought out the gold, loaded it upon wagons, and drove to the water's edge. Then they unhitched the oxen, and, putting their shoulders to the wheels, shoved the wagons into a deep place in the river.

That day the Niblung kings started on the journey, from which they never returned; for King Atli put them to death, because they would not tell what had become of the golden treasure, of which nothing now remained except the ring of Andvari, which Gudrun still wore. After the death of her brothers, Gudrun set fire to Atli's palace while he was sleeping; and, rushing to a cliff, threw herself into the sea. So on her finger, the ring of Andvari, the last piece of gold, went back to the water from which it was taken.

> Ye have heard of Sigurd aforetime, how the foes of God he slew;
> How, forth from the darksome desert, the gold of the waters he drew;
> How he wakened Love on the mountain, and wakened Brynhild the Bright;
> And dwelt upon earth for a season, and shone in all men's sight.
> Ye have heard of the Cloudy People, and the dimming of the day,
> And the latter world's confusion, and Sigurd gone away;
> Now ye know the need of the Niblungs, and the end of broken troth,
> All the death of kings and kindred and the sorrow of Odin, the Goth.

THE STORY OF ASLOG

as told by Eirikr Magnusson and William Morris

CHAPTER I

DURING prehistoric times in ancient Scandinavia – when the land was divided into a number of little principalities, over each of which a chief or king ruled, generally at war with his neighbour, the liege of the bordering state – there lived and ruled a famous family of chiefs called the house of Völsung. Of these Sigurd Fafnirsbane, or Snake-Killer, was the most renowned; he was espoused to the warlike but beautiful Amazon Brynhild, whom he had liberated from the charmed imprisonment of that aforenamed mythical huge snake, which had held her enthralled in a deep trance for a long time. The issue of this union was a little daughter, whom they called Aslog.

However, the great warrior soon afterwards visited the court of King Gjuke, whose daughter Gudrun became enamoured of the heroic Snake-Killer. Her mother, Queen Grimhild, noticing this, and being skilled in the black arts, prepared a charmed draught, which the unsuspecting Sigurd quaffed, with the result that he became inflamed with love of the princess, and, faithless to his betrothed Brynhild, married Gudrun. But her brother Gunnar was desirous of wedding the abandoned Brynhild, so far famed for beauty, strength and valour, and persuaded Sigurd to lend him his horse Grane, the noble steed noble indeed, for he is said to have measured twelve feet in height, and was not to be conquered by either fire or sword. Gunnar mounted this mighty charger, to plunge through the flames with which the dragon had surrounded Brynhild's castle. But, lo! The horse refused to obey the brave rider, and the Saga tells that Sigurd lent him his own apparition, that is, exchanged bodies with him for the time, so as to effect a passage through the fiery wall for the new suitor. This mythical trick succeeded, and the faithful Brynhild welcomed her truant lover, as she naturally thought he was, and then the nuptials were completed and thus she married Gunnar in the guise of Sigurd.

One day, some time afterwards, when Gudrun and Brynhild went into a limpid stream that flowed hard by the castle, inhabited in common by all the members of the Völsung clan, to wash their loose flowing hair, Gudrun, who was of a spiteful temper, began scoffing at her sister-in-law, saying that she herself was compelled to wade further into the stream that no drops of water that had laved Brynhild's hair might bespatter and contaminate her own tresses, which she weened they certainly would, as Brynhild was only an Amazon and not a princess. To this the insulted wife of Gunnar retorted that she was of royal descent; but the vicious Gudrun railed at the inferiority of Gunnar, her own brother, to the hero of her own choice, the far-famed Sigurd Fafnirsbane, and to the astounded Brynhild laid bare the whole secret whereby she had been beguiled into a union with Gunnar whilst assuming the garb and corporeal presence of Sigurd.

The injured Amazon, who now saw she had been defrauded of him she loved best, her betrothed lover, and tricked into wedlock with a man she did not love, resolved upon revenge. She easily persuaded Guttorm, another member of the Völsung family, who was jealous of Sigurd's great fame as a hero, to murder her faithless royal lover in his sleep; and thus revenge herself upon him, and Gudrun, who had erst deprived her of him. Guttorm performed this dark deed of blood, and murdered the sleeping man, and even Sigurd's little son, a babe of three years; but he also met his own death at the hand of his victim in the hour of his diabolical triumph. But when the revenge was accomplished, and Brynhild saw her dead lover cold and motionless at her feet, her heart was softened, and repentance came in utterings of deepest lamentations; words of consolation fell unheeded on her conscience-stricken spirit, and she fell upon her sword, pierced to the heart; and thus the proud Amazon followed her lover to the Halls of Valhalla, and her corpse was placed on the funeral pile of Sigurd, consumed by the same flames, and their ashes mingled in the same urn. But Atle, the brother of Brynhild, sought and obtained the hand of Gudrun, the widowed Megara. When, after some time, she had borne him two sons, he invited her two brothers, Gunnar and Hogne, King Gjuke's sons, to celebrate the event with a feast. He did this purposing to avenge Brynhild.

The two royal guests came suspecting nothing, but Atle, as cruel as he was treacherous, caused the palpitating heart to be torn from Gunnar's breast; and the younger brother, Hogne, he ordered to be flung alive into a pitful of venomous snakes. Pitying people, however, threw a harp to the captive in his loathsome prison, but as he had his arms tied behind him, he could only touch the vibrating strings with his toes, which he did, with the effect that he charmed his fell executioners, all but one, which twisted itself around his naked body until it reached his breast, and stung his heart, so that death speedily followed.

When Gudrun became aware of the cruel fate which had befallen her two brothers, she raved, mad with grief; and killed her own two innocent babes, the children of Atle.

When her dastardly husband with pomp and ceremony celebrated the funeral obsequies of his two victims, Gudrun, his spouse, brought him two beautiful cups, seemingly wrought of ivory, with golden brims, and filled with wine, urging him to pledge the memory of his two brothers-in-law. When he had complied with her request, she told him, with fiendish glee, while passion almost overpowered her, that the goblets were made of the skulls of their own two young children, and that thus she had avenged the death of her two brothers on the father of her own children. With this she rushed from the banqueting hall, frantic with rage and grief, only to return in the dead of night to set fire to the house in which the king slept, and in which conflagration he and his nearest retainers perished.

CHAPTER II

ALSO at the court of Sigurd, there lived an exiled king called Heimer, who was the accepted *skald* or bard of this chief and hero; and when Sigurd and Brynhild met their untimely end, the old kingly bard took their little daughter Aslog, then only a few years of age, and hastened into other petty states, to seek refuge and save the only surviving child of her race from the general carnage which raged amongst her infuriated kinsfolk. Better to conceal his infantile charge, he had a large harp constructed, in which he was able to hide the child.

And now began a period of strange adventures in the lone and wild woods through which their course lay. Sometimes, when far from the habitations of men, the old harper would allow his little darling to run by his side gathering flowers and berries from the wayside.

One evening, towards sunset, when Heimer was playing on his harp to a goodly throng of listeners that had gathered from a small hamlet whose cots lay scattered in a glen in the mighty woods, the clear manly voice of the aged minstrel rose in accents liquid and sonorous to the accompaniment of the harp, for he sang the heart-stirring lay about the love and fate of brave king Sigurd and his beloved Brynhild, the beauteous and faithful Amazon, who killed herself for grief with her own sword; the eager audience, of whom some were lying on the ground while others standing formed a ring around, looked at each other with amazement; for as the old man related in song, with almost inspiration, the touching story, they thought the very harp responded with sobs and stifled cries to the burden of the piteous tale.

He was indeed a wonderful harper who could make his very instrument echo the bitter grief that each felt within himself. Mellow tones seemed at last to soothe the awakened spirit of the harp, and then the old man departed from the wondering group, and soon betook himself with his instrument to a lonely path leading towards the bay.

The moon shone out and threw a mystic glamour over the forest scene. Then King Heimer stopped; his mien still betrayed a king, though despoiled of all save the nobility of soul within, and of which his whole bearing seemed conscious. He opened the foot of the harp and lifted out his little charge, Aslog, who had fallen asleep within, over-powered with grief at the recollection of her lost parents which the song had evoked in her loving and childish heart.

It was a cold evening, and the stars were out; so the old man bethought himself that he had better warm little Aslog in his embrace. Soon, locked in his arms, she looked up into his face and leaned her head against his cheek, while her silent tears trickled down into his long white beard, and lay like gems reflecting the silvery glimmer of the moon-beams which like a halo played round the group. "Hush, my little one, you have me still who loves you, and the good god Baldr, Odin's most beloved son, the god of Light and Song. He will protect you when I am dead and gone. Do you know, child, those rustics and warriors who listened to my song about Sigurd and Brynhild (may Baldr bless their union in Valhalla!) they, simple folk, thought the harp bewitched, because you muled and wailed, little one. Do not do so again, but cheer up ; we will soon arrive at a place of refuge and safety, where we will find friends that love us. If you weep in the harp to my playing, and bewitch the listeners, I shall have to call you my little witch, and you would not like that, King Sigurd's daughter! The old man had to sing out of tune to drown your sobs; give me now a kiss and say you love me as much as ever, though I won't let you cry. You cry indeed! The daughter of the famous hero and Amazon! Oh no, we will have no more tears now, only love and song. I see a lonely cot in the distance, for a spare light is twinkling invitingly. Now you must retire into your hiding-place for the night; in the cot it will be warm and quiet, and tomorrow at dawn we will proceed on our way, and then you will have something to eat." Another loving kiss, the blessing of the night, and the door was closed upon little Aslog, the fugitive princess child, a little prisoner cradled in music. The old man now resumed his staff, and descended the hill towards the sea.

Soon he reached the hut, and entering saw an old woman, who was alone at home. He asked to be permitted to stay there during the night, and that she would befriend him with something to satisfy his hunger. Heimer was weary and cold, but it was with difficulty that he persuaded the old woman to light the wood in the big open fireplace; at last, when a cheery blaze crackled among the twigs and branches, and Heimer stretched out his stiff and weary limbs, the woman's manner suddenly changed, and she became quite cheerful and friendly, for when the aged wanderer held out his hands to warm them at the genial flames, she discovered that he had a precious golden ring encircling his arm. It was the custom of the times to break pieces off for barter and for purchases. And when she went near the harp she discovered a piece of embroidered costly stuff showing through an aperture, being at the opening of the little door. An evil thought entered her wicked heart; she perceived the stranger was in disguise, and she determined to get possession of his valuables.

When her old man soon after came home, he also hungry, weary and shivering with cold, she told him in a whisper that in the press slept an aged wanderer, who as a beggar had asked for a night's lodging, but that he carried with him a large harp, in which was secreted a treasure of gold and valuable stuff. She urged him to murder the sleeping man, and then for the rest of their lives they would suffer from neither poverty nor want, nor would need to work any more. Ake, the husband, at first lent an unwilling ear to her proposal, but soon allowed himself to be persuaded, and the two wicked old creatures then speedily despatched their sleeping guest.

This crime accomplished, they eagerly hurried to the harp, and opened the little door of the instrument; but picture their surprise when out stepped a little girl, fair-haired and blue-eyed, just awakened by their bustle, and looking enquiringly around for her aged guardian. When little Aslog saw the sinister-looking couple, she ran frightened to old Heimer, where he lay stretched on the floor; but when she could get no answer to her repeated calls upon his name, even though she pulled him by his hands and beard, as she was wont to do, she at last realized the fact that her beloved protector was dead, and would speak no more to her. She burst into bitter sobs, clinging to her silent friend, and flung her little arms around his neck and nestled in his clothes and silvery hair.

The inhuman old wretches considered for a short time whether they should not murder the little girl as well; but her despair was so touching, and her rare beauty so winning, that at last they resolved to spare her and adopt her as their own child. To silence inquisitive people who might call at their lonely hut, she was forthwith dressed in coarse grey baize, as was customary with the children of bondsmen.

CHAPTER III

ASLOG was compelled to remain with the old people, who called her Kraka, and she grew up to become a most beautiful maiden, slender, tall and graceful, and with the inborn gait of a princess. All who saw her admired her wondrous beauty. Her native wit and wisdom were also most remarkable, though she spoke but seldom, and never with strangers, who therefore imagined she was deaf and dumb. Only with her grim wardens did she exchange a few words, when she was alone with them, and only then when their daily intercourse compelled her, for she loathed them from her inmost soul, because they had murdered her beloved and venerated guardian, and detained her, the daughter

Ragnar Lodbrok meets Aslog, who is called Kraka by her captors.

of Sigurd and Brynhild, a slave to wretched bondsmen. She repeated to herself every day the song Heimer had sung to his harp's accompaniment about her heroic parents, and thus she kept in vivid recollection for many long years the story of their loves and untimely fate.

There grew a tall pine tree by the hut, and when she looked upon its ever-verdant beauty, she thought of the stalwart form of her glorious father, and when she mirrored herself in the sylvan well, the recollection of her mother's features stood clear before her.

When Kraka had lived with the wicked old couple thus for more than twelve years – she was now sixteen years old – a Viking sailed into the creek one day with several galleys, and landed with his men near her home. It was no less a person than Ragnar Lodbrok, a hero famous all over the north for his deeds of daring. When the hut was observed by the mariners, some of the men were sent thither to bake some bread, of which provision they had been short for the last few days.

When the men returned with the hard-baked bread, it was found to be burned and wholly spoiled; upon this the Viking became greatly exasperated, and gave orders to have the negligent fellows severely punished. But the men tried to excuse themselves, and said that in the hut they had beheld such a beautiful maiden that they had quite forgotten all about the bread in the oven, and they could not help it, for she had quite bewitched them.

The Viking became interested at this, and asked who the girl might be. They answered that she was the daughter of Ake and Grima, the bondsmen who lived in the hut, though they could scarcely believe it, for they were such an aged and repugnant-looking couple, and the old woman such a vicious old harridan; and yet they said she was their daughter Kraka, their only child, who tended the goats on the mountain slopes. But her beauty, they persisted, was fairly bewitching, and her bearing that of a queen. "Impossible!" the Viking answered. "I cannot believe it. You have all seen my lamented consort, the incomparable Thora, and anyone who ever saw her ought not to speak of other women's loveliness." Yet the men maintained that the girl's rare beauty would in every respect vie with that of their dead queen. Then the chief ordered that Kraka should immediately be brought before him, and promised that if he really found her so exceedingly lovely as the men had given out, he would forgive them their negligence.

Kraka was soon brought, and Ragnar Lodbrok was even more bewitched than his men by her incomparable beauty, and was quite spellbound by the prudent and ready answers she gave to all his questions. The Viking thought her a fair prize, and took her aboard his own galley, and told her she should never return to the old people at the hut. Her radiant beauty at first repelled every advance from the wild and passionate hero of many lands, for she was virtuous as she was wise and beautiful; and this pleased her captor much, and he could not help admiring that lofty spirit which dared even him, the hero of his time. Ragnar was famed for always being kind and considerate to women, a virtue which in later times might have been called chivalrous; and though she concealed even from him her royal descent, he made her his lawful wife and queen.

Ragnar already possessed two sons, Eric and Agnar, by his former consort, and they found in Kraka a loving stepmother; indeed the young queen, through her many virtues and rare wisdom, endeared herself not only to her newly-found family, but to all the people over whom Ragnar Lodbrok ruled. Many years of happy married life followed, during which she presented her royal husband with five sons, all of whom became more or less famous in the warfares of the times.

When King Ragnar, already advanced in years, was on a visit to King Eisten Bele, one of the Swedish petty kings, he saw this chief's daughter Ingeborg, whose beauty quite captivated the gallant champion. "The princess" went the round of the table at the banquet given in his honour, and filled the goblets of the royal guest. Her beauty, and the wine, must have intoxicated him, for he determined upon separating himself from Kraka, whom he but knew as a bondsman's daughter, and thus unworthy to share his throne, and then marry Ingeborg, the daughter of a king, as more befitting his royal state. Eisten Bele readily consented to this union, to be contracted as soon as Ragnar had rid himself of Kraka. When the ice broke up Ragnar sailed away, promising to return during the summer to celebrate the nuptials with the fair Ingeborg.

Upon his return home he divulged nothing to Kraka of his design, but the news came to her through other channels at the court. Instead of upbraiding her spouse, she resorted to other means far wiser; she increased her loving attention to him, and was more charming than ever; and she told the king that at last she thought the right time had come to tell him who were her real parents, and that she was no vile bondsman's child. With unfeigned amazement he learnt that she was the daughter of Sigurd and Brynhild; he listened eagerly to the recital of her wondrous flight in the harp; effected by King Heimer, and to her tale of woe during her long captivity with Ake and Grima.

His joy to possess a queen of noble descent and equal to himself was sincere; he thought he had never loved her so well before, and dispelled all thoughts of parting with her. The image of Ingeborg vanished from his heart for ever, and no journey to Eisten Bele was taken to celebrate the contemplated union, which this warrior thought a great insult to him, as his daughter was a princess, and he the King of Upsala. But Eisten Bele got no opportunity to avenge this breach of promise, for Queen Aslog, the name she now resumed, persuaded her two stepsons to hasten to Upsala to war with its king in his own domains. This they did, but Agnar fell in the battle, which grieved his noble and grateful stepmother as if he had been her own son.

When Ragnar Lodbrok, on one of his seafaring expeditions, fell into the hands of King Ella of Northumbria, and by his victor was thrown into a pit filled with serpents, and there met his tragic death, which event is recorded in the *English Chronicles*, Aslog sent all her own five sons to avenge his death. She survived her spouse many years, a disconsolate widow, honouring the memory of the noble Viking who had rescued her from ignoble thraldom and made her queen of his heart and realm, Aslog, the little child princess, who had lain in a harp, and sobbed in harmony with its tremulous strings to the piteous lay recording the fate of her hapless parents.

RAGNAR LODBROK

as told by Eirikr Magnusson and William Morris

RAGNAR was the son of King Sigurd Ring, and his first wife Alfhild. His father, when an old man, had fallen deeply in love with Alfsol, the daughter of King Alf of Jutland. Her brothers refused to give her in marriage to so old a man, and when they were defeated in battle by Sigurd Ring, they poisoned her rather than she should become his wife. The king thereupon had her corpse carried on board his ship, which he steered out into the open sea, and then plunged his sword into his heart, thus dying beside the body of his beloved Alfsol.

Ragnar, therefore, although only fifteen years of age, was now king. He was remarkable as well for his great beauty as for the dauntless courage which he always displayed when he went with his followers on marauding expeditions to foreign lands.

On one of these expeditions he landed on the coast of Norway, and penetrated alone into the heart of the land. On gaining the summit of a hill, he threw himself on the soft turf to rest, and to enjoy the beautiful landscape which spread itself out before his view ; the green valley at his feet, the lake, sparkling like diamonds in the sunshine;, and the verdant meadows and cornfields. As he gazed on this fair picture, his mind was filled with the idea that the wild and warlike life he had hitherto led was after all far less satisfactory than a life of peaceful, quiet happiness.

As he thus pondered he suddenly became aware that two hostile divisions of soldiers had entered the valley; presently their trumpets sounded, and they rode at one another full-tilt, with their shields raised. His surprise was great to perceive that one of the divisions was led by a beautiful woman, who was mounted on a milk-white charger, and dressed in silver armour; while her lovely raven locks, escaping from under her helmet, fell in rich profusion over her neck and shoulders. She rode before her soldiers, cheering them on, and fighting the enemy herself with sword and spear. Many fell beneath her strokes but, the enemy being too strong for her little band to resist, they were obliged to retreat. Not so the heroic maiden; captivity or death threatened to be her doom, yet still she fought on with indomitable courage, her bright silver armour making her conspicuous wherever the battle was hottest.

Ragnar, seeing that she stood in sore need of help, could no longer remain an inactive spectator of the scene but, seizing his sword, hastened to her side, and fought desperately against the enemy. His sword made such havoc amongst the foe, and such numbers of their best warriors were slain that at length those who were left were obliged to seek safety in flight.

As soon as the battle was over, Ragnar straightway withdrew to his ship. There he learnt that the name of the soldier-maid was Lodgerda, that she ruled the surrounding country, and dwelt in a beautiful palace in the midst of her possessions.

The following day he repaired thither, and was received by Lodgerda with much joy and gratitude as her friend and deliverer. Ragnar remained a guest at the palace for three days, after which time, as he loved Lodgerda dearly, he besought her to become his wife, to which she joyfully consented.

Ragnar and Lodgerda lived very happily together for some time. She was an excellent wife to him, but she refused to leave her own country for his, nor would she resign to him her rights as sovereign. Ragnar passed three peaceful years at her side, but at last the warlike spirit woke again within him, and when he heard that the Danish Islands had rebelled against his rule, and become independent, he parted from his wife, who could not bring herself to leave her peaceful home for a strange country, and set out for his own kingdom alone.

In a very little while he succeeded in putting down the rebels, and proceeded to his palace at Hledra, covered with glory.

One day a stranger at his court showed him, in a magic mirror, a virgin of wonderful beauty. The king was so enchanted at the sight of her that he could hardly take his eyes from her face, and declared that the man who could call such a treasure his own must be the happiest being on earth.

"Yes, indeed," replied the stranger, "thou sayest truly, for this noble maid is not only famous for her beauty, but also for her wisdom and goodness. Her father, Herrod of East Gothland, asks her advice on all occasions, and if he follows it his enterprises are always successful. Now, however, both he and his daughter are in great distress. Some time ago, two of his warriors presented him with a griffin's egg, which was part of the plunder which they had brought home with them from a foreign land. It was hatched at the king's orders by a swan, and a curious little winged serpent came out of it. He gave the little creature to his daughter, who put it in a golden cage, and fed it with her own hands. It grew, however, so quickly that it was soon too large for the cage, and even for the room, and now it surrounds the whole house in which the princess lives. The monster is still submissive to her, but he guards her with a jealous eye, nor will he allow her to leave the house, or receive food from anyone but from the man who daily brings him an ox for his meals. No one dares attempt to touch him, for his eyes are like flaming fire, his breath is deadly poison, and with his tail he can break the strongest oak tree, as easily as if it were a reed. The king, therefore, in order to rid himself of this curse, has promised the hand of his daughter to whomever shall succeed in slaying the monster."

Before Ragnar had heard the completion of this tale, he had determined to set out on the adventure himself. He lost no time in procuring a garment of thick wool and ox hide, which he steeped in tar, for he knew that through such a garment neither poison nor venom could penetrate.

Accompanied by many warlike companions, he set out for East Gothland, and landed on the coast not far from the king's castle.

Wrapped in his tarred garment, and armed with a mighty spear, he started for the princess's abode.

There, surrounding the house with his huge body, he beheld the monster, apparently asleep. He attempted several times to stab him, but in vain; his spear could not pierce the scales of the serpent, which were hard and smooth as steel. Presently the monster raised its huge body, and tried to seize Ragnar in its jaws, hissing meanwhile with rage, and spitting its deadly venom at him. But as it thus coiled itself about, Ragnar perceived an exposed spot under its throat, where the scales appeared to be soft, and at this spot he aimed his spear, with all the strength he could muster. For a few moments the creature writhed and turned in agony, so that the house was shaken to its foundation, and then suddenly the great monster sank to the ground dead.

The princess, awakened by the noise, stepped to the window, and beheld the victor clothed in his rude garments, but before she had time to look upon him more closely he withdrew himself from her gaze.

Herrod, as soon as he received the news of the event, ordered a proclamation to be made, to the effect that the people should meet together in an assembly, in order to decide to whom the prize should be awarded.

On the appointed day Ragnar took his place in the assembly, clothed in his tarred garments. At the command of the king, two heralds carried about among the men the point of the spear, which had been taken from the serpent's body, in order to discover who among them possessed the shaft to which it fitted. When Ragnar produced the same, and fitted the point of the spear on to it, the king, taking him to be a poor man, exclaimed in astonishment: "Ha, thou Leather-Garments, and who taught thee that clever thrust? Comest thou from the Biarma Country, that thou hast such an odour of pitch and tar about thee?"

At these words Ragnar dropped his disguise and stood in his royal attire before the assembled people. "Ragnar! Ragnar! It is the king himself!" cried a multitude of voices, and Herrod, stepping down from his throne, embraced him, saying: "Thou shalt in future be called Lodbrok (Leather Garments), in remembrance of thy valour, and I will give thee the hand of my daughter in marriage."

The king kept his word, and the Princess Thora joyfully consented to become the wife of her brave deliverer. Nor had she ever any cause to regret her choice, for her husband was so devoted to her that he even gave up his marauding expeditions in order to remain at her side. Their happiness was augmented by the birth of two sons, Eric and Agnar. But fate suffers no perfect happiness to be on earth and ere long Thora died in the arms of her disconsolate lord.

And now peace and happiness fled from the palace, and sorrow and mourning reigned in their stead, for Ragnar was inconsolable for the loss of his wife.

At length one of the noblest of his warriors stepped before him, and represented to him how that he was still young and in the prime of life, and that it was a sin for him to waste his best years in mourning for his departed queen. His words roused the sleeping ardour of the king, and soon he was once more tossing in his ship on the billowy ocean, where, amidst dangers and diverse adventures, he strove to forget his great sorrow.

One day, landing on the coast of Norway, he sent his servants inland, to prepare food and bake bread. After wandering about, they came to a lowly peasant's hut, and on entering, they found within it a cross, hideous old woman, sitting cowering over the fire. They asked her to help them make the bread, but she excused herself on account of her great age. Just then a young peasant girl entered the cottage, and the men, on seeing her, stared at her with open mouths, and could not find words to address her, for they had never before seen so exquisitely lovely a woman.

"Yes, yes, that is my daughter," croaked the old hag. "See, Kraka, these men would make bread, and do not know how."

Without making any reply, the girl set about preparing the dough herself, and when she had put the loaves into the oven, she directed the men to watch them, as she had other work to do. But the men only had eyes for the beautiful girl, who with wonderful adroitness went about the cottage, cleaning and putting everything to rights.

In consequence of their negligence, some of the loaves were burnt, and when they returned on board the ship they were scolded and punished for their carelessness. They declared, however, that the king himself would have been guilty of the same negligence had he endeavoured to watch the bread in the presence of such a beautiful maid.

Their words aroused the curiosity of the king, and he gave orders that this wonderful maiden should be brought before him on board his vessel on the following morning. She was to come unattended, and yet not alone; naked, and yet clothed; fasting, and yet full.

This strange command was given to Kraka, who accordingly appeared before the king the next day, with a fisherman's net wrapped in folds about her, and accompanied by a shepherd's dog. She had taken some of the juice of a leek, so that she was neither fasting nor full. In this way she obeyed the command of the king to the letter.

Ragnar was much impressed by her wisdom, but still more so by her wonderful beauty, her fair silken locks and blue eyes, in which the light of heaven was reflected.

He straightway offered to make her his queen, but she, having no great faith in the constancy of man, desired him to complete his voyage, and then, if he should still be of the same mind, to return to Norway, and repeat his offer.

The king submitted to the will of the peasant girl and departed. His devotion to her, however, was unchangeable, and immediately on his return from his voyage he fetched her from her peasant home, and took her to his palace at Hledra as his bride, and there celebrated his marriage-feast.

Kraka bore her husband four sons, the eldest of whom, named Iwar, was very handsome, and had strong broad shoulders, but his lower limbs were so weak that he had always to be carried about. The other three sons were strong healthy youths, who awaited impatiently the time when they, like their half-brothers, Eric and Agnar, should be permitted to go on distant voyages, and return with rich plunder from foreign lands.

Meanwhile the people had begun to murmur and complain that a peasant girl had been set upon the throne; and the courtiers, who were as dissatisfied as the people, repeated these murmurings to the king.

Ragnar, greatly displeased at these complaints, set out for Swithiod, to pay a visit to his friend, King Eistein. He was cordially welcomed at the court, and the daughter of the mighty king waited upon him herself, and filled his goblet with sparkling wine, and sat beside him at the board.

Ragnar was enchanted as well by her beauty as by her conversation, and when the courtiers pointed out to him the advantage of an alliance with the princess, he allowed himself to be persuaded, and asked for the king's consent to his marriage with his daughter. This the king granted, and it was arranged that as soon as their betrothal had been solemnized Ragnar should return home, and, under some excuse, divorce his peasant-wife.

When he arrived at his palace at Hledra, Kraka came out as usual with a glad and smiling countenance to welcome him home. She seemed not to notice his cold greeting, but did her utmost to provide him with every possible comfort after his journey, and asked if he had brought any news. On his replying surlily that he had none to give, she informed him that she had heard a strange report about his best friend; that he had wished to divorce his rightful spouse, in order to marry a king's daughter, and that the betrothal had already been solemnized.

"What knave informed thee of that?" cried Ragnar, angrily.

"My chattering magpies," she quietly replied. "Thou knowest them, for they were present at King Eistein's court during thy stay there. Full of anxiety I sent them after thee, and they brought me a faithful report of thy doings. If thou dost indeed intend to carry out thy plan, I will return to the peasant-folk, whom people believe to be my parents. They murdered my foster-father Heimir, and now thou wilt destroy the happiness of my life. But before thou doest anything rash, listen to me, and I will reveal to thee a secret. Know then that my name is not Kraka, but Aslog, for I am the daughter of King Sigurd the Dragon-Slayer, who ranks as high over all the kings of the north as the sun ranks above the stars. My mother was Brynhild. When my father was foully and secretly murdered by his brothers-in-law, Gunnar and Hagen, the good Heimir, for fear of the murderers, bore me away in a harp from the unhappy land, and after wandering about for a long time, came to the peasants' hut, in which thou foundest me. The two inhabitants of the hut, thinking the harp contained great treasures, murdered my faithful protector in his sleep by night, but did not dare to make away with the child which they discovered in place of the gold they had expected to find. Thus I grew up with them in the cottage. They allowed me to keep my mother's wedding-ring, together with her picture, and the letter which she wrote before her death. Here is the proof of my story," Kraka continued, producing the letter and the ring, "and yet another token has Odin revealed to me; it shall be made manifest when our unborn babe shall behold the light of the world, for in his eye he shall have a mark like a tiny serpent."

As she ceased speaking, she laid aside her royal jewels, and turned to depart, but Ragnar, who stood shamefaced and abashed before the noble woman whose royal descent he now recognized, besought her to stay. She loved him so dearly that she could not withstand his entreaties, but remained with him, and in due time presented him with a little son, who bore on him the prophesied mark of distinction, and was therefore called Sigurd the Serpent-Eyed.

Meanwhile Eric and Agnar, the sons of Ragnar's first wife Thora, had made their names famous by their warlike deeds. They had opportunity of displaying their valour in the war which now broke out with King Eistein, who was enraged at Ragnar's rejection of his daughter.

Eric and Agnar landed on the Swedish coast, but they both fell in the battle which ensued, for Eistein's host was too strong for them, and their ranks were thrown into confusion by the enchanted bull, which the king had ordered to be driven amongst them.

When the news of their defeat and death reached Ragnar's court, his third son Iwar forthwith set out to avenge his brothers' untimely end. No sooner was the battle opened, however, than the huge enchanted bull rushed bellowing as before amidst the soldiers, causing terror and confusion in the ranks. Iwar therefore lost no time in seizing his mighty bow and arrow; and taking aim at the monster, he pierced it through the heart, so that it fell dead on the field. After this the battle was easily won, Eistein himself being struck down whilst attempting to fly for his life.

Ragnar's sons engaged in many other wars and piratical expeditions. Their combined forces conquered the rich town of Wifelsburg, after which they marched to Luna in Etruria. They found it strongly garrisoned, and therefore sent messengers into the town to say that they came with peaceful intentions, merely to buy victuals, and that their captain, Hastings, who was sick to death, wished to be baptized and received into the Christian Church. Delighted with this news, the inhabitants immediately opened communication with the strangers, and the holy ceremony of baptism was performed over the sick man, the governor of the town standing sponsor.

A few days later an emissary was sent to inform the inhabitants that Hastings was dead, and that his dying wish had been that his corpse might be allowed a resting place in the Christian Church, to which he had bequeathed his riches, with the desire that the priest should annually say three masses for his soul. The messenger ended by declaring that if this was allowed to take place, it was his belief that the whole army, who intended, unarmed, to accompany the bier of their leader to the grave, would consent to be baptized.

The request was granted. On the day of the funeral the church was so crowded by the clergy, nobles and citizens of the town that there was hardly any room left for the Northmen.

The requiem was solemnly chanted, the blessing was spoken, and the body of the departed soldier was just about to be lowered into the grave when the lid of the bier sprang open, the dead man rose up in his shroud, with a drawn sword in his hand, with which he at once slew all who came within his reach. The rest of the soldiers likewise drew forth their arms, which they had kept concealed beneath their garments, and massacred without mercy the unarmed people who filled the church. They then rushed out into the streets, plundering and murdering wherever they went, and setting the town on fire.

This was the strategy by which means the Northmen possessed themselves of the town of Luna.

While his sons were engaged in these warlike expeditions, King Ragnar himself was not idle. He determined on an invasion of Britain, in order to force King Ella to pay him tribute. For this purpose he had two new ships built, large enough to carry a great number of soldiers, and with these he landed on the British coast. He devastated the country in a terrible manner, and engaged in many bloody battles, but he never received any wound, for Aslog had woven him a magic garment, through which neither shot nor sword could penetrate.

One day his ships were driven by a storm into a Northumbrian bay, where they struck upon a rock and foundered. He, however, with many of his men and some arms, succeeded in gaining the shore. Here they soon encountered Ella's forces, but the brave soldier, nothing daunted, did not hesitate a moment, with his handful of followers, to commence the attack. He fought without flinching in the hottest part of the battle, but as his brave soldiers fell around him, he was at length surrounded by the enemy, and taken prisoner. No one recognized him, and as he refused to answer any of the questions put to him, King Ella, in anger, ordered him to be thrown into a dungeon full of serpents.

At first Aslog's magic garment protected him, from any hurt, but the guards, when they perceived this, deprived him of it, and he soon after succumbed to their venomous stings.

Thus died brave King Ragnar, like a hero as he was, uttering neither cry nor complaint under his slow torture, but singing in rich clear tones a dirge of the Northland.

THE STORY OF KORMAK

as told by Edward Ernest Kellett

IN the days when Athelstan the Mighty ruled over England; when witches still had power and elves still danced their rings; when "stitch" was still caused by goddesses that shot invisible arrows into a man's side; when "wise women" could foresee the future, or make a man invulnerable, or change themselves into animals, in those days a certain man, named Ogmund, set sail from Norway to go to Iceland. He carried with him the twin pillars of his high-seat, images of Thor and Odin, for these had within them his luck. And when he drew near to Iceland he cast these same pillars overboard. And they came ashore in Midfirth, where dwelt a chief named Skeggi. Skeggi welcomed Ogmund, and gave him a plot of ground whereon to establish himself and build a house. Now it was the belief then that if in measuring for a house, a man found the meteyard too short, then would the fortune of the house be shortened also; and three times did Ogmund measure, but three times did the meteyard fall short. Wherefore men deemed the luck of that house would be scant; yet Ogmund built there.

Ogmund took to wife a woman named Dalla, who bore him two sons: the elder was called Thorgils, and he was quiet, gentle and slow to move. The younger was called Kormak; he was gloomy, passionate and hasty of temper, black-haired, tall and strong; a good *skald* or poet, and his verses were easily remembered. When these two had just reached early manhood, Ogmund their father died, and Thorgils took the household in hand. Men reckoned him a good bonder. As for Kormak, he stayed at the house a while, but did little therein.

Not far from thence, at a place called Tongue, lived a chief named Thorkell; he had a son also named Thorkell, whom they called Tooth-gnasher; proud men were both father and son. A daughter had Thorkell, whose name was Steingerd: bright-eyed was she, beautiful-haired and the fairest of maidens. She was away from home, at a house called The Peaks, near to the farm of Thorgils and Kormak. Now one day it happened that Kormak and Tosti, a friend of his, had gone some distance from their home after their sheep; and they stayed the night at The Peaks, for they were weary. Large was the hall, and fires were lit for the guests. Now Steingerd and her maid were eager to see what guests had come that night; so they came and peeped over the door of the hall; and as they did so, Kormak spied her feet below the door. Whereupon he whispered a *visa* to Tosti:

"Lo the feet of the maiden
Below the door;
With love hath she struck me
To my heart's core:
Ill-luck will she bring me,
Sadly I fear;
That maiden brings danger
Whene'er she draws near."

Now Steingerd saw that she had been seen; so she ran along the passage, until she came into the hall at the far end, behind the high-seat. Here she deemed she would be hidden by the carved pillars, and she stood and gazed at the young man. But of a sudden the fire flamed up, and its light flashed upon her bright eyes, so Kormak saw her once again:

"Lo, those are the maiden's bright bright eyes!
Methinks they will harm me in wondrous wise."

So spake he to Tosti; but meanwhile, Steingerd and her attendant were speaking of him; and Steingerd, as the manner of women is, took pleasure in making light of him, that she might hear her handmaid praise him.

In the morning Kormak saw her as she was combing her hair; and the handmaid said to him, "What wouldst thou give for a wife with such hair and such eyes as Steingerd's?" And he answered, in yet another *visa*:

"I price one of her eyes at three hundred in silver,
And the head she is combing at five hundred."

Then said the handmaid, "Pity is it that she thinks not the same of thee," but she knew well what were Steingerd's true thoughts of him.

"As for the whole of her," said Kormak, "I would value it against Iceland, and Denmark, and England, though I might rule over all three." Then came Tosti, and asked him to go out after the sheep; but what were sheep to Kormak then? Better loved he to stay in the house, and to play chess and tables with Steingerd, than to look after cattle on the hills. Late was it ere he could bring himself to go home. And when he reached home, he told his mother of his love, and said to her, "Mother, make me fine clothes, that I may find more favour in Steingerd's sight."

"Alas!" said Dalla. "Well I perceive the evil that is coming on our house. Hast thou thought how this will seem in the eyes of Thorkell her father, and of his son?"

Now Thorkell was proud and haughty, and when men told him that Kormak loved Steingerd he was aflame with wrath. "Who is this Kormak?" said he. "Is he much better than a thrall of Midfirth-Skeggi?" Now there was a man named Narfi, a low man and an insolent, whom Thorkell kept in his house; and he heard these words of the father. Wherefore, one day, when Kormak was at the house, for Steingerd had now come to Tongue, he seized some sausages that were on the fire, and thrust them in Kormak's face. "How likest thou these kettle-snakes?" said he in a kind of doggerel rhyme. Kormak, not wishing then to quarrel, for Steingerd was by, said he liked them well; but in the evening, when he was about to go home, he saw Narfi and remembered these insolent words. So he stayed him, and bade him take back what he had said. "Not so," said Narfi; "if thou like not the fare, thou needest not come to the dinner." And at that Kormak struck at him with his axe, but Narfi fled from him, and so escaped for a season.

Now there was a witch-wife named Thorveig; she dwelt at Stanstead in Midfirth. She had two sons, Odd and Gudmund, violent men both. To them spake Thorkell, and promised Odd many gifts if he and Gudmund would lie in wait for Kormak. So they watched for their chance. And one day, when they were in the great hall and Steingerd was on the dais, they saw Kormak coming towards the door. So these two brethren rose up to slay him as he entered the door. And Odd seized a sword that was there, and Gudmund a scythe. But Kormak chanced to see them, wherefore he thrust his shield into the room before him, and bent the scythe and broke the sword. Then Thorkell came out and said that Kormak was ever a brawler, and a madman in his words; then sent he Steingerd out of the hall, and said that Kormak should never see her more. At that Kormak spoke a verse:

"Let my foes, these brethren, whet their swords,

Yet shall they not slay me;

Let them set on me in the open field,

It will be as though two ewes attacked a wolf."

Now, later, Kormak found that Steingerd was in a certain house; so he went thereto, and when he found it locked he broke it open and talked with her. But she said, "Little care hast thou of thy life, for the sons of Thorveig are seeking after thee." "Little indeed care I," said Kormak, and abode there all that day. And as he departed, he saw three men waiting for him in a dale; these were Odd, Gudmund and Narfi, whom Thorkell had sent to watch for him and slay him. So he spake another verse:

"Three men lie in wait for me;

They strive to keep my maiden from me:

But the more they seek to hinder us,

The more we love each other."

And at that moment the three sprang out on him. The two brethren fought bravely, but Narfi hung behind, for he was fearful and a coward. Now Kormak fought like a lion, and the two brethren could not slay him; wherefore the fight was long, and Thorkell deemed it were best to go to help the brethren. But when he donned his armour Steingerd clung to him so that he could not go. The end was that Kormak slew Odd, and wounded Gudmund so that he died soon thereafter.

Then went Kormak to Thorveig. "Thou canst not abide longer in these parts," said he; "thou must flit thee abroad at such a time, nor will I pay thee any were-gild for either of thy sons." Thorveig answered, "It is likely enough that I must yield to thee and go hence; and as to the were-gild thou hast the power to deny it; yet shall I pay thee thy due reward never shalt thou desire to have her save when thou canst not get her." "Do thy worst, thou evil woman," said Kormak. A little later he told these words of Thorveig's to Steingerd, and she was sad about them, for she feared the power of the witch. Kormak replied,

> "All the rivers shall run backward,
> Ere I leave thee, lady mine!"

"Boast not thereof, said she. "Many a little thing may bring thy boasts to naught." "Fear not," answered he; "dost thou choose me for thy husband?" "Surely," replied she. "Then urge thy father to let me wed thee." After that, Kormak gave Thorkell great gifts for Steingerd's sake, and many men of mark took up the cause and pleaded for Kormak with Thorkell. And the end of it was that Thorkell gave way, and consented to give his daughter to Kormak. But so soon as this was done, the mind of Kormak began to change, for Thorveig had wrought mighty spells. When Thorkell began to speak about the dowry, Kormak thought himself not fairly dealt with therein, and quarrels began; insomuch that when all things were arranged for the bridal, Kormak came not to it; and all men thought that a deadly shame done to Steingerd, and her father, and his whole house.

There was a man named Bersi, who lived at Sowerby not far from Tongue. Many a duel had he fought, and therefore was he known as *Holmgang* Bersi, or Bersi the duellist. To him came Thorveig when she was driven from Midfirth; and Bersi received her well, and gave her a portion of land west of Midfirth. Now Thorkell, after the shame put upon him by Kormak, remembered Bersi, and deemed he would be a great help if it came to an open quarrel with Kormak. So Narfi was sent to Bersi, and was told to offer him Steingerd to wife. Narfi went, and Bersi greeted him well. "Men say, Bersi," said he, "that Steingerd and thou would make a good match. Nor is there need to think of Kormak, for he has shown he thinks no more of the maiden." The end was that Bersi was betrothed to Steingerd, but Steingerd's own heart was not in the matter; and she sent Narfi to tell Kormak thereof. Little pleased was Narfi with his errand; for well knew he how hasty was Kormak with his blows; so he rode with a shield in front of him, and stared all round like a frightened hare. Now when he came to Kormak's home, he found him building a turf-wall, and beating it with a mallet. "What tidings, Narfi, that thou comest thus to me?" "Slight tidings: we had many guests last night." "Who were your guests?" "*Holmgang* Bersi, and seventeen others, for he had come to his bridal." "Who was the bride?" "Steingerd, Thorkell's daughter," said Narfi. "Ever dost thou bring ill news," said Kormak; and he rushed upon Narfi and smote him with the mallet so that he fell from his horse stunned. "Ill done was that," said Kormak's brother Thorgils. "Not so," replied Kormak; "'tis but that a churl hath got his deserts." Soon Narfi came to himself, and told them all about the wedding. "Did Steingerd know of it beforehand?" "Not until the very evening they came thither," said he. "But thou wilt find it a lighter thing, Kormak, to ill-use me than to fight with Bersi."

Now when Kormak knew that Steingerd was wedded to another, all his love for her came back as it were a flood. Straightway he took his horse and weapons, and started to rush after Bersi. "Whither wilt thou?" said Thorgils. After him who hath stolen her whom I love," said he. "Vain is thy errand," said Thorgils; "long since will Bersi have reached his home: yet will I go with thee." For no man will I tarry," said Kormak; and forth he rode, so that ere he had gone far he foundered his horse. And Thorgils with seventeen men found him near Thorveig's home. Now Bersi had come to Thorveig but a little while before, and she lent him a boat to cross the firth. "But ere we part", said she, "I would give thee a little gift. 'Tis this shield; methinks thou canst not be wounded if thou earnest it. Small is this gift in return for the home thou hast given me." Bersi thanked her, and so they parted. And Thorveig, by second-sight, knew of the coming of Kormak and Thorgils; wherefore she sent men to bore holes in all the other boats. Straightway came Kormak and the rest, and asked Thorveig for a boat. "Not for nothing will I do thee that service," said she: "here is a boat which I will lend thee for half a mark." Thorgils said two ounces would be more than enough. "Waste not time," said Kormak; he leapt into the boat and Thorgils after him. But scarcely had they gone far, when it filled beneath them, and hard work had they to come back to land.

"Thou deservest punishment rather than pay, thou evil woman," said Kormak. "A little jest was it of mine," said Thorveig; and with that Thorgils paid her the money. Meanwhile Bersi had got safely home.

Now after this naught would content Kormak but that he should send a challenge to Bersi, though Bersi offered him his sister Helga to wife. "That is well offered," said

Thorgils; "for Helga is deemed a good match." "Not so," said Kormak. "What are all the women in the world to Steingerd?" Wherefore the challenge was sent.

Now when Dalla, Kormak's mother, heard thereof, she was displeased with him. "Thou hast done foolishly," said she; "for Helga is a good match, and Bersi hath not his equal as a fighter in all Iceland. Moreover, he hath a sword called Whiting which naught can resist, and a healing-stone which will cure all his wounds; and by these hath he come through a score of fights; and yet more hath he Thorveig's spells to aid him: what hast thou against all these?" "My good axe," said Kormak.

"Little boots that," said Dalla. "Go hence to Midfirth-Skeggi, and borrow his great sword Skofnung: that alone can break the spells." Now Skofnung was indeed a mighty brand, and a wise man holding the same could fail not of victory. For there was tied to it a small wallet, which must not be touched: the sun must never shine on the hilt; and it must never be worn save when the owner was making ready for battle. If drawn in haste it would shriek; but if drawn with heed it would do strange things; a snake would creep out from under the hilt, and then, if the blade were duly slanted, it would creep back again in sign of good luck.

Therefore, when Kormak went to Skeggi and begged for his sword, Skeggi would not give it. "Slow is the mind of the sword," said he, "and thou art hasty. Little good wilt thou do it, and little will it do thee." But Dalla went to Skeggi and asked for it. "I will lend it", said he, "if he will do all I tell him; otherwise it will go hard with him." And he told Kormak all the needs of the sword. Kormak took it, and straightway forgot all that Skeggi had told him. In his house he dragged the sword from its sheath, and it came out shrieking; and so hastily did he draw it that he tore off the wallet therefrom. "Alas," said Dalla, "all is over with thee. I should have known how it would be, hasty-tempered as thou art!"

Nevertheless, Kormak carried Skofnung with him to the holm. So swiftly went he, that he kept not the sun from the hilt: Skofnung shrieked as he was drawn, and when the snake crawled from under the guard, Kormak slanted not the blade. Wherefore the luck of Skofnung fled from him.

In those days it was the custom at the *holmgang* that each man should smite thrice at the other's shield, one first and then the other; and if no blood was shed, then should they fight without shields. Now Bersi had brought three shields, and the third was that which Thorveig had enchanted: yet, had Skofnung been duly dealt with, little would have booted her enchantments. So they smote in turn, and each shield was split in turn, till it fell to Kormak to strike at the magic shield. And so it was that when he smote, Skofnung was broken, fire flew from the shield, and the point of the blade was driven back on to Kormak's hand, so that blood fell on the rug whereon they fought. Then men went between them, and said that Kormak was conquered. Little liked he his fate; but he had to pay the ransom, and to tell Skeggi how he had fared with the sword. Skeggi said that it had happened as was to be expected from such a man as Kormak. Long was it ere the wound was healed, and longer ere Kormak had peace of mind, for he loved Steingerd, and could not bear that another should have her. As for Skofnung, the more men strove to grind it to a point, the worse it was.

Long stayed Kormak at home, eating his heart with care and grief. Then it came to pass that Bersi had yet another *holmgang*; and in this he was grievously maimed: therefore Steingerd, scorning to be the wife of a maimed man, and also loving Kormak, put him away and went home to her father's house. "Now," thought she, "Kormak will surely wed me." But Thorveig's spell was still mighty; and as before he loved her not.

Now Steingerd was given in marriage once again, this time to a certain man named Tintein, who dwelt in the north of Iceland. And no sooner did Kormak hear thereof, than his love welled up once more. "I cannot bear", he said to Steingerd in one of his verses, "that thou shouldst be wedded to a tin-man; never shall I smile now thy father has given thee to such a nithing." Steingerd said, "Thou wouldst not have me when thou mightest; little good is it to wail now thou canst not." And she told Tintein of Kormak's words. Thereupon, Tintein spake to his brother Thorvard. And Thorvard watched, and saw that Kormak oft tried to get speech with Steingerd. Wherefore Thorvard summoned Kormak to the *holmgang*. All men knew that Kormak was the better sword-player; therefore went Thorvard to a wise woman named Thordis, who, though she was friendly to Kormak, yet prepared Thorvard for the battle by many spells. Not long thereafter, Kormak came to Thordis, and begged her to prepare him likewise. "Alas!" said the wise woman. "Thou hast come too late: I knew not that I as preparing an enemy of thine; yet, for the friendship that is between us, I will undo the spells I have laid upon him. But I fear thy hastiness; take heed therefore to speak no word except I speak to thee, whatever thou seest me do." Now to undo the spell she had to slay three geese on the holm or place of battle. And three nights she went with Kormak to slay a goose there, but such was his hastiness that each night he spake to her; so that at last she said to him, "Vain is it to try to help thee, so hasty as thou art: hadst thou but obeyed me, I had given thee victory tomorrow, and also had broken the spells of Thorveig, so that thou shouldst have married Steingerd and loved her till thy death-day; but now it cannot be." Angry indeed was Kormak, but it availed him naught to rave. Wherefore the battle came on, and Kormak did not lose in it, yet did he not win Steingerd.

Now Steingerd and Tintein set out for Norway, and it happened that Kormak and Thorgils his brother set sail about the same time. And on the voyage Tintein's ship was attacked by Vikings, but Kormak was near and saved it, not for love of Tintein, but for love of Steingerd. And so they went together to the court of King Harald of Norway; and here Kormak saw Tintein often in the company of Steingerd, and liked it ill. One day it came to pass that he saw them on their ship together in the harbour; wherefore he was suddenly angry and seized the tiller of his own boat and hurled it at Tintein so that he fell stunned. Many such quarrels had they; and at last Tintein and Steingerd left Norway for Denmark.

Now one day, when Kormak was cruising in his ship, he saw another ship coming towards him, and when it drew near he saw that the captain thereof was Tintein. But Tintein said no words of wrath to him, but asked his help: "For", said he, "certain Vikings attacked us and carried off Steingerd, and I would have thy aid in taking her back." "Assuredly will I help thee," said Kormak; "where lie those pirates?" "Not far hence," said Tintein. So Kormak sailed with Tintein, and, as luck would, he came up with the pirates in a certain harbour, when most of the men were ashore. He rushed on board, and slew the first man he saw and that was Thorstein, the man who had carried off Steingerd: and the rest of the crew either were slain or swam ashore. Thus

Steingerd was taken back again; and Tintein said to Kormak, "She is thine by law of conquest take her and go in peace." But scarce had Tintein said these words, when Kormak felt in himself that he could never wed her. So they parted, and never saw one another again.

Little more need one tell of Kormak. With Thorgils sailed he about the British Isles; and men say they founded Scarborough, and called it after Thorgils's other name, Scard; but the end was that in Scotland he fell in combat with a giant or *blot-risi*. So died Kormak Ogmund-son, whose fate it was never to wed the woman he loved, nor to love her except when she was wedded to another.

And as for Thorveig, so men say, she died in the manner following. As Kormak was sailing to Norway, a walrus rose out of the sea, and made as though it would rush at the ship of Kormak. But Kormak smote it with a long pike; hard and true smote he it, so that it straightway sank, and never rose again. But as she sank, men say they saw her eyes, and they were the eyes of Thorveig the witch: for she had made herself a walrus to slay Kormak, and had been slain herself. Howsoever this be, at that very hour Thorveig fell sick in her house in Iceland, and died in her bed.

THE TALE OF GEIRMUND HELL-SKIN

as told by Edward Ernest Kellett

 GEIRMUND and Hamund were the twin sons of King Hjor. And this is the story that tells why the twain were both called Hell-skin. At the time when King Hjor had to go to a kings' moot, his queen was "not well", and while the king was out of the land she bore two sons; and they were fine children, but that was the greatest mark upon them, that never had men seen darker skins than were on those children. The queen set little store by them, and deemed their colour of ill omen. Now there was a thrall named Lodhott, who was set in charge of other thralls. He was married, and his wife bore a son at the very time that the queen bore the twins: and this boy was so exceeding fair, whom the thrall's wife had borne, that the queen deemed her own sons but ill-favoured, to compare with him. Wherefore she devised to make an exchange with the handmaid; and though the handmaid deemed even as the queen that her own son was the fairer, yet dared she not deny to make the bargain. So the queen took the thrall's son, and spread it abroad that he was her own, and called his name Leif, while the handmaid took the twins and brought them up in thrall fashion, till they were three winters old; but Leif had the honour of a prince. Yet the twins showed tokens of their true birth.

Now it came to pass that Bragi the *skald* came to King Hjor, and abode with him some time. And when the king one day went a-hunting, there were but few left in the palace. Bragi was in the window-seat, with a reed in his hand; and the queen was lying in an alcove, so hidden that none could see her. Leif sat in the high-seat, and played with a gold ring. And the twins, thinking the hall empty save of Leif, and seeing him thus playing, drew near; and Geirmund said to his brother, "How were it if we took the ring from Leif, and played therewith ourselves awhile?" "Ready am I," said Hamund. So they ran up and took it from Leif; whereupon he wept bitterly. Then they said, "A strange thing surely, that a king's son should weep to lose a gold ring!" And, pulling him from the high-seat, they mocked at him.

Now all this Bragi saw: wherefore he rose and went to the queen, and, touching her with the reed, spake a verse:

"Twain are in hall, both know I well,

Hamund and Geirmund, Hjor's sons are they;

And Leif the third, Lodhott's child;

Thou didst not bear him: few viler could be!"

Thereupon the queen arose, and went forth with the boys, and took back her own, restoring Leif to his mother: for she deemed as was indeed true that they had in them the high spirit that it was likely, from their birth, that they would have. And at eventide, when the king returned and sat in his high-seat, then went the queen to the king, taking the two lads with her, and told him all she had done, and of the exchange with the handmaid, bidding him deal as he deemed fit. Then the king, looking at the boys, said, "Of a truth I perceive that these boys are of my race; yet never have I seen such dark-skinned boys as they are." Therefore were they thenceforward both surnamed Hell-skin. And as soon as they were full grown they went out of the land a-harrying, and gained both wealth and glory, steering with skill a great ship a long while; insomuch that it is said in some sagas, and specially in the saga of Rolf the Black, that those brothers were held the greatest Vikings among sea-kings of that time.

THE SAGA OF HORD

as told by Edward Ernest Kellett

THIS is the story of one whose luck was evil from his youth, and who came to an ill end through a curse laid unthinkingly upon him by his own mother when he was a child. For in those days men had to take heed to their words: inasmuch as, if they spake unadvisedly with their lips, the Weird Sisters listened, and would assuredly suffer not the words to fall to the ground.

There was a man named Grimkell in the south-west of Iceland, silent and dour, but just and honourable; never failing in doing sacrifice to the gods. He sought in marriage Signy, the daughter of Valbrand, a widow, wealthy, whom men deemed a great match. But Valbrand thought Grimkell no unequal husband for her, and hesitated not to consent; though Torfi his son, thinking the twain unlikely to agree, set his face against the thing, and said ill-luck would arise therefrom. Yet was the bargain hanselled and carried through.

Valbrand, being old, went not according to custom to the bridegroom's house, but sent a friend of his, whose name was Kol, instead. With Kol went Grim, the son of Signy by her former marriage, and thirty men besides. Evil were the omens on that journey: a horse was lost in a snowdrift, and Grim wished even then to turn back, but Kol made him go on. Grimkell gave them a great feast, wondering much, howsoever, that neither Valbrand nor Torfi had come with the bride.

Signy was proud and fond of show: Grimkell, as was said, was silent and loved not company and merry-making. Soon therefore the pair began to disagree, and might have quarrelled, but that Grim, loving them both, ofttimes played the peacemaker. He was gentle and honest; but ere long he wedded and left the stead. His wife was Gudrid, the daughter of Hogni, a man of wealth. Grimkell stocked his farm right royally, so that Grim speedily became rich. He and Gudrid had a son whom they called Geir.

Now Signy had a dream. She saw a great tree growing, with such mighty branches that it overspread the house; but it bore no blossoms.

This dream she liked ill, wherefore she told it to her foster-mother Thordis, a woman skilled in omens; but Thordis liked it no better. "This is the meaning," said she. "Thou wilt bear a son, strong and fair, but there will be no love lost between him and his kin." Soon thereafter did Signy bear a son, whom she called Hord: fair and strong; but there was this marvel about him, that he walked not till he was three winters old; and men deemed this unlucky. Now one day when Grimkell was sacrificing in the temple, Signy sat on a stool, with a necklace across her knees that was an heirloom and a great treasure. The child, seeing the glitter of the necklace, rose to his feet having never walked before and came to his mother, snatched at the necklace, and broke it, so that the pieces fell on the floor. Signy, in hasty anger, cried out, "See this child! Unlucky are his first steps, his next will be worse, and worst of all his last!" Grimkell, hearing the words, and knowing that the Weird Sisters must have marked them, spake no word, but took up the child and carried him to Grim and Gudrid. "Rear him for me," said he, "for his mother draweth ill-luck on him." They took him and brought him up with Geir; but Signy, angered with herself and with Grimkell, thenceforward saw less of her husband than ever. Shortly afterwards a maid-child called Thorbjorg was born to her at Torfi's house, and she died in giving her birth. Torfi liked not the child that had caused this ill, and bade that she should be thrown into the river. But the man, instead of so doing, carried her to Grim and Gudrid, who took her also, and brought her up with Geir and Hord.

Now Grimkell, hearing this, was wroth with Torfi, and would fain have slain him; but Grim and the lawman, Thorkell the Moon, a just man, won him over to take as atonement six hundred ounces of silver. When Torfi came to pay it, Grimkell said, "I ask it not for myself: pay it, and the interest thereon, to Hord when he reacheth man's estate." Torfi answered, "I will pay it if Hord is a better man than his father!" "Be it so," replied Grimkell. "Little good in any wise will it do him, seeing whence it comes. But boys take after their mother's brothers; wherefore I deem that Hord will turn out worse than I." At this there arose a great shout, and things came nigh to bloodshed; and though the two men fought not at that time, little love was between them thenceforward. Thus early was Hord the cause of quarrel among his kin.

At twelve years Hord was a match for most boys of sixteen; and at fifteen he was a head taller than the most part of full-grown men; and he had further this gift, that no glamour could make him see things save as they truly were. He had the keenest eyesight of all men, and in all sports was the greatest champion. Geir also, though less than he, was tall and strong; and the two were ever together, and had but one mind between them.

Now it chanced that a ship came from Norway, the owner whereof was a man called Brynjolf. At the "Thing" Brynjolf met Grimkell, and said, "Gladly would I see thy son Hord, of whom I have heard much praise." And just then Hord and Geir passed by: so Grimkell called Hord, and made him known to Brynjolf, who, looking on him, saw that fame had not erred in praising him; and he said, "If thou desirest to go out with me to Norway, I will be thy partner and give thee a half-share in all our gains." "That is a strange word," said Hord, "to one thou hast never seen before: yet will I go with thee if but I can gather enough goods to trade with." Geir, too, was eager to go; and he urged Hord to take a man with them called Helgi Sigmundson, Hord liked this not, for, seeing things as they were, he perceived in Helgi a hasty temper that would bring ill-luck: yet did he yield to Geir. Grimkell gave them a large sum of money, and store of merchandise wherewith to trade: and so they set sail, and arrived at Bergen with a fair wind.

This was when Harald Greyfell was king in Norway, and about the time when Edgar the Peaceable reigned in England. Harald received Hord well, gave him leave to trade, and made him his man. Soon it was seen how noble Hord was: he did great things in war, and gained wealth and high renown. For one thing he did he won especial fame. There was a howe on a hill, wherein was buried an ancient Viking. Men said he had a great sword in his hand and a precious ring on his finger: yet none dared to enter the howe to get these treasures. Hord, hearing thereof, entered the howe, fought with the Viking, and, overcoming him, took sword and ring. Of which deed the fame spread far and wide, insomuch that the Jarl of Gautland gave him his daughter Helga to wife; and, though Helga was the paragon of women, it was said that such a man as Hord was no ill match for her.

Meanwhile in Iceland his sister Thorbjorg had grown up and had wedded a man called Eindridi. Soon after this marriage Grimkell died, and, what was great scathe, Grim and Gudrid died also. Eindridi and Illugi, who had married Grimkell's eldest daughter, saw to the sharing of the lands and goods. Soon afterwards, Hord, being then thirty years old, returned with Helga his wife, Helgi Sigmundson, and a train of followers. Little ill-luck had been his thus far; but the Weird Sisters had not forgotten. He met Eindridi and Illugi, and fairly they dealt with him. Eindridi would take no more than Thorbjorg's share; and Illugi entertained him so royally throughout the winter that Hord said he was happy in having found such a brother-in-law. But next he bethought him of the money due to him, by the award of the lawman, Thorkell Moon, from Torfi. So he went to Torfi and asked for it. Torfi replied, "I mind me of my words to thy father, that I would pay thee only if thou wert a better man than he. No proof do I see that thou hast yet excelled thy father." Hord answered, "I boast not myself so highly, but the money is mine and I will have it." So saying, he rode thence and told Illugi of Torfi's unfair dealings. Straightway the twain gathered a band of men, and rode to Broadbowstead, where Torfi dwelt; and Torfi, seeing the host, came forth and said, "Now see I plainly thou art thy father's son: what I said was but to prove thee. Take thy money, lands, and all; and I give thee to boot sixty head of sheep as seal to the friendship that ought to be between men so near of kin." Hord took the gift, but, seeing Torfi as he was, loved him but little more for his yielding and his words.

Now among Torfi's men was a yeoman named Aud, whose horses strayed often into Hord's lands, doing great damage. Wherefore one day Hord said to Helgi Sigmundson, "Go forth and drive away these horses." Helgi went forth, and found Sigurd, Aud's son, driving the horses home. "Wherefore art thou so slack in tending thy beasts?" said he. "Thou and thy father are the pests of the land." Upon which, Sigurd answering no less fiercely, a quarrel arose, and the end was that Helgi slew Sigurd. Soon thereafter came Hord, and saw what had befallen. "A knave art thou," he said to Helgi, "to slay a harmless lad: it were but just if I slew thee in thy turn; yet will I spare thy life. But my mind bodes me that this is the beginning of ill-luck to thee, and that upon me also it will drag the evil that hath been foredoomed." So saying, he went not forthwith to tell Aud, but, casting a cloak over the boy, departed homeward.

A little later he went to Aud, and said, "Sore grief is thy son's death to me, and much against my will it came to pass. Self-doom I give thee: name thy own price for the were-gild; none shall say that I have dealt unfairly with thee." "It is too late," said Aud. "I have been to Torfi, who hath taken up my case, and hath promised to pursue it to the utmost." Whereat Hord, feeling a sudden rush of wrath, which men deemed to have come from the Weird Sisters, drew his sword and cried, "This for calling in Torfi against me!" and slew Aud. Nor did he cease therewith, but set fire to his stead and burned it to the ground. And when this was done, the fury ran out of him.

And Torfi, hearing of this, summoned Hord to answer for it at the Althing or Moot of all Iceland. Hord said he would scorn himself to answer Torfi, who had ever been his enemy; but he sent Helgi to Eindridi, asking him to take up the case at the Althing. Eindridi replied that he had at that time a case at a smaller Thing, having promised to help Illugi therein. "But", said he, "if Hord will come to my stead he shall not lack for aid from me." Helgi returned to Hord, and, saying naught of this last offer, told him that Eindridi refused to help him. Thus it was that, when the case came on at the Althing, there was none to speak on Hord's behalf, and he and Helgi were alike outlawed.

When Hord heard the news, he mocked thereat, saying, "Torfi hath had me outlawed; but what care I?" And, destroying all such property as he could not carry with him, he went over to Geir's house at a place called The Flats. There, having left little spoil for Torfi to take, he fortified The Flats, and lived thenceforward as a free-booter, Geir willingly joining with him. And finding the cattle too few to feed so great a company, Geir and Helgi went forth to a farmstead called Waterhorn, slew the herdsman, and drove off the cattle. Hord liked this ill. "Ye may rob openly," said he, "but stealing of this kind must cease." Yet could he not hinder his men from doing much that he liked as little as this.

The news of this deed at Waterhorn spread far and wide, and made a big stir. But more news soon came. There was a man named Kolgrim, living no great way off; and he asked the Flat-men to play games on the ice at Yuletide. At these games the Flat-men ever got the worse, but could see no reason therefor, till they thought that

Kolgrim had laid an evil charm on their shoes, which were made of ox-hide from stolen cattle. When they told Hord of this, he said, "Little good are we if we cannot avenge ourselves," and came himself to the games, and fought so furiously that six of his enemies lay dead on the ice. As for a seventh, whose name was Onund, he was sore wounded, but dragged himself thence; yet, as he came near his house, he said, "I must sit down and bind my shoe," and sitting down he died straightway. That place was ever after known as Onund's Knoll. Such things made men resolve to make an end of The Flats and of the outlaws dwelling there, whose numbers increased continually as other outlaws joined them. At the summer Thing men met and planned to destroy them; and Hord, hearing thereof, and knowing that, however long he held out, famine would conquer in the end, bade the men remove to a holm or island in the firth by Dinner Ness. This isle runs sheer down into the sea, and few men were needed to defend it against thousands. Two hundred went with Hord, taking boats from the boat-sheds of any men that lived near by. There they built a great hall on the very edge of the cliff, and cut underground passages, so that if need were they could escape thereby. They had but one lack there was no sure supply of water: therefore they built a great tank, and sent men from time to time in a seal-boat to the river mouth to bring fresh water from thence, which they emptied into the tank. And they made laws. All men were to obey first Hord and next Geir. If any were sick, and recovered not within three days, they threw him over the cliff. All men had to swear an oath to keep these laws, and to be faithful unto death. Of these the chief were Thord Kott, Thorgeir Girdlebeard of whom none spake a good word and Helgi Sigmundson, who was scarce better than Thorgeir. In that fortress were Helga, Herd's wife, who was no whit in endurance behind any of the men, and her two sons Grimkell and Bjorn.

Three years was Hord in that holm, and daily were there battles, and robberies, and evil deeds, in which Thorgeir was the worst; nor could Hord restrain his men from such, though he knew they brought ill-fame upon him. Sometimes the men of Geir's Holm, for so that isle was called, had the better in fight, and sometimes the worse; but all men feared them and desired their destruction. Of these three years the saga tells many things, which here we pass over and come to the end.

None hated the holm-men more than Ref, the *godi* or priest, a chief and a great fighter. Ref had a brother called Kjartan, strong of his hands likewise, but not held to be a truth-teller, evil-minded and not greatly beloved. Their mother was a very old woman named Thorbjorg Katla, a witch whose spells were mighty. Katla boasted that by her spells and glamours she was safe from the holm-men, howsoever they might strive to harm her. This boast came to the ears of Geir, and he was minded to put it to the proof; wherefore he set out with Thord Kott and eleven others to the house of Katla. Drawing near thereto, he left two men to guard the boat, and set Thord on a rock to keep watch, while with the others he came toward the house. But Katla, knowing by her arts that a boat had set forth, straightway came to her door and raised such a mist and glamour that no man could see his fellow. Then, sending a messenger to Ref, she waited; and Ref came in haste with fifteen men. They found Thord on the rock, and forthwith slew him, and then turned to the shore where Geir was. Suddenly the mist lifted, and the bands saw each other, whereon began a fierce fight. All Geir's men were slain, and three of Ref's; as for Geir, he was sore wounded, and had a hard task to reach the holm, where Helga, who knew leechcraft, tended his wounds.

A little later, Hord, deeming that Eindridi had been faithless to him, for he trusted the tale of Helgi, sent men to set fire to Eindridi's house. Small success had the men; yet the chiefs, feeling that an end of these dangers must be made, held a moot to plan the taking of the holm; and one said this and another said that. And as they were thus talking, a woman rode into the Moot even Thorbjorg, the wife of Eindridi and Herd's sister. "Hearken," said she; "I know your devisings. As to what may hap to the rest, I care not; but whosoever slays Hord, let him know that I will be his bane!" At this a dead silence fell on the crowd; but at length they said, "Even so an end must be made of the holm-men, or the land will perish." And Ref said, "Force against the holm is vain; fraud must be tried. Let therefore a man go thither, and take the oath as one of them; and when he hath gained their trust let him say that if they scatter and go back to their homes their lives will be spared." Torfi deemed this advice good. "But first," said he, "let us move to the Ness, out of hearing of any of Hord's men." Next day they dined at the Ness, wherefore it is called Dinner Ness unto this day. And then they looked round for a man to go. "Whoso goes", said Torfi, "shall gain great honour. Moreover, I deem that by now the holm-men, by their evil deeds, have lost their luck, and will not see things as they are." Then said Kjartan, "I have my own score to settle with the holm-men, and will go. But if Hord be taken, ye shall give me that treasure of his, the ring of gold which he took from the cairn." "So shall it be," said Torfi.

Now there was a man named Thorstein, who had sworn never to harm the holm-men. His boat Kjartan took, and went over therein. The men welcomed him, for Weird had cast a glamour on their minds, and any tale would they believe. Hord alone, who ever saw things as they were, was not deceived. "But see," said Geir, "he has come over in Thorstein's boat, and Thorstein has promised never to betray us." "Thy eyes are blinded," said Hord; "an ill man is Kjartan for a friendly errand." "I will take thy oath if thou willest," said Kjartan. "Thy oath is as thy mere word, worthless," said Hord. Nonetheless the men, who were fey and weary of their narrow life, disobeyed Hord, and would go: nay, he was gladdest who got to the boat first. Kjartan took them round a point that hid them from the view of the holm-men, and here were they all slain. Then Kjartan came back; and now Geir was eager to go, for he too was fey and beglamoured. "Thou art bewitched," said Hord; "seest thou not that Kjartan hath returned alone? Had he been true he had brought witnesses of his truth." But the doom was on Geir, and he went, and many with him. As they came round the point, Geir saw the throng of bonders. "Ill-luck follows ill-rede," cried he; "ever hath Hord seen farther than I," and straightway sprang into the water. But a man named Orm, a friend of Eindridi, who was the best of javelin-throwers, saw him, and forthwith hurled a javelin, which struck Geir and slew him. Men said that was the best throw that had ever been heard of. All the other men were then slain.

Much was Kjartan praised for his craft; and Torfi said, "Few can be left: wilt thou try yet again?" He answered, "I will put the knob on the stick', and set forth for the last time.

Now there remained on the holm but Hord, Helga, their two sons, Helgi Sigmundson, and a few more. And Helga saw the death of Geir from the cliff, and bade Hord look. He looked, and saw naught. "Never ere this hast thou failed to see things as they are," said Helga; "I fear doom is on thee." Then came Kjartan, and

Hord said, "Wherefore came Geir not back with thee?" "He waiteth to take the peace along with thee," said Kjartan. "Looks lie if thou speak true," said Hord. "Then thou art afraid to come," said Kjartan. "Naught fear I," replied Hord; "nor wilt thou doubt that ere the day is over." Then he said to Helga, "Come thou also." "Nay," said she; "I perceive that thou art fey; and 'tis said that there is no help for a doomed man." So saying, she wept sore.

Hord stepped into the boat, and said no word till they reached the shore; and there he saw the body of Geir with the javelin right through it, floating on the waters. "Not long", cried he to Kjartan, "shalt thou rejoice in thy treachery," and with the old Viking's sword clove him to the waist. But just then the boat ran ashore, and straightway the men seized him, and Eindridi bound him fast, and Helgi with him. "Fast dost thou bind me," said Hord. "So did ye hold me fast when ye strove to burn me in my house," said Eindridi. "Will no one slay him for me?" But all remembered the words of Thorbjorg, and stood still.

Suddenly Hord broke loose, snatched the axe from Eindridi's hand, and rushed through the midst of his foes. Ref pursued him, being on horseback, but he too remembered Thorbjorg, and dared not smite him. And then had Hord escaped his enemies, but the "war-fetter", that fear which the gods send on the bravest, of a sudden descended on him, and held him fast, so that the men overtook him again, and dragged him back. "Not ye could hold me," said he; "but 'tis some evil power that hath come upon me." With that he leapt forward, and saying that none else should have the glory, slew Helgi with one blow of his sword. And just then came up Thorstein. He, knowing naught of Thorbjorg's words, gave Hord his death-blow.

So died Hord. Men praised him for his courage, and said his ill-deeds were less his own than those of others. "But there was a doom on him," said they, "and he was not a lucky man. What is fated none can shun."

To Thorstein, Torfi would fain have given the great sword; but when Thorstein heard of Thorbjorg's threatening, he would have chosen not to have earned the reward. The chiefs then planned to go over to the holm for Helga and her sons, meaning to slay the boys; but that night they stayed still, and next day it was too late. For Helga was a paragon among women. She took her younger child Bjorn on her back, and swam with him that night to the mainland. Then, leaving Bjorn, she swam back and carried Grimkell over in like manner. The night they spent in a cleft of the rock, which was afterwards called Helga's Cleft. Then all three went to Eindridi's house, and called Thorbjorg out. When Thorbjorg came forth, she spake no word, so deeply moved was she. But she put the three in an outhouse, and waited for Eindridi.

When Eindridi returned, she bade him tell her the whole story of Herd's death, and he told her. Then she said, "Thy wife will I not be, unless thou slay Thorstein." Little did he like the work, but, forasmuch as he loved her, he did so, and then came back to tell her. "Fulfilled is my vow", said she, "that I would be the bane of Herd's slayer; yet remains there another thing." "Speak thy mind," said he. "Even now never will I be thy wife save thou promise to shelter Helga and her two sons, if so be they come to us for help." "An easy promise is that," said he, "for assuredly they are dead. Strictly did we search the holm, and found them not: wherefore it is our belief that they threw themselves into the sea and perished therein." Then went Thorbjorg to the outhouse and brought in Helga and the lads. "Too crafty hast thou been with me," said Eindridi; "yet will I keep my word to thee." And so did he, receiving them into his house, and bringing the children up as his own.

Hord was thirty-nine years old when he died. For thirty-six of these he was in honour and good fame, and for three an outlaw. But men deem that few have surpassed him, first because of his wisdom in counsel and skill in fight; secondly because of the noble woman who was his wife; and lastly because of the vengeance that was taken for him after his death.

And here endeth Holmverja Saga, or the Story of the Holm-men.

THE TALE OF GRETTI AND GLAM

as told by Edward Ernest Kellett

SO Gretti rode to Thorhall's stead, and the bonder greeted him well. He asked whither he wished to fare, and Gretti said he willed to abide there overnight, if so it seemed good to the bonder. Thorhall said he would be glad enough therefor: "But few think it profitable to guest here for long; thou wilt have heard tell what is here to face, nor would I desire that thou shouldst come by any danger through me; and though thou thyself shouldst come off unscathed, yet know I that thou shalt lose thy horse, for none that come here can keep un- harmed their goods." Gretti said there was supply of horses whatever happed to this one. Thorhall rejoiced greatly that Gretti would be there, and welcomed him with both hands. Gretti's horse was tied fast in the stall, and then went they to sleep; and the night passed in such wise that Glam sought not the house. Then said Thorhall, "Well hath been thy coming to me, for every night hath Glam been wont to ride the house and break the panels, whereof thou canst see the marks." Gretti said, "Two ways may that be taken: either he will not rest for long, or the ridings may cease for more than one night; I will abide here yet another night, and see how it fares." Afterwards they went to see the horse, and behold, no harm was done to it; and the bonder deemed this even as the rest, such was the luck of Gretti. So Gretti abode another night, and the fiend sought not the house that night either, which seemed to the bonder a sign of hope; but when they went to see the horse, the stall was broken up, and the horse dragged out of door, and every bone in him broken in sunder. This did Thorhall tell to Gretti, and bade him take heed to himself, "for certain is thy death if thou abide Glam". But Gretti said, "It is little indeed to do for my horse, if I abide the fiend." The bonder said, "Ay, but small good wilt thou do, for he is not of human shape: yet do I own that every hour seems good to me when thou art here." So the day goes on; and when men should go to sleep, Gretti said he would not go out of his clothes, and lay down in front of the bonder's locked chamber. He had a rug over him, and twisted one fold under his feet, and another under his head, and looked out through the neck-hole. In front of the bench on which he lay was the house-pillar, strong and firm, and Gretti set his feet against that pillar. The door was all broken, but in its place was set a hurdle, which men had hastily fashioned for that end; and the cross-wainscot was broken also. All the beds were taken away, and very inhospitable seemed that hall. A light burned therein through the night.

And when a third of the night had almost passed, Gretti heard without a great noise; then was there a sound overhead, and the roof was ridden, and that so violently that every beam cracked. This went on long; and then the steps came down off the roof and came to the door; and as the hurdle was fastened over it, Gretti saw that the fiend put in his head, and it seemed terribly big and wondrously harsh of feature. Glam came in slowly, and stretched himself up when he had entered the door; he loomed up toward the roof, and laid his arms on the cross-beam, and so glared through the hall. Gretti lay still, and stirred no whit. Then saw Glam that a strange heap was lying on the bench, and he came towards it and seized it; but Gretti set his feet against the pillar and yielded not. So Glam tugged thereat even harder, and yet could he not drag the rug away. Then tugged he a third time; and this time he pulled

Gretti from the bench; nay, the rug came in sunder between them. Glam stared at the rent, and wondered much who could be so hard tugging against him; and at that Gretti leapt in under his arms, and grasped him round the waist, and hoped that Glam would give way and fall; but the demon pressed on Gretti's wrist so hard that he was bowed down by the force thereof. And Gretti stayed himself at all the seats, and set his feet against all he could, to hold himself back, and the pillars of the hall started from their sockets, and all that was in their way was broken. Glam strove to drag him from the hall, and Gretti strove to stay within; for hard as it was to hold up within the house, well knew he that it would be harder without; but Glam increased his might, and notwithstanding all Gretti's strength did Glam drag him out of the hall and into the porch; and there he drew him even towards the door. And at the door Gretti suddenly thrust hard against Glam, so that he, not expecting it, fell backwards, and Gretti fell face downwards upon him. There was a moon that night, and at whiles it shone forth, and at whiles it was covered by the clouds; and when Gretti saw Glam's face his strength left him, so that he could not draw his sword, but lay between this world and the next. And then did Glam show forth his accursed might, more than other aftergangers, in that he spake thus: "Great daring hast thou shown, Gretti, that thou hast faced me; yet deem it not strange that thou shalt gain little luck thereby. For thou hast yet achieved but half thy full strength, yet shalt thou never be stronger than now; and henceforth all thy luck shall turn to evil: thou shalt be an outcast and a wanderer, and whenever thou art alone thou shalt see these glaring eyes of mine till loneliness shall be a horror to thee; and this same horror shall drag thee to thy doom."

And when the demon had thus spoken, the weakness ran off Gretti that had been upon him; then drew he his knife, and hewed the head from Glam and laid it by his thigh. Then came out Thorhall, who had clothed himself while Glam was speaking; but he had dared not to draw nigh till Glam was dead. He thanked Gretti, and praised him much, that he had vanquished this unclean spirit. Then burned they Glam to cold ashes, and after that they bare the ashes away in a scrip and buried them where neither men nor cattle were wont to tread.

Thorhall sent messages to the nearest hamlet, telling what had been done; and that

was the saying of all men that never had there been in the land such a man for strength and daring as Gretti, Asmund's son.

But thenceforward Gretti was never as he had been before; and this was the difference, that whereas of old he feared nothing, now he had become afraid of the dark, so that he never dared to fare alone after night had set in, for he seemed then to see phantoms of every kind.

THE TALE OF THIDRANDI

as told by Edward Ernest Kellett

NOW toward the end of the time when Iceland was yet heathen there came rumours of a greater god than Odin or Thor from over the sea; and some men wondered whether, if that god came, they would worship him or cleave to the old gods. For there were strange whispers that this "White Christ" was a god that would reward the men who served him. Of such men was Hall of the Side, a just man and a true; and it was deemed that Thorhall of Horgsland, a friend of Hall's, knew more of the coming change than he would say, for he was a great spa-man, and foresighted. Hall and Thorhall loved each other much; and when Hall went to the Thing he would guest at Horgsland, and Thorhall would often stay long whiles at the house of Hall. The eldest son of Hall of the Side was called Thidrandi: he was the best-loved youth in all Iceland, handsome and kind-hearted, and good to the poor, and blithe with every bairn he met, so that men's hearts went out to him. Now one summer, when Thidrandi was eighteen years old, it chanced that Thorhall was staying with Hall; and men began, as they ofttimes did, to speak well of Thidrandi and to praise his ways. But Thorhall held his peace, saying neither good nor bad. At last Hall said to him, "Why art thou so silent about my son Thidrandi, seeing that to me thy words are of more account than all other men's?" Thorhall answered, "It is not that I mislike aught about him, or that I am slower than other men to see that he is the best of youths: rather is it that I know he will always have many to praise him, but I forebode he may not be long with us, and then, the more men have praised him the sadder wilt thou be."

And as the Yule-feast drew near, Thorhall waxed more and more sad. "Wherefore art thou sad?" said Hall. "I like not this coming feast," said he; "for I forebode that a spa-man will be slain there." "That need not grieve thee," answered Hall. "I have an ox called Spa-man: him will I slaughter at the feast, and no harm shall befall thee, though thy boding be fulfilled." "Not for myself was my fear," said the prophet, "but for great tidings and strange, which I foresee, but which I will not tell forth as now." "Then shall we put off the feast?" "Not so; for what must be shall be, let men do as they will." And when Yule came there were few men at the feast, for the weather was cold and very wild. And as men sat at the board at even, Thorhall said, "This is my boding, that it were better for no man to go out this night, whatever happenings he hear outside: let him pay no heed, whoever knocks or cries." Hall said to his men, "Hearken to Thorhall, for great things hang upon his words: what he forbids let no man do." Now Thidrandi was waiting on the guests: he was, as ever, courteous and well-beloved of all. And when night fell, Thidrandi put guests in his own locked bed, and slept outside in the hall. And when men slept, there came a knocking at the door; and all men made as if they heard it not, for the warning of Thorhall was strong upon them. But at the third knock Thidrandi said, "Great shame it is to us to make as if we slept, and men without on such a night as it is: these are guests my father bade to the feast, who have been lost, and are but just arrived hither." So he took his sword in his hand, and went out; but he saw no man. So he went a little farther, and heard a sound of riding from the north: that was a company of nine women, all with drawn swords, and dressed in black garments.

Then he heard a sound of riding from the south: that was a company of nine women, all in white garments, and riding on white horses. Then he would have turned back and told his vision; but lo! The black-stoled women came between him and the door, and made at him with their swords; nor was he slack to defend himself.

Now, a long while after, Thorhall awoke, and called Thidrandi; but there was no answer.

"Slow is he to answer," said he; whereupon men rose, and went out. The moon was now bright, and the frost clear, and they found Thidrandi lying sore wounded. So they carried him in; and when they had speech with him, he told them all even as it had happened. At daybreak he died, and they laid him in a howe after the old heathen fashion. And they made inquisition to find who had slain him; but no man knew of any enemy of Thidrandi's; as indeed all men loved him. Then Hall spoke to Thorhall, "What deemest thou of this strange deed?" said he. "I know not," answered he; "but this is my guess thereat: those women will be none other than the fetches of your friends, and the goddesses ye worship. Not long hence will be a change of faith in this land, and better gods will come to drive out the old; and thou, Hall, shalt take to these new gods; wherefore these have come to take toll of thee beforehand, in revenge for what thou shalt do to them. And those in white were the better ones, that strove to help Thidrandi; but so it was not to be."

Hall liked so ill the death of his son that he bore not to stay at his old home, and moved thence to the place that was afterwards called Baptism River. And there also Thorhall visited him; and one morning, as he looked out of the window, Hall saw him smile. "Why smilest thou?" said Hall. "Therefore I smile," said he, "because I saw every howe and cairn opened, and all the ghosts, and Discs, and fetches, both small and great, passing away, and making Flitting-day." And soon after came great tidings, as we shall now tell.

For even then King Olaf of Norway was sending out Thangbrand to teach the new faith in Iceland. And Thangbrand came to Side on Michael's Day, and did the service for St Michael. For whom doest thou these strange things?" said Hall. "For Michael the Archangel," said Thangbrand. "And what is his power?" asked Hall. "It is to meet the souls of the dead, and take them to their appointed place." "If his power be so great," said Hall, "then great indeed must be the might of him who gave him the power," said Hall. "God hath put that thought in thy mind," said Thangbrand; and he went on and told the story of the White Christ, and of his birth and death and rising again. And Hall and all his house believed the story, and were baptized by Thangbrand in Baptism River, which keeps that name unto this day. And so the boding of Thorhall was fulfilled; for a better race of gods had come to Iceland.

THE TALE OF HALLBJORN HALL

as told by Edward Ernest Kellett

THERE was, in Iceland, a *skald* or poet called Thorleif, skilled in all *drapa*s and *visa*s, and knowing all kennings and metres: he was renowned far and wide in that country. When he died, men laid him in a howe. And not far from that howe dwelt a bonder named Thorkell, gentle of disposition, and wealthy, but not of great rank or honour. His shepherd was a lad called Hallbjorn, whose eke-name was Hali. And Hali had keen desire to make a praise-song on the poet of the howe, and oft-times, when by the howe, tried to make that song. But forasmuch as he was no *skald*, and knew not the devices and ornaments of song, he got not the poem made; and could attain no further than these words, "Here lies the man".

Now it was that one night he was lying, as often, by the howe, and striving zealously to achieve that lay of praise to the howe-dweller, but as ever he succeeded not. Then at last he fell asleep; and in his sleep he seemed to see that the howe opened and a man came forth, great and tall, and well set up. He came up the hill to Hallbjorn, and said to him, "Here liest thou, Hallbjorn Hali, and eager art thou to do that which thou art not by fate gifted to do, namely, to make a song of praise to me. And the choice lieth thus: either thou wilt attain the gift, and that in higher measure than most other men and this is the more likely chance or else thou shalt fail, and then needest thou no more strive to attain the gift. I will speak in thy ears a *visa*; and, if so be thou rememberest that *visa* and hast it in mind when thou wakest, then wilt thou be a *skald*, widely renowned throughout the land, and sing the praises of many chiefs; and great shall be thy gain therefrom." Therewith he came yet nearer, and drew out the lad's tongue, and spake this *visa*:

"Here lies the man; since time began the best of poets he;

Whene'er he sang the rafters rang with merriment and glee."

"Now", said he, "must thou learn the art of poetry, to make a due praise-song on me when thou wakest, and it must be well wrought, with the right words and metre, and specially with kennings." Then he turned toward the howe, and entered therein, and closed it behind him; but Hallbjorn woke, and seemed to see his shoulders as he vanished.

But he remembered the *visa*; and after a while went home with his sheep, and told men what had happened to him. And afterwards he made the praise-song on the howe-dweller, and went far and wide through the land, singing songs about many chiefs, and gaining great glory and good gifts from the chiefs for his songs, so that he became a man of wealth. And of him many things are told, both in Iceland and abroad, though they be not here written.

BRAND THE GENEROUS

as told by Edward Ernest Kellett

 ONE summer there came out from Iceland to Norway a man named Brand, the son of Wermund. He was always called Brand the Open-handed, and well he deserved the name, for he was always giving. Now, at the time he came to Norway, King Harald Hardrada was in Drontheim, and staying with the king was a man named Thjodolf, a friend of Brand's; and Thjodolf spoke many things of the open-handedness of Brand, so much so that the king smiled and scarce believed the half of what he said.

At last the king said, "Well, Brand is now in Norway: we will test whether he is as generous as thou sayest. Go to him, and bid him give me the cloak he is wearing."

Thjodolf went straightway, and found Brand in a little house, measuring linen. He was in a scarlet kirtle, and over the kirtle was a scarlet cloak, which he had thrown loose over his shoulder while he measured the linen; and hanging to his wrist was a gold-handled axe.

"The king wishes to have thy scarlet cloak," said Thjodolf.

Brand answered him not a word, but let the cloak slip from his shoulders and went on with his work. Thjodolf took it up and went back to the king.

"How did it fare with thee?" said Harald.

"Brand spake no word," answered Thjodolf. Moreover, he told all about Brand's behaviour and about the axe with the gold handle.

Harald answered, "Truly is he an open-handed man; yet meseems he has no small pride about him, forasmuch as he spake no word. Go back to him, and tell him I would have his axe with the gold handle."

"I like not to go on such an errand. It may be he will deem I am jesting with him, to ask his weapon."

"Nevertheless", said Harald, "thou shalt go, or else what must I deem of all thy boasting of his open-handedness? I shall hold him no generous man if he withholds the axe."

So Thjodolf went and asked for the axe.

Again Brand spake no word, but in silence gave him what he asked.

Thjodolf departed, and told the king even as it had fared with him.

The king answered: "Now begin I indeed to fancy he is more generous than other men; yet will we test him yet again. Go and ask him for his scarlet kirtle."

"I like not to go on such an errand; he will surely, this time, take me for an ill-timed jester."

"Nevertheless thou shalt go," said Harald.

So Thjodolf went the third time.

"The king wishes yet another gift, thy scarlet kirtle," said he.

Again Brand spake no word; but he stepped out of the kirtle, cut one sleeve from it, and kept the same: the rest he gave to Thjodolf, who fared therewith to the king.

"Now", said Harald, when he saw the gift, "now see I indeed that Brand is not only generous but high-minded also. Well do I see his riddle; he meaneth that I am a man with but one hand, even the hand that takes ever and not the hand that gives. Go now yet again to him, and bid him follow thee to me."

And so was done. Brand followed Thjodolf to the king, who smiled at him and said, "Thou shalt see that I have the other hand also; I will give thee precious gifts and great honour."

And Brand abode in the king's court, and well did men see that the king held him in high esteem.

THE STORY OF VIGLUND

as told by Edward Ernest Kellett

IN the days of Harald Fairhair there was a great chief in Norway named Thorir: he was married to a noble woman, and had a daughter named Olof. Olof, even when very young, was a paragon among maidens, and skilled in all womanly arts; wherefore her name was lengthened, and she was called Olof the Star. Thorir loved her much, and would suffer no man to talk with her; and he built her a beautiful bower, roofed with lead and girded around with railings of iron. And when she grew in years, many men, rich and great, sought her hand; but Thorir would give her to none of them, nor did she desire to look on them. So went the days by.

Now the story takes in other names. There was a man named Ketill, who ruled in Raumarik: a great man, wise and with many friends; his wife Ingibjorg was of high descent, and their two sons, Gunnlaug and Sigurd, were nobly taught in all that should become men: they rode out often to shoot deer or birds, and excelled in all sports. Ketill was a great *holmgang*-man: he had been in twenty duels, and had had the victory in all; moreover, he was so persuasive of tongue that, when men heard him speak, they ever deemed that things were as he said. King Harald loved Ketill much.

Now it so happened that Harald made ready his ships to sail south, and took with him Ketill's sons; but Ketill himself abode at home, for he was now somewhat stricken in years. So the king sailed, and came to Rogaland, where was a jarl that ruled in the land, Eric by name, a mighty chief, and well-dealing with his friends. When Eric saw the king, he gave him good welcome, and brought him to his house with songs and much joy. And the king was pleased thereat, for the jarl spared naught to make him blithe: good drink was brought forth, and the men were soon drunken. And after fair harping, the jarl took the king to show him all his estate. In an orchard was there a grove, where sat three boys playing at tables; all three were handsome, but one passed the others. And afterwards they took to wrestling, and that one was a match for the other two. So the king asked their names, and Eric said, "Sigmund and Helgi, and Thorgrim is the third; he is not of the same mother as they." Then the king, seeing how strong and handsome Thorgrim was, took him to himself, and made him his henchman. And as time went by, the king laid great honour on Thorgrim, so much so that his name was lengthened, and he was called Thorgrim the Proud. And as the days went by, Jarl Thorir came to the king's court, and with him Olof Star; and Thorgrim cast eyes on her and loved her, nor did Olof disdain his love. But, even at that time died Ingibjorg, the wife of Ketill; and Ketill asked of Thorir his daughter Olof to wife. Now, as Ketill was a great chief, and King Harald urged the suit, Thorir agreed thereto; but men say that Olof would have chosen rather to take Thorgrim; but it was not so to be. So the bride-feast was fixed for the next Yule, at the house of Jarl Thorir.

Now Thorgrim was out harrying that summer; and when he returned, he heard that Olof was betrothed to Ketill; whereat enraged he went to King Harald, and asked that he would help him against Ketill. "Not so," said the king, "for Ketill is my friend." "But Olof and I have plighted troth; nor will I break my word with her; and if thou, O king, wilt not help me, then will I no longer be thy henchman." "Do as thou wilt," said the king; "but I deem thou wilt nowhere find greater honour than with me." So Thorgrim took leave of the king, and went alone till he came to the house of Jarl Thorir. And when he came there, he found the house all made ready for the marriage-feast: bright lights in the hall, and the finest entertainment, and Ketill the bridegroom there also. Thorgrim came forward, and said, "Hast thou, Ketill, chosen to wed Olof?" Ketill said that it was even so. "And did she give thee her consent?" said Thorgrim. "I deemed", said Ketill, "that Jarl Thorir could dispose of his own daughter, and that a bargain would hold that was made with him." "This say I," replied Thorgrim, "that Olof and I have plighted troth, and she hath promised to have no man but me; or is that so, Olof?" And Olof said it was even so. "Then must I have her," said Thorgrim. "Her shalt thou never have," cried Ketill; "and I have had dealings with greater men than thou art, and come not off worse than they." At that suddenly all the lights went out, and there was great confusion in the hall; and when the lights were brought in, then was Olof vanished, and Thorgrim likewise. Then men seemed to know that he had done this, and so it was, for he had bidden his men put out the lights, and he had carried Olof to

his ship. Men thought that Ketill had taken great shame from this, and the king made Thorgrim an outlaw for what he had done.

Now that was the "landnam-tide" in Iceland, when men were taking land there, and Thorgrim came to Iceland, to Snowfellsness. There dwelt a man named Holmkell, a kindly man, whose wife was Thorbjorg, a harsh woman. Their sons were Jokull and Einar. Now Thorgrim bought land close by Holmkell's stead, and great friendship grew up between them two. In Iceland Thorgrim made the wedding-feast for Olof; and there, a year later, was born their first-born son, whom they called Trausti. A year later was born their second, Viglund; and it happened that in the same year was born a maid-child to Holmkell and Thorbjorg, whom they named Ketilrid; and it was said there was no fairer pair in all these parts than Viglund and Ketilrid. Now Thorgrim spared no trouble to teach his sons manly deeds; but Thorbjorg loved not her daughter Ketilrid, and would teach her none of the arts of ladies. Wherefore it came about that Holmkell gave Ketilrid to Thorgrim to foster; and so she and Viglund grew up together. Olof had a third child, a daughter Helga; and so it was that, in all games they played, Viglund and Ketilrid were on one side, and Trausti and Helga on the other. And some men say that Viglund bound himself by oath to Ketilrid; but others say that she would none of that for fear of her mother, yet told him that she would choose him rather than any man.

Now is it to be told that Jokull and Einar took after their mother, and behaved themselves unwisely in that country: Holmkell liked their ways ill, but they heeded not his advice, and rather did worse the more he warned them. They had a fighting-horse, brown of colour, very wild and fierce, whose teeth were sharp and terrible, like the teeth of no other horse. Viglund had also a horse, tawny in colour, the best and fairest in that neighbourhood; and of these horses there will be a story later.

Now one day Einar came to his mother, and said, "Ill seems it to me that Thorgrim the Proud has such renown in these parts: methinks if I might deal an insult to Olof Star, that might minish his pride much; or, if he sought vengeance therefor, it is not certain that he would come out higher than I. She said that that was well said, and was even as she would have desired. So one day, when Thorgrim was not at home, Einar and his brother Jokull rode to Thorgrim's stead. But Olof's handmaid spied them coming, and deemed from their looks that they were after no good; so she told Olof. And Olof said, "Take my mantle, and wrap thyself therein, and sit at the high-seat, so that they may think that thou art I; and I will see that no harm befalls thee." So the handmaid did; and when the young men came to the door, another servant told them that Olof was at the high-seat. So they went thither, and thought it was really Olof, and talked with her. Suddenly in rushed a man with a drawn sword; he was not tall, but very furious. "Hence," said he, "and greet Thorgrim the Proud; for he is riding into the garth!" They sprang up and looked, and beheld Thorgrim with a throng of men; whereupon they leapt on horseback and rode for their lives. But soon it was spread abroad that the man with the sword was Olof herself; wherefore the young men got nothing but shame and laughter from that journey. Thorgrim said to Olof, "Forasmuch as they did not get their end, and for the love I bear to their father Holmkell, I will seek no vengeance as at this time."

Now another day also Jokull and Einar rode to Thorgrim's stead; and Jokull asked Viglund whether he would give him the tawny horse. "Not so," said Viglund. "Then will you match him against my brown?" said Jokull. "That may be," said Viglund.

"I deem the horse then better than given," said Jokull. "Things do not always go as one deems," answered Viglund; and then they appointed a time for the horse-fight. When the time came, the brown horse was brought out, and it took both brothers to hold him, so terribly did he behave. Next came out Viglund's horse; and scarce had he seen the brown when he rushed at him, and smote him so hard with his forefeet that he dashed out all his dreadful fighting-teeth; nor was it long before he dealt so rudely with him that the brown fell down dead. At this Jokull and Einar were so angry that they took their weapons and attacked Viglund; nor did they cease till Thorgrim and Holmkell came up and parted them; but even so one man had fallen of Viglund's company and two of Jokull's. Holmkell and Thorgrim still kept their friendship; and when Holmkell heard of the love between Viglund and Ketilrid he rejoiced thereat, but to his wife Thorbjorg and her sons it was a bitterness. Soon was it said abroad that no pair were the equals of Viglund and Ketilrid in all that might become man and maid.

It is told that one night Jokull and Einar stole out to Thorgrim's stead, and came to the pasture where was the tawny horse, and tried to drive him and the other horses home. But that could not be, for he resisted bravely; and at last they grew so angry that they sought at him with their weapons and tried to kill him. Even so it was long ere they attained their end, for he fought long with hoofs and teeth; yet at last they brought it to this, that they slew him with spear-thrusts. And then they feared to drive the other horses home, for they saw that men would know they had slain him; therefore they dragged him over a cliff, trusting that it would be thought he had fallen over and so killed himself. Then they went home. Their mother knew all they had done, and in truth urged them on to it.

Now when Viglund and Trausti came to the stables, they missed their horse, and found him under the cliff; but such were his wounds, they saw he had been slain, and they seemed to know who had done it. But when they told Thorgrim, he said, "Keep yet the peace; if it so goes as I expect, they will do some other thing that will entangle them." And so it was: for not long after, the oxen of Thorgrim were lost, and men said that Holmkell's sons had done that also. And when Holmkell heard that said, and further found out that it was even so, he took his horse and rode to Thorgrim's house, and told him that he deemed his sons had done Thorgrim that scathe. "Wherefore", said he, "I leave thee to put thy loss at what sum thou wilt, and I will pay it." So Thorgrim put it at the sum he thought just and fair; and he and Holmkell parted with great friendship.

There was a woman named Kjolvor, who dwelt at Hraunskarth; she was a great witch, in every way ill-thought-of and unholy in her dealings, a great friend of Thorbjorg. Now Thorbjorg and her sons offered her a hundred in silver to do some harm to Viglund and Trausti as she saw best chance so to do; for they had great envy of those brothers, and, moreover, they had heard of the love between Viglund and Ketilrid. And indeed Viglund and Ketilrid loved each other dearly; for it is the nature of love to burn more brightly the more men try to check it or wish it harm; and so they continued loving till death. Now Kjolvor knew that one day Viglund and Trausti were out fishing with a man named Bjorn: whereupon she went into her house and, by her enchantments, made bad weather come up over the sea. When Viglund saw it coming, he said, "It seems best to me that we fare home." But Bjorn was so great a seaman that he deemed no weather too bad to sail in; so he said, "We will not fare home till we have loaded the ship with fish." And Viglund said he should be the master. Then came the bad weather wind, frost, storm and hail; and Bjorn said, "Now will we turn home." "It had been better earlier," said Viglund, "yet will we say naught of that." Trausti and Bjorn rowed, but made no way, and the ship began to fill under them. Then Viglund took the oars and bade Bjorn bale and Trausti steer; and so mightily did he row that they made land at Dinner Ness. Next day they fared home, and Ketilrid rejoiced much to see them, for she had thought them dead.

Now the story returns to Ketill in Norway: he took ill the loss of Olof Star, and wished for vengeance; but he grew old and could not take it himself. His sons Sigurd and Gunnlaug grew into mighty men, and his daughter Ingibjorg was the fairest of women. Now a certain man of the Vik sought Ingibjorg to wife: his name was Hakon; he was rich in money and strong of his hands. Ketill said to him, "I give thee my daughter on this condition, that thou go first to Iceland and kill Thorgrim." So Hakon set sail; and when he reached Iceland, Jokull and Einar met him, and Hakon told them his errand. At that they rejoiced greatly, and promised him, if he killed Thorgrim, that he should have Ketilrid to wife. Then they took him to their home, where Thorbjorg gave him good welcome, but Holmkell liked things little.

Now after a time Hakon asked these brothers where the fair woman was that they had promised to give him to wife, "for I would fain see her". They said she was out fostering with Olof the Star. Then Hakon asked that she might be fetched home: "And with your help I doubt not then that she will take me to husband." A little later Thorbjorg said to Holmkell, "That will I, that Ketilrid should come home to us." "It seems to me", said he, "that she is better where she is." "Not so," said Thorbjorg; "I would rather seek her myself than that she should wed Viglund; it is my wish that she marry Hakon." Now Holmkell thought it better to seek her himself than that Thorbjorg should go: wherefore he set out. And when Viglund saw him coming, he said to Ketilrid, "Here is thy father; methinks I know that he desires to flit thee home; but I bid thee remember all our speech together, and what we have plighted." Ketilrid answered, and wept much: "Long have I thought that we should not be able to be together: almost I think it better we had said naught to each other; and it is not clear that thou lovest me more than I thee, though I say less thereof than thou. Now I see that all this is my mother's doing; I have had little love from her this long time, and likely it is that our days of joy are over if she has her way. Now either shall we see each other no more, or my father's wish will prevail; and that is not likely, for it is hard for him to strive against my mother and my brothers, and they are all set against my will." Then Viglund kissed Ketilrid, and it was easy to see that parting was a grief to them both.

Now when Holmkell came, Ketilrid told him that he should rule in this matter; and together they rode home; but all in Thorgrim's house were sad to lose her, for she was gracious to every man. And at home, despite her mother, she would have none of Hakon; and her father Holmkell aided her therein; and so many days passed in which she said no word to Hakon, Now about this time there were games at a place called Esjutarn; and Holmkell's sons came to the sport with Ketilrid; Thorgrim's sons also came. Ketilrid rejoiced to see them, and talked long with Viglund. Then she said, "I will lengthen thy name, and call thee Viglund the Fair; and I give thee this ring as a christening gift." And Viglund gave her a ring in return. Now this came to the ears of Jokull and Einar, and they liked it ill; so Thorbjorg saw to it that she went not out alone again.

In those games Viglund and Jokull came against each other in the ball-game, and Viglund threw the ball further than Jokull. At this Jokull was wroth, and hurled the ball in Viglund's face, so that the skin of his forehead was all torn. Trausti bound it up with a piece of his dress; and when that was done, Jokull and Einar had gone off home. So Trausti and Viglund went to their house, and when Thorgrim saw them, he said, "Welcome, son and daughter!" "I am no daughter," said Viglund, "though this bandage makes me look like one." And they told Thorgrim what had passed. "And didst thou not avenge thyself on Jokull?" said Thorgrim. "He was gone before I had finished bandaging the wound," said Trausti. But the two brothers waited not long for vengeance; for ere the games were over, Viglund met Jokull and smote him with the ball in the forehead, even as Jokull had smitten him before. Jokull tried to strike Viglund in return, but Viglund rushed in under his arms, and threw him mightily to earth, so that he lay stunned, and had to be carried home by four men holding a sheet at the corners, and it was some time ere he was whole.

And Viglund visited Ketilrid at her father's house, and talked with her, and played tables. Her brothers were then not at home, but when they heard of his doings they lay in wait with ten men to kill him and Trausti. Ketilrid saw their ambush, and bade Trausti and Viglund to go home some other way; but they answered, "We will alter our purposes for no man." So they came to a certain stackyard, and there Jokull and his men burst out upon them. And Jokull said, "'Tis well we have met; now will I take vengeance for the fall thou gavest me and for the blow." "Be it so," said Viglund; and fought so well and bravely that he was the bane of two men, while Trausti slew another. Then the other nine drew off, and went back home, and told Holmkell that Viglund and Trausti had without cause slain three of his men. At this, for the first time, Holmkell was wroth; and, when Hakon again asked for Ketilrid's hand, he refused no longer. Hakon gave up all thought of returning to Norway or of marrying Ingibjorg; and he deemed also that he would never attain to killing Thorgrim. But Ketilrid liked the marriage ill, and when Viglund heard the news he was sore pained at heart. And again he came to her house, and she told him that it was against her will that it had happened. "And now we must part; but go not home the way thou earnest, for Hakon and my brothers, and men beside, are waiting to kill thee." "Not so," said Viglund, "for it comes into my mind that now Hakon and I must settle things between us for ever." So he and Trausti went out, and he came to the stack-house as before. There were twelve men awaiting them, but the two brothers fought hard and well, until at last there were left but Jokull, Einar and Hakon on the one side, and the two sons of Thorgrim on the other. Then said Jokull, "Let Einar fight Trausti, and Hakon Viglund; and I will sit by." So Trausti fought Einar, until both fell. Then Viglund fought Hakon; this battle lasted long, for Viglund was exceeding weary, and Hakon strong and courageous; yet it ended so that Hakon fell dead, and Viglund was sore wounded. Then sprang up Jokull: he was fresh and without wound, and long did he fight with Viglund. Now Viglund felt himself growing weak with loss of blood, and thought he might fail to finish with Jokull for his weakness; therefore he suddenly changed his shield to his right arm and his sword to his left, for he could use either hand equally, and smote Jokull's arm off at the elbow. At that Jokull went backwards, nor could Viglund follow him for weakness; but he seized a spear lying close by, and hurled it at Jokull; and it came between his shoulders and out at the breast: then Jokull fell down dead. As for Viglund, he fainted from the blood-rush, and lay there as it were a corpse.

Then men rode to Holmkell's house and told him the news that both his sons were killed, and Hakon, and Thorgrim's sons also. And when Ketilrid heard it she fell down in a swoon. When she came to herself, her mother said, "Now is revealed all thy love for Viglund, for thou didst faint when thou heardest he was dead; well is it that ye are now parted for ever." Holmkell said she had paled as much for her brothers as for Viglund. "Be that so or not," said Thorbjorg, "now seems it to me that we should gather men and kill Thorgrim the Proud." "Not so," said Holmkell: "little is Thorgrim's blame for the death of our sons; and as for Viglund and Trausti, what more could they lose than their lives, which are lost already?"

Now Viglund and Trausti lay some while on the field; but at last Viglund came to himself and staggered to his brother, and saw that there was still life in him. As he was wondering what to do, for he was too weak to carry another, he heard a slight moving over the ground, and he looked and saw his father Thorgrim therein. Thorgrim took them with him to a certain underground dwelling, where their mother Olof was; she bound their wounds and tended them long in secret, until, after many months, their hurts were healed. Nearly all men fancied they were dead. Holmkell buried his sons in a howe called Kumli's Howe; he and Thorgrim divided not their friendship, but were agreed to bring the matter neither to law nor to private doom. And so things were for a time.

Now the story shifts again to Norway. Men came to Ketill and told him all that had happened: how that Hakon was dead and Thorgrim yet unpunished. And forasmuch as Ketill deemed it a shame to him that vengeance came slowly, he bade his two sons, Sigurd and Gunnlaug, take up the case and go to Iceland to kill Thorgrim. Now both of them had taken vows: Gunnlaug that he would refuse no man help if it were a case of life and death, and Sigurd to return no man evil for good. Little did they like their errand, yet for their father's sake they set sail. Now off the coast of Iceland there came a great storm, and their ship was broken near to Thorgrim's stead. Thorgrim heard of this, and took them into his house, and gave them all they needed. There Sigurd saw Helga, Thorgrim's daughter; and some men said that love passed between them, but that came not into wide knowledge. Viglund and Trausti still lay hidden, nor did Ketill's sons hear aught of them. One day Gunnlaug said to Sigurd, "Shall we not take vengeance on Thorgrim? Methinks it were now easy to do." "Speak never again thereof," said Sigurd. "That were to repay ill for good; for he hath taken us in after our shipwreck, and helped us in every way." And Gunnlaug never spoke thereof again.

Now when it had come about that Thorgrim's sons were healed of their wounds, they asked their father what it was best in his mind that they should do. He answered, "That seems to me good, that ye should embark on shipboard with the brothers Sigurd and Gunnlaug, and say, as is even true, that it is a matter of life and death, and ask them for a faring from Iceland; and, methinks, they will grant you this request, for they are good men both." And so it was done. Men say that Ketilrid was sore grieved that winter: she slept little and wearied much. But that same night, when Ketill's sons were due to set sail, went Viglund to her, and Trausti also; great was her joy to see them. "I deem myself free of all ill," said she, "now that ye are healed of your wounds." Then Viglund told her of his purpose abroad; and she was glad thereat. "I rejoice that ye are safe," said she, "howsoever it goes with me." "Wed no other man," said Viglund, "while

I am hence." "That will my father decide," said she. "I will never go against his will; yet it may well be that I shall find pleasure with no one as with thee." Then Viglund bade her trim his hair, and she did so; whereupon he said, "No other shall trim my hair than thou while thou art in life." Then they kissed and parted; and easy was it to see that it grieved them sore to sunder; yet so it had to be. A little later Holmkell found his daughter greeting much. He asked why it was so sad to her. "Dost thou wish me to avenge thy brothers?" said he. "Know of a truth that 'tis for thy sake I have spared these other brethren; but if it be thy will, I can easily have them slain." "So far is my thought from that", quoth she, "that I would neither have had them outlawed nor have chosen to send them penniless out of the country; nor would I, were it in my choice, take any other than Viglund to be my husband." When Holmkell heard that, he took his horse and rode after the brethren. When Trausti saw him, he said, "Here rides Holmkell all alone; it were an easy way, and not a noble way, to get Ketilrid, if thou wert to slay Holmkell." Viglund said, "If so were that I should never see Ketilrid again, yet would I never harm Holmkell: small gratitude were such a deed for all the good that he hath done me; and Ketilrid hath grief enough, though her father be not slain he who hath willed her naught but happiness." "Thou hast spoken well," said Trausti. Now Holmkell rode past them and then turned back; and when they came to where he turned, they saw there money and a gold ring and a rune-stick carved, whereon were cut all the sayings of Ketilrid and Holmkell, and this besides, that she gave that money to Viglund for his journey.

Afterwards they went to the ship, and there were Sigurd and Gunnlaug ready to sail, and a land-breeze blowing. Viglund called to the ship, and asked if Gunnlaug were on board, and whether he would give him passage to Norway. "Who are ye?" said Gunnlaug. "We are Vandred and Torred," said they. "What urges you to sail abroad?" said he. "Our life lies on it," answered they. "Come into the ship," said he; and so did they.

Now when they were some way out into the sea, Gunnlaug asked the strong man why he called himself Vandred. "I called myself so", said he, "because great dread is round about me; but my real name is Viglund and my brother's is Trausti: we are the sons of Thorgrim the Proud." At that Gunnlaug was silent a space, and then said,

"What is now to do, Sigurd? For well I know that Ketill our father will have them slain so soon as they come to Norway." "Surely", said Sigurd, "we must do to them even as their father Thorgrim did to us namely, that he saved our lives." "That is nobly spoken," said Gunnlaug, "and so let us do."

They had fair weather, and came easily to Norway; and when they came to Raumsdale Ketill was not at home. When he returned he sat in his high-seat with his men around him; then he greeted his sons: "But who are these unknown men?" Sigurd said, "They are Viglund and Trausti, the two sons of Thorgrim the Proud." "Up, men," cried Ketill, "and seize them! I would Thorgrim were with them, that I could deal so with him!" But Sigurd said, "Not so did Thorgrim deal with us, for he took us in after shipwreck, and did to us even better than the day before; and now wilt thou slay his sons, though guiltless? Nay, for we will be their comrades, and one fate shall happen to the four of us!" Then said Ketill, "I cannot fight with my own sons," and the wrath ran from him. Then said Gunnlaug, "This is my advice, that Thorgrim keep his wife Olof, and that she have her inheritance from her father Thorir; that Trausti marry our sister Ingibjorg, and that Sigurd marry Helga, Thorgrim's daughter." To all did that advice seem good; and according to that advice was it done. They stayed there that winter in great friendship; Trausti wedded Ingibjorg, and in the summer they all went a-harrying: all were men of renown, but Viglund gained more renown than any; yet had he little delight, for never was Ketilrid out of his thoughts. So went three years by.

Meanwhile strange things had happened in Iceland. A man named Thord came to Holmkell's stead, and asked the hand of Ketilrid; and because of the urgings of Thorbjorg, and also because Viglund delayed, at last Holmkell gave her to Thord; but she liked it ill. And that same summer came Viglund home from his harrying; and all the other men had their hair trimmed: but he said, "No other will I have to trim me, save Ketilrid; so did I promise her when we parted." Then next summer they all came out to Iceland, and told Thorgrim of the peace made with Ketill, whereat Thorgrim rejoiced greatly; but sad was Viglund when he heard that Ketilrid had been betrothed to another man. Still were his thoughts on her, so that when he made lays on her, her name came both at the beginning and at the end of his verses.

Now Viglund and Trausti set out to find the dwelling of Thord. So they called themselves by other names – Viglund called himself Orn, and Trausti was Hrafn – and set sail. Long were they on the voyage, for the wind was contrary. And when they came thither, Thord received them kindly, and bade Ketilrid do well by them. Now Ketilrid knew Viglund, but Viglund did not know that she knew him. Thord was stricken in years, and, as old men will, he slept in the afternoon; and Viglund came in with drawn sword, and said to himself, "How easily could I slay him!" But Trausti had followed him, and said, "Do not so ill as to kill a sleeping man, and him old; bear thy fate manfully." So Viglund put up his sword; and all that winter, though he saw Ketilrid many a time and oft, he said no word of love to her.

Now, as summer came on, old Thord set out from home, and came back with many men: Thorgrim the Proud, and Olof his wife, and Helga, and Holmkell, and others. Then Viglund and Trausti received them in Thord's house. And Thord stood up and spoke, "Well know I who ye are, Orn and Hrafn; ye are the sons of Thorgrim; and I know well what was between thee, Viglund, and Ketilrid. Now will I tell thee who I am: I am Helgi, thy father's brother, and I have taken Ketilrid only that she might be given to no other: I have kept her here with me, but married her not. Now, therefore, take her at my hand: right sure I am that Holmkell will refuse her not. For it is my advice that ye and Holmkell be reconciled, and that ye live in peace hereafter."

And so it was: Viglund went up to Holmkell, and a peace was made between them; and he and Ketilrid were wedded with great splendour. And here ceases this saga. To us who have copied it, there seems much pleasure therein.

KING HELGE AND ROLF KRAKI

as told by Eirikr Magnusson and William Morris

HELGE, king of Denmark, was a brave hero, and loved nothing better than daring expeditions.

He landed one day on a lonely island, at a time when hill and vale, meadow and cornfield, were clad in summer's richest garb. But he and his wild warriors were blind to nature's charms; their one aim was to secure as much plunder as they could. So they took the inhabitants prisoners, and then possessed themselves of their cattle and their goods.

Now amongst the prisoners there was a young maiden named Thora, who differed from her companions as much as the moon differs from the stars. The king was deeply moved at the sight of her wonderful beauty, and when he heard the sweet tones of her silvery voice, and learnt that she was of royal birth, he offered her his hand, his heart and his throne. She did not refuse him, and the wedding was celebrated amidst much rejoicing. The happy bridegroom remained a week on the island, spending the days in wandering through the shady groves with his lovely bride beside him. Then he took her back with him to his home at Hledra, where they lived contentedly till the following spring.

By that time Helge was beginning to tire of the monotony of his quiet life, and was filled with a great longing to resume his expeditions to foreign lands. His love for his wife had passed away; he looked on her only as a hindrance to his future plans. Therefore when he embarked in his vessel he forbade her to remain at the palace, and commanded certain of his courtiers to take her back to the lovely island where he had first found her.

After the lapse of many years, a sudden storm one day compelled Helge to take refuge in the nearest port. On landing, he soon recognized the picturesque shores and shady groves where he had once wandered so happily with his fair bride. He made inquiries for Thora, but she had disappeared; no one knew anything about her. Could she be dead? Or had she been carried away by pirates? Such were Helge's thoughts as he wandered through the woods and meadows which he knew so well. But suddenly he stopped short in his wanderings, for there before him, gazing into the clear waters of a murmuring brook, he saw her sitting, younger and more beautiful than ever.

He hastened towards her with outstretched arms, but just as he would have clasped her to his breast, he suddenly became aware that it was not his wife, but a stranger, who rose to greet him. Nevertheless, he was sure that he detected in her a strong resemblance to his dear Thora, not only in her outward appearance, but also in the silvery tones of her voice. Convinced that she had been sent by the gods to recompense him for the loss of his former queen, he addressed the maiden, who told him that her name was Yrsa, and that she came from a distant part of Saxony. Her beauty was such that Helge loved her at first sight, and as he believed that she had been sent him by the gods, he besought her to become his bride. Knowing him to be a brave and noble hero, the maiden gladly consented to his proposals, and then for the second time Helge brought a queen to Hledra.

With his advancing years, King Helge became more quiet and thoughtful than formerly, and loved to pass his leisure hours in the company of his fair young wife and Rolf, his little son. How he rejoiced when the child smiled up into his face, and tried, when only six years old, to draw his father's battle-sword from its sheath!

One day, the king and his beloved Yrsa were sitting on a mossy bank in a pine wood, watching with infinite pleasure, the innocent gambols of their child. Helge was telling his wife how much he loved her, and assuring her that no power on earth should ever part them, when suddenly the bushes near them rustled, the boughs were parted by a white hand, and out stepped a female figure, clad in black from head to foot, and thickly veiled. As she advanced towards them, she threw back her veil, and behold there stood Thora, aged and pale, and altered, but still Thora, Helge's rightful spouse. "Traitor!" she cried. "As easily as a lighted torch could destroy this mighty forest, so easily can one word from me set the death seal to thy happiness!" Then Yrsa knew that this was indeed Helge's first wife who stood before them, and that she had no longer any right to stay with her beloved lord.

With a piteous wail of despair, she fell fainting to the ground, while Helge, bending over her, vowed that nought but death should ever rob him of his fair wife. He would have clasped her in his arms, but Yrsa motioned him away, murmuring in broken accents, "Never more, Helge. We have loved each other truly, but now we must part for ever, for Thora is thy lawful spouse. May be the gods will take pity on us, and bring us together again in Valhalla, but on earth we may meet no more. Farewell!" With these words she vanished into the dark forest, and the king was left alone in his misery, for Thora, too, fearing her husband's wrath, fled from him into the wood.

Helge now determined to use all the means in his power to recover his lost Yrsa. First he sent messengers to her, but in vain, for she would not listen to their words. Then he started with warriors to find her himself, and force her to conae back with him, but when she heard that he was coming, she fled into the interior of Saxony, whither also he resolved to follow her.

In the meantime, Adils, king of Upsala, who was in want of a wife, heard of the great beauty of the Saxon princess, and knowing that she lived in daily terror of Helge's pursuit, he determined to offer her protection by making her his queen. So when the spring came, he sent his ambassadors to Saxony to plead his suit with Yrsa, who lent a favourable ear to his proposals, and returned with the messengers to Swithiod, for there she hoped to be safe from the persecutions of Helge. But though she was surrounded by every possible luxury at the court of Upsala, the young queen was far from happy, for her heart was still full of love for her lost husband.

When Helge heard of the union between King Adils and Yrsa, he too was filled with sorrow. Knowing, however, that his forces were not strong enough to invade Swithiod, he dismissed his army and tried to think of other means by which to regain Yrsa. Meanwhile he fell into a state of the deepest melancholy, from which nothing could rouse him except the sight of his son Rolf, who was rapidly growing from a child into a man, and was so tall and slim that he was surnamed Kraki, which means a pole.

But the excellence of his son could not console Helge for the loss of his wife, and as he knew Adils to be an avaricious man, he determined to offer him some of his richest treasures if he would consent to give him his beloved Yrsa once more. Accordingly he selected the most valuable jewels from his treasury, and with these and a few brave warriors he started for Upsala.

King Adils was filled with greed at the sight of the sparkling jewels, and readily consented to Helge's proposal. Thinking, however, that it would disgrace him were it known that he sold his wife for gold, he bade Helge either fly with her secretly or carry her away by force.

The two kings having come to this agreement, Helge was admitted into the presence of the queen. When his eyes fell upon her lovely form, he stood like one entranced, for though she looked older than in former days, yet she was to him what she had always been, the pearl of the north, the most beautiful and the most noble of women.

He spoke of the great love he bore her, told her of Adils's unworthiness, and implored her to come to him once more. But rising majestically from her seat, Yrsa thus addressed him: "I will not listen to thine entreaties, for even if I were to go with thee, we could never be happy together as long as Thora lives. Our union could only disgrace us in life, and condemn us in death." Helge, though deeply moved by these words, would not give up his purpose; he attempted to seize her, and carry her away by force, but rushing on to the balcony, she cried out that if he came one step nearer she would throw herself over. He dared not approach her, and at length yielded to her entreaties that he would leave her, and torment her no longer by his presence. So with aching heart he bade her farewell, and quitted the palace.

But King Adils, bitterly disappointed at having to give up the treasures, commanded his servants to lie in wait for his guest in a dark forest, and there to rob him of his jewels as he passed by. And so it happened that as Helge was returning home through the wood with heavy heart, he and his companions were suddenly attacked by a large band of ruffians. A desperate struggle ensued, in which Helge and his party were overpowered by numbers, and foully slain. The murderers then took possession of the treasures which they found on the dead bodies, and carried them to King Adils, as they had been commanded.

Rolf was only fifteen years old at the time of his father's death, but he was so much beloved by the Danish people that they unanimously chose him king in his father's stead. He was a brave and noble youth, and soon became renowned as a mighty hero.

All the neighbouring monarchs were subject to him, and his praise resounded through many distant lands.

After the lapse of several years, Rolf conceived a desire to visit the scene of his father's murder. He therefore started for Upsala, and on arriving at the palace was joyfully welcomed by his mother Yrsa; whilst Adils caused a great fire to be made at the entrance to the hall, as though in honour of his guests. But when Rolf and his comrades were all seated at the banquet, King Adils ordered his servants to make the fire larger and larger, until at length, when the heat was beginning to be intolerable, he and his followers quietly left the hall by a secret door. Not long had they done so when the clothes of the guests who were seated nearest the blazing mass caught fire. Then Rolf, in order to save himself and his companions from destruction, flung his shield on to the rising flames, and springing over it, called on the rest to follow his example.

In the courtyard they were met by Queen Yrsa, who told them of a place of shelter where they might conceal themselves for the time, but she advised them to depart early the next morning, since Adils was bent on their destruction. Before leaving them, she gave Rolf a silver goblet containing all the jewels which Adils had stolen from his father Helge.

Rolf and his companions straightway betook themselves to the place of safety which the queen had pointed out, and after refreshing themselves with meat and drink, lay down to rest. A few hours later Rolf awoke, and found that the roof which sheltered them was on fire, whilst the doors were blocked from the outside with huge stones and beams. He lost no time in arousing his comrades, and by their united strength they succeeded in throwing down one of the side walls, and so escaped from an untimely and horrible death. After routing and putting to flight the armed warriors whom Adils had set around the house. Rolf and his companions mounted their steeds and commenced their journey homewards. But they soon became aware that their enemies were in pursuit, for the distant sound of horses' hoofs became clearer and clearer every moment. "It is Adils and his followers!" cried Rolf. "Strew the golden treasures in the road that will arrest their progress." The men did as they were bidden, whilst Rolf himself emptied the contents of the silver goblet which his mother had given him.

His plan succeeded, for when the pursuers saw the treasures lying in the road, they gave up the chase, and eagerly dismounted to collect the booty. Adils, however, continued the pursuit, till just as he had almost reached the fugitives his eye fell on a costly ring lying at the side of the track. His avarice proved too strong for him to resist, and reining up his steed, he bent down to pick tip the bauble on the point of his sword. At the same moment Rolf, perceiving his advantage, turned upon his pursuer and stabbed him through the back, ere he had time to raise himself from his stooping posture.

"Live!" he cried, laughingly. "Live if thou canst with this remembrance of thy loving son!" With these words he picked up the jewel, and putting spurs to his horse, rode away with his followers, leaving the enemy far behind.

Rolf now returned to Hledra, where he was warmly welcomed by his faithful subjects. There he ruled with wisdom and gentleness. Unhappily his reign was destined to be a short one, for ere long he was slain in battle, while fighting in his country's cause. His soul was borne by the gods to the Halls of Valhalla, but the memory of the brave young hero lives still in the songs of countless minstrels, and in the hearts of a loving people.

Rolf and his men throw jewels and gold to distract their pursuers

HALFDAN THE BLACK

as translated by Samuel Laing

HALFDAN FIGHTS WITH GANDALF AND SIGTRYG

 HALFDAN was a year old when his father was killed, and his mother Asa set off immediately with him westwards to Agder, and set herself there in the kingdom which her father Harald had possessed. Halfdan grew up there, and soon became stout and strong; and, by reason of his black hair, was called Halfdan the Black. When he was eighteen years old he took his kingdom in Agder, and went immediately to Vestfold, where he divided that kingdom, as before related, with his brother Olaf. The same autumn he went with an army to Vingulmark against King Gandalf. They had many battles, and sometimes one, sometimes the other gained the victory; but at last they agreed that Halfdan should have half of Vingulmark, as his father Gudrod had had it before. Then King Halfdan proceeded to Raumarike, and subdued it. King Sigtryg, son of King Eystein, who then had his residence in Hedemark, and who had subdued Raumarike before, having heard of this, came out with his army against King Halfdan, and there was great battle, in which King Halfdan was victorious; and just as King Sigtryg and his troops were turning about to fly, an arrow struck him under the left arm, and he fell dead. Halfdan then laid the whole of Raumarike under his power. King Eystein's second son, King Sigtryg's brother, was also called Eystein, and was then king in Hedemark. As soon as Halfdan had returned to Vestfold, King Eystein went out with his army to Raumarike, and laid the whole country in subjection to him.

BATTLE BETWEEN HALFDAN AND EYSTEIN

WHEN King Halfdan heard of these disturbances in Raumarike, he again gathered his army together; and went out against King Eystein. A battle took place between them, and Halfdan gained the victory, and Eystein fled up to Hedemark, pursued by Halfdan. Another battle took place, in which Halfdan was again victorious; and Eystein fled northwards, up into the Dales to the herse Gudbrand. There he was strengthened with new people, and in winter he went towards Hedemark, and met Halfdan the Black upon a large island which lies in the Mjosen lake. There a great battle was fought, and many people on both sides were slain, but Halfdan won the victory. There fell Guthorm, the son of the herse Gudbrand, who was one of the finest men in the Uplands. Then Eystein fled north up the valley, and sent his relation Halvard Skalk to King Halfdan to beg for peace. On consideration of their relationship, King Halfdan gave King Eystein half of Hedemark, which he and his relations had held before; but kept to himself Thoten, and the district called Land. He likewise appropriated to himself Hadeland, and thus became a mighty king.

HALFDAN'S MARRIAGE

HALFDAN the Black got a wife called Ragnhild, a daughter of Harald Gulskeg (Goldbeard), who was a king in Sogn. They had a son, to whom Harald gave his own name; and the boy was brought up in Sogn, by his mother's father, King Harald. Now when this Harald had lived out his days nearly, and was become weak, having no son, he gave his dominions to his daughter's son Harald, and gave him his title of king; and he died soon after. The same winter his daughter Ragnhild died; and the following spring the young Harald fell sick and died at ten years of age. As soon as Halfdan the Black heard of his son's death, he took the road northwards to Sogn with a great force, and was well received. He claimed the heritage and dominion after his son; and no opposition being made, he took the whole kingdom. Earl Atle Mjove (the Slender), who was a friend of King Halfdan, came to him from Gaular; and the king set him over the Sogn district, to judge in the country according to the country's laws, and collect scat upon the king's account. Thereafter King Halfdan proceeded to his kingdom in the Uplands.

HAFLDAN'S STRIFE WITH GANDALF'S SONS

IN autumn, King Halfdan proceeded to Vingulmark. One night when he was there in guest quarters, it happened that about midnight a man came to him who had been on the watch on horseback, and told him a war force was come near to the house. The king instantly got up, ordered his men to arm themselves, and went out of the house and drew them up in battle order. At the same moment, Gandalf's sons, Hysing and Helsing, made their appearance with a large army. There was a great battle; but Halfdan being overpowered by the numbers of people fled to the forest, leaving many of his men on this spot. His foster-father, Olver Spake (the Wise), fell here. The people now came in swarms to King Halfdan, and he advanced to seek Gandalf's sons. They met at Eid, near Lake Oieren, and fought there. Hysing and Helsing fell, and their brother Hake saved himself by flight. King Halfdan then took possession of the whole of Vingulmark, and Hake fled to Alfheimar.

HALFDAN'S MARRIAGE WITH HJORT'S DAUGHTER

SIGURD Hjort was the name of a king in Ringerike, who was stouter and stronger than any other man, and his equal could not be seen for a handsome appearance. His father was Helge Hvasse (the Sharp); and his mother was Aslaug, a daughter of Sigurd the worm-eyed, who again was a son of Ragnar Lodbrok. It is told of Sigurd that when he was only twelve years old he killed in single combat the berserk Hildebrand, and eleven others of his comrades; and many are the deeds of manhood told of him in a long saga about his feats. Sigurd had two children, one of whom was a daughter, called Ragnhild, then twenty years of age, and an excellent brisk girl. Her brother Guthorm was a youth.

It is related in regard to Sigurd's death that he had a custom of riding out quite alone in the uninhabited forest to hunt the wild beasts that are hurtful to man, and he was always very eager at this sport. One day he rode out into the forest as usual, and when he had ridden a long way he came out at a piece of cleared land near to Hadeland. There the berserk Hake came against him with thirty men, and they fought. Sigurd Hjort fell there, after killing twelve of Hake's men; and Hake himself lost one hand, and had three other wounds. Then Hake and his men rode to Sigurd's house, where they took his daughter Ragnhild and her brother Guthorm, and carried them, with much property and valuable articles, home to Hadeland, where Hake had many great farms. He ordered a feast to be prepared, intending to hold his wedding with Ragnhild; but the time passed on account of his wounds, which healed slowly; and the berserk Hake of Hadeland had to keep his bed, on account of his wounds, all the autumn and beginning of winter.

Now King Halfdan was in Hedemark at the Yule entertainments when he heard this news; and one morning early, when the king was dressed, he called to him Harek Gand, and told him to go over to Hadeland, and bring him Ragnhild, Sigurd Hjort's daughter. Harek got ready with a hundred men, and made his journey so that they came over the lake to Hake's house in the grey of the morning, and beset all the doors and stairs of the places where the house-servants slept. Then they broke into the sleeping-room where Hake slept, took Ragnhild, with her brother Guthorm, and all the goods that were there, and set fire to the house-servants' place, and burnt all the people in it. Then they covered over a magnificent waggon, placed Ragnhild and Guthorm in it, and drove down upon the ice. Hake got up and went after them a while; but when he came to the ice on the lake, he turned his sword-hilt to the ground and let himself fall upon the point, so that the sword went through him. He was buried under a mound on the banks of the lake. When King Halfdan, who was very quick of sight, saw the party returning over the frozen lake, and with a covered waggon, he knew that their errand was accomplished according to his desire. Thereupon he ordered the tables to be set out, and sent people all round in the neighbourhood to invite plenty of guests; and the same day there was a good feast which was also Halfdan's marriage-feast with Ragnhild, who became a great queen. Ragnhild's mother was Thorny, a daughter of Klakharald king in Jutland, and a sister of Thrye Dannebod who was married to the Danish king, Gorm the Old, who then ruled over the Danish dominions.

OF RAGNHILD'S DREAM

RAGNHILD, who was wise and intelligent, dreamt great dreams. She dreamt, for one, that she was standing out in her herb-garden, and she took a thorn out of her shift; but

Viking warriors on the attack

while she was holding the thorn in her hand it grew so that it became a great tree, one end of which struck itself down into the earth, and it became firmly rooted; and the other end of the tree raised itself so high in the air that she could scarcely see over it, and it became also wonderfully thick. The under part of the tree was red with blood, but the stem upwards was beautifully green and the branches white as snow. There were many and great limbs to the tree, some high up, others low down; and so vast were the tree's branches that they seemed to her to cover all Norway, and even much more.

OF HALFDAN'S DREAM

KING Halfdan never had dreams, which appeared to him an extraordinary circumstance; and he told it to a man called Thorleif Spake (the Wise), and asked him what his advice was about it. Thorleif said that what he himself did, when he wanted to have any revelation by dream, was to take his sleep in a swine-sty, and then it never failed that he had dreams. The king did so, and the following dream was revealed to him. He thought he had the most beautiful hair, which was all in ringlets; some so long as to fall upon the ground, some reaching to the middle of his legs, some to his knees, some to his loins or the middle of his sides, some to his neck, and some were only as knots springing from his head. These ringlets were of various colours; but one ringlet surpassed all the others in beauty, lustre and size. This dream he told to Thorleif, who interpreted it thus: there should be a great posterity from him, and his descendants should rule over countries with great, but not all with equally great, honour; but one of his race should be more celebrated than all the others. It was the opinion of people that this ringlet betokened King Olaf the Saint.

King Halfdan was a wise man, a man of truth and uprightness – who made laws, observed them himself, and obliged others to observe them. And that violence should not come in place of the laws, he himself fixed the number of criminal acts in law, and the compensations, mulcts or penalties for each case, according to everyone's birth and dignity.[1]

Queen Ragnhild gave birth to a son, and water was poured over him, and the name of Harald given him, and he soon grew stout and remarkably handsome. As he grew up he became very expert at all feats, and showed also a good understanding. He was much beloved by his mother, but less so by his father.

HALFDAN'S MEAT VANISHES AT A FEAST

KING Halfdan was at a Yule-feast in Hadeland, where a wonderful thing happened one Yule evening. When the great number of guests assembled were going to sit down

---

1   The penalty, compensation or *manbod* for every injury, due the party injured, or to his family and next of kin if the injury was the death or premeditated murder of the party, appears to have been fixed for every rank and condition, from the murder of the king down to the maiming or beating a man's cattle or his slave. A man for whom no compensation was due was a dishonoured person, or an outlaw. It appears to have been optional with the injured party, or his kin if he had been killed, to take the mulct or compensation, or to refuse it, and wait for an opportunity of taking vengeance for the injury on the party who inflicted it, or on his kin. A part of each mulct or compensation was due to the king; and these fines or penalties appear to have constituted a great proportion of the king's revenues, and to have been settled in the Things held in every district for administering the law with the *lagman*.

to table, all the meat and all the ale disappeared from the table. The king sat alone very confused in mind; all the others set off, each to his home, in consternation. That the king might come to some certainty about what had occasioned this event, he ordered a Finn to be seized who was particularly knowing, and tried to force him to disclose the truth; but however much he tortured the man, he got nothing out of him. The Finn sought help particularly from Harald, the king's son, and Harald begged for mercy for him, but in vain. Then Harald let him escape against the king's will, and accompanied the man himself. On their journey they came to a place where the man's chief had a great feast, and it appears they were well received there. When they had been there until spring, the chief said, "Thy father took it much amiss that in winter I took some provisions from him – now I will repay it to thee by a joyful piece of news: thy father is dead; and now thou shalt return home, and take possession of the whole kingdom which he had, and with it thou shalt lay the whole kingdom of Norway under thee."

HALFDAN'S DEATH

HALFDAN the Black was driving from a feast in Hadeland, and it so happened that his road lay over the lake called Rand. It was in spring, and there was a great thaw. They drove across the bight called Rykinsvik, where in winter there had been a pond broken in the ice for cattle to drink at, and where the dung had fallen upon the ice the thaw had eaten it into holes. Now as the king drove over it the ice broke, and King Halfdan and many with him perished. He was then forty years old. He had been one of the most fortunate kings in respect of good seasons. The people thought so much of him, that when his death was known and his body was floated to Ringerike to bury it there, the people of most consequence from Raumarike, Vestfold and Hedemark came to meet it. All desired to take the body with them to bury it in their own district, and they thought that those who got it would have good crops to expect. At last it was agreed to divide the body into four parts. The head was laid in a mound at Stein in Ringerike, and each of the others took his part home and laid it in a mound; and these have since been called Halfdan's Mounds.

FRITHIOF THE BOLD AND FAIR INGEBORG

as told by Eirikr Magnusson and William Morris

 DURING King Bele's rule his land was one of the most prosperous and fertile of Norway. He was celebrated for his noble deeds, and for his many famous campaigns in distant lands. His faithful friend and companion in all his expeditions was Torsten Wikingson. Naturally the country flourished under the protection of two such noble men, and no enemy ever dared invade their territory. At the time that our story begins they were both old men, but whenever they sat in the Assembly of the Nobles they had always good advice to give, and when they told of the wonders of foreign lands, and of their adventures in former years, the guests listened in such breathless silence that they forgot to empty their goblets.

The palace of the king, in which was a hall spacious enough to entertain two thousand people, was situated on a hill. In the valley beneath flowed a brook, beside which the two friends would often take their walks, sometimes also ascending a little eminence, which projected into the sea, from which they had a lovely view of the surrounding country.

One day when they had mounted this little hill, they threw themselves down on the green turf to rest, and their conversation turned to bygone days, and to their approaching departure from this world. By-and-by they sent for their three sons, who presently joined them. First came Helge, Bele's eldest son, whose expression was dark and sinister, for he was in the habit of spending most of his time in the temple, where the priests initiated him in the mysteries of the oracle. Next came Halfdan, a laughing merry boy, and between these two, and a head taller than either of them, was Frithiof, Torsten's son, who had a manly countenance, and seemed to be conscious of his superior strength.

"My sons," said the king, as they approached, "you stand on holy ground, for your fathers, being old men, are weary of their long labours, and now intend quitting this world." He then proceeded to give them his parting advice, and to explain to them his last wishes, exhorting them to live together in love and unity, and to devote themselves to the good government of the country that he left to their charge. "To thee, Helge," he continued, turning towards his eldest son, "I leave the special care of thy sister Ingeborg. Be a father to her, but on no account force her to do anything against her will, and above all in her choice of a husband she is to be perfectly free."

After they had said all they wished, Bele and Torstei dismissed their sons with their blessings, directing them as a parting request to raise on the spot where they were then resting a monument, with an inscription which should make known to all who visited the place that they had been faithful to one another till death, and that they had ever protected the rights of their people.

As soon as the funeral was over, and the monument erected over the ashes of the departed heroes, Frithiof returned to Framnas, his father's estate. Here he found many costly heirlooms, amongst others, a magnificent bracelet, the clasp of which was formed of a sparkling ruby, and which was so wonderfully made that it would exactly fit any arm. Besides this he found a sword called Angurwadel, which had a golden hilt, and a blade with a peculiar sparkle, and also a beautiful ship, *Ellide*, which had been a present from the mighty sea-god Æsir, on the occasion of his being entertained by Wiking, an ancestor of Torsten's.

Twelve warriors were equipped, ready to fight for and to defend Frithiof in case of war, and indeed there was nothing wanting in the mansion which human heart could possibly desire. Nevertheless Frithiof felt lonely and unhappy, for he missed the one being who was dearer to him than all else in the world. But he knew where to find his beloved, for she was no other than fair Ingeborg, King Bele's daughter and Helge's sister. He had been brought up with her, and therefore knew well how to value her pure and loving heart, which he could not but know had, since childhood, belonged to him. He determined therefore to seek her, and ask her if she would share with him his life and his fortunes.

Early the next morning Frithiof set out for Helge's palace. On arriving he entered the great hall, the walls of which were adorned with tapestry and arms, and in the centre of which grew an oak tree so tall that the top had grown through an opening in the apartment, and its foliage spread over the glass roof. At first sight he thought the hall was empty, but presently he perceived fair Ingeborg, seated at the foot of the oak, engaged in embroidering a sky-blue mantle, with a gold border. She did not hear him as he softly approached and stood looking over her shoulder examining her work. He saw that she was embroidering on the mantle a figure of Baldr, but what was his delight when he recognized in the young and beautiful god a likeness of himself! A cry of joy escaped his lips; Ingeborg started, turned hastily round, and sank into her lover's arms. For a happy hour they sat together talking over the days of their childhood; until at length Frithiof spoke of the object of his visit to his beloved, and of his hopes for the future. "But", said she hesitating, as she sat with her trembling hand clasped in his, "thinkest thou that my brother Helge, who now stands in my father's place to me, will give his consent?" "Children," interrupted Hilding, the instructor of Torsten and Ingeborg in their childhood, who had entered the apartment unperceived, "build not your hopes on Helge. He is proud of being a descendant of Odin, and will not willingly give his sister in marriage to the son of a peasant." "Then will I demand her hand from the community," cried Frithiof, "which surely ranks above the son of Odin."

Accordingly the young hero hastened to Framnas, and embarking in his ship *Ellide*, made his way to the hill which contained the ashes of Torsten and Bele. Here he found the kings administering justice, and immediately laid his request before them, adding that Ingeborgf favoured his suit, and that King Bele would probably have sanctioned it, as he had allowed them to be brought up together. In ending his speech, he promised to be the faithful friend and protector of the land. "Thou holdest thy head high," replied Helge, "but the daughter of Odin is not for the son of a peasant. She is destined to marry none but an equal; and as for my country, I am able myself to protect it." "A peasant girl", said Halfdan, "is more fitted to sweep thy palace than the daughter of Odin." "Or, if thou art in want of employment," continued Helge, sarcastically, "become my servant. Thou canst have a place amongst my menials." "I am a free man," cried Frithiof proudly, "and from the community will I demand the hand of fair Ingeborg. But in the meantime, come not thou too near my sword." And with these words he drew Angurwadel from its sheath, and with a mighty stroke cleft the king's golden shield, which hung on a tree hard by.

KING SIGURD RING'S COURTSHIP

IN the royal palace at Upsala, enthroned beneath a canopy of gold and surrounded by five hundred warriors, sat the aged monarch, Sigurd Ring. Graceful maidens waited on the king and the courtiers, and filled their goblets with sparkling wine; but no sounds of merriment were to be heard in the palace; all was hushed and sad, and the king himself sat stern and silent on the throne. He was thinking of his departed queen, who had died many years before, leaving him and his orphaned children lonely and forsaken in the great palace, which looked deserted now it was no longer graced by her royal presence. As the king sat sadly thinking of the happy bygone days, one of the youthful courtiers, seizing a harp, sang, in clear and manly tones, a song to the memory of the departed queen, whom the angel of death had so soon called away from the side of her devoted spouse. From this song he drifted on into another, in which he sang the praises of a beautiful and pure maiden, who dwelt in Hilding's mansion, and who might be tempted to regard with favour the mighty monarch of the North, and to bring joy and contentment into his palace once more, by coming to grace it with her fair presence. As the song ended, it was loudly applauded on all sides, for many of the court- iers present had formerly been Hilding's companions-in-arms, and having seen fair Ingeborg in his house, had learnt to appreciate her noble character and high intellect, and deemed her worthy to share the throne of their beloved ruler, and to be a second mother to his orphan children. The king listened with favour to their advice, and thought it would be well to follow it. "For," said he, "though she be still young, if she should choose me of her own free will, and be a kind mother to my orphan children, I will vow to love and honour her as I did the departed queen."

Accordingly he despatched messengers, laden with costly gifts, to Helge's court, to persuade him to give him his sister Ingeborg in marriage. Helge, after having sump- tuously entertained the messengers, offered sacrifices in Baldr's temple, in order to ascertain whether or no the god favoured Sigurd Ring's proposal. He declared that the signs were unfavourable, and that, therefore, he could not give his sister in marriage to the king. Halfdan, sneering at Sigurd Ring's advanced age, declared that it was a pity he had not come to court his bride himself, for in that case he would with his own hands have helped him to mount his steed. The messengers, infuriated by Helge's refusal and Halfdan's ridicule, returned to their country, and told the king what had occurred, which so incensed the aged monarch that he immediately declared war against Helge, exclaiming that he would soon prove that he had strength enough left to chastize two impertinent boys.

Late at night fair Ingeborg sat in Baldr's temple, where she had been placed by her brother Helge, to protect her in case of danger during the ensuing war with Sigurd Ring. Frithiof had promised to visit her there, and though she anxiously awaited his arrival, she yet feared the anger of Baldr, whose temple, at that hour, it was sacrilege for any layman to enter. Weary of watching, she at length stepped out into the starlit night, and advanced as far as the golden chain which marked the boundary of the sacred grove. Presently she heard footsteps, and the next moment her lover had sprung lightly over the barrier which separated them, and stood beside her.

"Oh! Think of Baldr," exclaimed she in terrified accents, "the holy god, whose temple thou pollutest."

"Baldr is a gentle, loving god," replied Frithiof, "and will not chide us for our love. Tomorrow, dearest Ingeborg, I shall demand thy hand of the community, which assembles on Bele's Hill. In return, I will promise the services of my good sword in the war against Sigurd Ring; and I will fight for our cause, for our love is chaste and pure as the stars above us, and as the god of virtue and innocence on whose ground we stand."

The next day the assembly met together on Bele's Hill to make preparations for the approaching war. "Where is Frithiof?" was demanded on all sides. "If he fights for us, All-Father is sure to give us the victory." As they spoke, Frithiof, the picture of youth, beauty and strength, approached, and stepping into their midst, made known to them his request.

"The hero Frithiof, the protector and friend of our country, is worthy of the daughter of Odin," such was the unanimous decision of the assembly.

"I accept the verdict," said Helge, "but Ingeborg shall never be given to one who has broken through the holy boundary of Baldr's territory, to deceive a foolish maid with protestations of love. Frithiof, thou didst converse last night with Ingeborg in Baldr's grove – deny it if thou darest!"

"Deny it!" cried a thousand voices simultaneously. "Deny it, and Odin's daughter shall be thine!" But if his life had depended on his answer Frithiof could not have told a lie. He answered in a firm, clear voice: "I did hold converse with her in the grove of the Temple; surely that is no outrage on the god of Love?" He could say no more, his voice was drowned by the clashing of shields and swords.

"Woe, woe to the polluter of the holy Temple!" was the cry on all sides, and the warriors shrank from him as from a pestilence.

"Banishment or death to the desecrator of the Temple," said the king, "such is the law of our country. But nevertheless I will be merciful to the man who calls himself the protector of the land. Let him go to Angantyr, the king of the isles, and demand from him the tribute-money which has not been paid since my father's death. And if he should return unsuccessful, let him be deprived of honour and banished from the land. What say you, my friends, do you approve of my decision?" His words were instantly followed by a clash of arms, which signified the assent of the community, and Frithiof, on hearing it, strode haughtily from the assembly, his countenance darkened by the passion which glowed in his breast.

Once more fair Ingeborg sat in Baldr's temple at night, and awaited the coming of her lover. As soon as she heard the sound of his footsteps she went out into the grove to meet him, and he, springing over the golden chain as before, joined her where she stood. He then told her all that had occurred, and ended by assuring her that he would soon succeed in obtaining the tribute-money from Angantyr, either by persuasion or by his sword.

"When I have done so I will send the money, to Helge," said he, "for then will the people who disown me now acknowledge that I have redeemed my honour. But thou, dearest Ingeborg, must follow me to Angantyr's island.

"My ship *Ellide*, which lies ready on the shore close by, will take us first there, and then further towards the south, to a beautiful land where perpetual summer reigns, and where the trees bear golden fruit. In this country there lived formerly a free and noble people, but they have gradually sunk into bondage. It shall be our endeavour to win back for them their freedom, so that they shall flourish once more, and then will we live together peacefully in this happy land."

"Sweet hope indeed," replied Ingeborg, in tears, "but I cannot go with thee."

"Thou canst not! And who shall prevent thee?" cried Frithiof.

"It is my honour that prevents me," said Ingeborg, "thy honour and mine. Were I to accompany thee, the world would blame me, and look down upon me, and then wouldst thou too cease to love and honour me."

Long did Frithiof try to win her over, but in vain ; the virtuous maiden was not to be moved from her resolution.

At length Frithiof was overcome with grief and passion. "Persist in thy heartless resolve," cried he. "I leave thee to pursue my lonely wanderings, and soon I trust to find, in the grave, the peace I have in vain sought on earth." He turned to go without even bidding her adieu, but she laid her soft hand upon his arm, and held him back.

"Frithiof," said she, "wilt thou rob me of the knowledge of thy love, the only comfort that remains to me in my lonely hours? Sometimes, when for days I have wept and mourned thine absence, I look up at the sky at night, and in the stars I think I see thy beloved image, and hold thy hand in mine, and dream that I shall hold it so for ever."

"Ingeborg!" cried Frithiof. "Thou dost not dream! The gods have sent thee a vision of the future. Listen! I shall sail straightaway for Angantyr's isle, and return with the tribute-money, before Sigurd Ring has had time to invade the land. He will not be able to withstand my sword; I shall conquer him, and then will the people no longer refuse to give thee in marriage to the deliverer of their country." Saying this, Frithiof clasped round her arm, as a token of their plighted troth, the golden bracelet with the precious ruby, which had been left him as an heirloom by his father, and after holding her once more to his heart, he left her, and made his way to the shore, where lay *Ellide*, his ship, in the charge of his faithful friends, who were ready to accompany him to Angantyr's island.

VOYAGE

THE rising sun saw Frithiof's ship dancing merrily on the waves, and rapidly making her way towards Angantyr's isle. The voyage lasted several weeks, during which time they encountered more than one heavy storm; but thanks to Frithiof's courage and experience at sea, they at length arrived safely at their destination.

Angantyr made the strangers welcome, and entertained them at his court, with all possible hospitality; but when Frithiof informed him of the object of his visit, he replied: "I have never paid tribute to any land, nor will I do so now, and whoever demands it of me must obtain it by the sword. But out of gratitude for the help which Torsten and Bele rendered me when I needed it, it has been my wont to send them yearly a gift from my treasury. Thou, Frithiof, being their heir, art entitled to a like gift." With these words he handed to Frithiof a purse filled with gold.

Frithiof, satisfied with having accomplished the object of his visit to Angantyr, was now all impatience to set sail for his own country; but he was unwillingly compelled to delay his departure, as his vessel needed repairing after the heavy storms she had endured; and then the autumn winds setting in drove great icebergs from the North into the vicinity of the islands, and rendered their departure an impossibility. During the winter, therefore, they were forced to remain the guests of Angantyr. Frithiof alone was dissatisfied at this arrangement: his heart was ever in Baldr's grove, which contained all that was dear to him in the world, and he could not dispel the dark presentiments that clouded his soul when he thought of how long he had been parted from his beloved.

Spring returned at last, with its blue sky and its budding trees and flowers. There was no longer any obstacle to prevent the departure of Frithiof and his friends, and they accordingly set sail at once to return to their own country. After a prosperous voyage of some weeks, they at length came in sight of land, and by-and-by they could distinguish Baldr's temple as it rose against the sky.

Frithiof, who stood at the helm, strained his eyes to catch the first glimpse of his beloved home. As they approached still nearer to the land, he could see the hills and valleys, the woods, and even the silvery brooks of his native land. But suddenly he beheld a sight that filled him with dismay, for on the spot where formerly had stood the noble castle of his ancestors, nothing was now to be seen but a heap of black and smouldering ruins! The shore was quite deserted; none of his faithful subjects were there, as in former days, to welcome him home.

Presently the vessel reached the strand, and Frithiof disembarked. As he did so, a solitary bird came fluttering round him, which he instantly recognized as his favourite falcon. It flapped its wings impatiently, as if it would reveal some secret, but Frithiof could not understand its signs. As he stood awestruck and wondering with the bird on his hand, he saw old Hilding, the friend of his childhood, approaching. He hailed him with delight, and implored him to tell him at once all that had occurred during his absence.

"It is a sad tale to tell," said Hilding. "Soon after thy departure, King Sigurd Ring invaded the land; a bloody battle ensued, in which Helge was beaten. As soon as he saw that the battle was lost he took to flight, but in doing so he threw a burning torch into the hall of thy castle, cursing its owner, who was not there to protect it against the enemy. The conqueror then offered to make peace, on one condition, namely that fair Ingeborg should be given him in marriage. But she, true to her absent lover, refused to consent to this. Then the nobles of the land did their best to persuade her to accede to the King's demands, representing to her that on her depended the weal or woe of the land, until at last, after a fearful struggle with herself, she consented to become a martyr for her country's sake."

Frithiof, on hearing these fatal words, turned first deadly pale, and then crimson with anger.

"Woe, woe to the man", cried he bitterly, "who ever again believes in the promises of a woman!"

"Calm thyself, Frithiof," said Hilding; "endure that which the gods, and not man, have ordained."

"I cannot endure it calmly," cried he. "Come, today is Midsummer Day, and the priest will be offering sacrifices in Baldr's temple. Thither we will go, and I will show them how well I can aid them in their sacred duties!"

THE WOLF IN THE TEMPLE

IT was evening, and the priests were assembled in Baldr's temple to offer sacrifices to the god. In their midst, and assisting them in the slaughter of the victims, stood Helge. Suddenly a clash of arms was heard in. the outer court, succeeded by the sound of Frithiof's voice. The next minute Frithiof himself entered the temple, and striding up to where the king stood, he flung a purse full of gold into his face, crying: "Here is the ransom, by which I redeem my honour. But I have yet to avenge the destruction of Framnas, and above all to recover the bracelet, which thou hast stolen from fair Ingeborg to adorn the image of Baldr."

Hardly had the words escaped his lips when he caught sight of the bracelet on the arm of the god, and hastening to the spot, he tried in vain to loosen it from the arm, on which it seemed to have grown. At length, by using all his strength, he succeeded in wrenching it away, but in doing so the violence of the sudden shock loosened the image from its stand, and it fell with a crash on to the pile where the priests were offering the sacrifices. In an instant there was a tremendous blaze; the flames rose so high that they set fire to the rafters and to the tapestry on the walls, and before long the whole temple was on fire. A fearful tumult arose; the people rushed hither and thither, bringing water, and tearing down the burning tapestry and woodwork. But their efforts were all in vain; the flames spread every moment, making the sky blood-red for miles around. Frithiof, who had never in his life submitted to any man, found himself obliged to submit to the gods. In great distress of mind he wandered away from the sad scene, where human aid was no longer of any avail, and as he passed through the people they fled from him, crying out: "There goes the desecrator of the temple! The wolf in the Holy Place (*Warg i wewn*)!"

KING SIGURD RING'S COURT

FRITHIOF was now an exile, feared, hated and shunned by everybody, with nothing left to him but his ship *Ellide* and the faithful friends who had accompanied him on his voyage to Angantyr's Isle. In this ship he now traversed the seas far and wide, engaging in many battles, and gathering around him many brave warriors, who accompanied him in their own ships on his bold enterprises. Victory attended him everywhere, and kings and princes paid him tribute, for the terror of his name had spread far and wide.

Nevertheless he found neither rest nor peace for his soul, for the curse of the offended deity, whose temple he had destroyed, seemed ever to be upon him; neither could he tear from his heart the memory of her who had been so cruelly stolen from him, for in the clouds he seemed constantly to see her fair image, and in the rushing of the waters to hear her gentle voice. He believed that if he could but see her once again, and hold her hand in his, he should be at peace once more.

Impressed with this idea, he set out for King Sigurd Ring's Court, knowing that that was the only place where he had a chance of seeing her. Not wishing, however, to be recognized as Ingeborg's lover, he wrapped himself in a bearskin, and procured a staff to lean upon, that he might be taken for an old man, and in this disguise he entered the palace of the king. Here he found many guests assembled, who were drinking and making merry, so that at first his entrance remained unnoticed. But no sooner had the courtiers caught sight of the stranger who stood in the doorway than they began to ridicule him and point at him. One of them even ventured to pluck at his bearskin, upon which he seized the offender in his strong arms, and turning him upside down, stood him on his head. Having thus displayed his strength, no one dared again to molest him. The king, however, who had heard the disturbance, cried out to know what the noise was about, and on being informed, commanded the stranger to come forward, and state his business. Frithiof, stepping before the throne, forthwith told the king how, after weathering many storms, his ship had at last been wrecked on Sigurd Ring's coast, and that having heard that the king was celebrated for his hospitality to strangers, he had ventured to seek shelter at his court. "Instead of hospitality, however," he concluded, "I have received nothing at thy court but contempt and ridicule, for which I have not hesitated to chastise the principal offender."

"Well said," replied the king; "but now I pray thee drop thy disguise, for I know thee to be other than thou seemest."

At these words Frithiof let the bearskin fall from off his shoulders, and great was the astonishment of all present to behold, instead of an aged cripple, a tall and powerful man, in the prime of life, dressed in a costly suit of sky-blue and gold, with a silver girdle round his waist. The king begged him to be seated, and requested the queen to present him with a goblet of wine. Ingeborg, blushing, approached the guest, and as she handed him the goblet she trembled so that some of the wine was spilt on her fair hand.

"I drink to the queen," cried Frithiof joyfully, as he raised the goblet to his lips, for he knew now that Ingeborg not only recognized him, but that she loved him still.

During the whole of the ensuing winter, Frithiof remained the guest of King Sigurd Ring, who soon learnt to love the stranger, and to find in him a faithful friend and companion.

One day, as they were driving on the ice in a sledge, the ice suddenly gave way, and Frithiof, by dint of his great strength and presence of mind, succeeded in dragging the sledge out of the water, thereby saving the king's life, while the other courtiers had kept away as far as possible from the scene of danger. When spring came round again, he frequently accompanied the king when he went hunting, but the aged monarch sometimes felt fatigued before the end of the hunt, and would stop to rest. On one of these occasions, he wished to stay behind alone with Frithiof, who in vain represented to him the danger of remaining unattended in the wood. The king would not be convinced, and anon he fell asleep, with his head resting in Frithiof's lap. Presently two birds, one black and the other white, came flying down from the trees above. The black bird fluttered close to Frithiof, and whispered in his ear: "Now is thy time, if thou hopest ever to call the queen thine own. The king is in thy power, thou hast but to thrust thy sword into his heart, and in this lonely wood no one will be the wiser."

But the white bird's song was in a very different strain. "The eyes of the gods", it sang, "penetrate even into the darkest woods. They would know of the evil deed, and would find means of punishing the perpetrator." "But think," continued the black bird, "think of the beauty of the queen. Courage, be not a coward; one stroke of thy sword, and she is thine for ever." And Frithiof did draw his sword; for one instant he held it aloft, then with all his strength he flung it from him, so that it fell down a precipice close by. No sooner had he done so than the black bird screamed and disappeared, but the white one spread its wings and flew straight up to Heaven.

The king, awakened by the clatter of the sword as it fell, raised his head, and turning to Frithiof, exclaimed:

"This sleep has indeed been blessed to me, for it has taught me to appreciate the true worth of the man whom I received in my palace as a stranger, and have since entertained as my guest. I confess now that I recognized thee, Frithiof, from the first, for I had heard so much of the hero who, exiled from his native land for setting fire to Baldr's temple, was feared by everyone on land and sea. I expected thee to come with an army to rob me of my kingdom and my wife; instead of which thou camest in a beggar's garb, perhaps, thought I, intent on a foul murder. I wished to prove thee, Frithiof, therefore I rested just now on thy knee. Thou hast nobly stood the test, and art indeed a hero, for not only hast thou conquered brave warriors on the field of battle, but above all thou hast conquered that subtle enemy who whispers his poisoned words into the ears of men, and tempts them to evil deeds. Therefore I am now prepared to bequeath to thee my kingdom and my wife, for thou art worthy of them! Befriend my young son, and make of him a hero such as thou art. As for me, it is time I quitted the world, but I will die a death worthy of a warrior I will betake myself to my vessel, and there await my fate."

"I thank thee, my king," replied Frithiof; "but it is thy son, and not I, who shall succeed to thy throne. I am an unhappy exile, pursued by the vengeance of the gods, and a peaceful life is denied me. A warlike life must be mine; I am destined to battle against wind and wave, and to fight against the anger of the god whom I have offended. Adieu, my king! Greet fair Ingeborg from me, and bid her walk no more upon the shore, for fear the waves should wash my corpse to her feet." So speaking, the unhappy man strode away into the wood, no one knew whither.

Shortly after this, the king Sigurd Ring called together the free nobles of his land, and, telling them that he felt it was time for him to depart from this world, bade them choose for themselves a new king. Beside him stood his young son, Ragnar Lodbrok, the child of his first wife, who, though only fifteen years of age, was a strong brave youth, bearing a marked resemblance to his father. The nobles were unanimous in choosing him for their king, and lifting him upon the royal shield they carried him about in triumph.

The aged monarch now took a tender farewell of his people and of his young son, exhorting them to maintain peace, and to devote their lives to the good of their native land. He then embarked in his vessel, which had previously been filled with tow steeped in oil, and as the fresh breeze which sprang up drove it out into the open sea, he took a burning torch and flung it into the hold of the vessel. In a few minutes the whole ship was on fire, and those on shore could see the mighty flames rise higher and higher, and reflect themselves against the sky; till, as the burning vessel drifted away, the red light of the flames grew fainter, and at last disappeared below the horizon.

It was evening, and Frithiof stood alone on Torsten's Hill watching the sun, as it sank to rest in the western sky. As he stood thus the happy days of his childhood rose upon his memory, the days which he had spent in fair Ingeborg's company, when they had wandered together in the fields and valleys, plucking the wild flowers, and carving their names on the bark of the trees. But suddenly this fair picture was darkened by the memory of the two brothers who had been the destroyers of his peace and happiness, and the authors of the crimes he had committed.

"Vengeance!' whispered a small voice within him.

"Yes, vengeance!" cried he aloud. "Vengeance on those who have blighted the fair prospect of my life! When that is accomplished then I too will die, and my blood shall atone to the gods for my crimes. Oh, hear me, father Torsten," cried he, "give thy son some sign by which he may know that he is heard."

The waves continued to break upon the shore, and the gentle wind to sigh in the valley; and the stars came out one by one; but no sound or sign was sent to comfort him. Presently he turned his eyes upon the hill where Baldr's temple had formerly stood, and looking up towards heaven, he perceived a faint light in the sky, which, as he gazed, grew stronger and brighter, and in the midst of it appeared a vision, which he instantly recognized as the image of Baldr's temple.

Overcome with wonder and joy, he sank upon his knees, and covered his face with his hands. He understood the vision which his father had sent him; neither death nor blood was demanded of him as the expiation of his crime; but a new temple in place of the old one was the atonement which the god required.

Frithiof therefore lost no time in seeing the great work commenced. A thousand hands were employed in the construction of the building, celebrated architects were sent for from the south, and in a wonderfully short space of time a new and beautiful temple stood upon the site of the old one, overlooking the green valley and the mighty ocean.

The day of consecration arrived. Within the temple stood Frithiof, gazing up in contentment at the image of Baldr, who was seated on a throne, in a recess of sky-blue and gold.

Presently the priests entered, burning incense, and they were followed by twelve men, bearing harps, who walked round and round the altar, singing praises to the god. These again were followed by twelve virgins, who took up the song of praise, filling the temple with their melodious voices. A holy calm stole over Frithiof's soul, for he knew now that he was at last reconciled to the god. But suddenly a shadow came between him and the light; he looked up, and beheld the king, clothed in the royal robe of purple.

In an instant all his peace of mind had vanished; bitter hatred filled his heart, and his hand involuntarily sought the hilt of his sword. But he thrust the blade back into its sheath, murmuring: "Not here in the holy temple; in a more suitable spot will I revenge myself."

"Not here," repeated a voice in his ear. He turned, and saw the high priest standing beside him, who continued: "Dost thou suppose that the god will remain ignorant of thy deed of vengeance, though it be not wreaked within the walls of his temple? Dost thou think to reconcile thyself to Baldr by this building of stone? He demands a far different temple of thee, a temple of peace and goodwill in thine heart, and if thou hast it not, thou art still far from being reconciled to him. Know that Helge is no more; he fell in battle against the Finns; but Halfdan approaches, tendering thee his hand in friendship."

"Alas! It is too late," replied Frithiof. "The curse of the god is still upon me. I know it by the wild hatred which fills my heart whenever my enemy is near me."

"Say not so, my son," answered the priest; "knowest thou not that Baldr, the god of peace and love, will gladly give thee the strength to forgive thine enemy, if thou

Frithiof in battle in France

dost but ask him for it? See," he continued, pointing to Haider's throne, "he beckons thee to him, he would be reconciled to thee."

As the old man spoke, Frithiof lifted his eyes toward the throne, and as he gazed on the image of the god, the spirit of love and peace seemed to enter into his heart. At this moment he saw Halfdan, who had noiselessly approached, standing beside him, anxiously waiting to know whether he would consent to be reconciled. Frithiof hesitated no longer, but flinging away his sword, frankly tendered his hand to his enemy.

No sooner had he done so than sounds of melodious music were heard; the door at the end of the aisle opened, and Ingeborg, radiant and lovely as ever, robed in a wedding garment, entered the temple, and advanced to her brother's side. In her hand she held a wreath of roses, which, still wet with the pearly drops of the morning dew, looked as if they had been watered by tears of joy.

Frithiof was overcome with happiness at the sight of his beloved Ingeborg, and as he approached her, she stepped forward to meet him, and wrapping her soft arms about him, leant her head upon his breast.

So the days of sorrow and battle were over at last for Frithiof, and now he might look forward to peace and contentment in the future, for fair Ingeborg and he were at length one, never more to be parted.

THE BATTLE OF BRAVALLA

told by Eirikr Magnusson and William Morris

IN the land of Swithiod (Sweden) there ruled a king named Ingiald. He was not a good king, for he was by nature cruel and cunning. This was chiefly the fault of King Swipdager, in whose charge Ingiald had been placed when a child. Swipdager, in order to engender courage in him, had given him a wolf's heart to eat, in consequence of which his nature had become like that of a brute beast.

On the day of his father's funeral, when many of the neighbouring princes and rulers had assembled together at a grand banquet, given in memory of the late king, Ingiald swore a great oath that he would soon conquer all the surrounding provinces.

The goblet was freely circulated among the assembled guests, who presently succumbed to the potent influence of the wine, and fell asleep upon the couches. Ingiald then gave orders that the palace should be surrounded by armed men, while he himself set fire to the hall where his guests lay sleeping. The soldiers stationed without made it impossible for them to escape, so that they all perished miserably in the flames. The treacherous king then took possession of their provinces.

Ingiald had two children, a son named Olaf and a daughter named Asa. His daughter was very beautiful, but she, unfortunately, inherited her father's cruel, cunning nature. She wedded Gudrod, king of Skaney, who loved her so dearly that he could refuse her nothing; in consequence of which he allowed himself to be persuaded by her to go to war with his brother Halfdan.

Halfdan, thus suddenly attacked, was defeated, he himself falling on the battle-field; but Gudrod did not live long to enjoy his conquest, for he was soon after secretly murdered by a friend of Halfdan's.

Halfdan's son Iwar now arose, determined to avenge his father's death. Collecting the scattered remnants of his army, he marched against Asa's forces. As the hostile factions approached each other, Asa rode through the ranks of her soldiers, encouraging and exhorting them to fight bravely against the enemy. But her enthusiasm awakened no response; the men stood silent with bowed heads.

Presently the horns sounded for the attack; the enemy advanced; then with one accord Asa's soldiers lowered their arms, and greeted Iwar, Halfdan's son, as their king. Asa, seeing that she was deserted, fled from the field, and sought an asylum at her father's court. He too, however, was threatened with desertion, but he hoped during the winter to be able to collect a formidable army.

On one of the islands belonging to King Ingiald, he and his courtiers held a carouse, while the beautiful Asa filled the goblets with rich and sparkling wine. But on the third day of the feasting there came messengers to the island, who spread terror among the revellers, for they reported that Iwar had made a passage through the snow and ice to Swithiod; that peasants and soldiers alike had gone over to his side, and made common cause with him against the tyrant. The island was already surrounded; no ship was left by which Ingiald could make his escape. Death or captivity stared him in the face, but he chose rather to die by his own hand than fall a victim to his bitter foe. He therefore watched his opportunity; when his courtiers were all asleep in the banqueting hall, he and his daughter Asa, after having made fast all the doors to prevent their escape, set fire to the palace. They then ascended the battlements, where they stood surrounded by flames, as Iwar's army approached, until the whole palace was consumed by the fire, and they and all the courtiers perished in the burning ruins.

The victorious Iwar now marched to Upsala, where he offered thank-offerings, and received the homage of the people of Swithiod, His conquests extended far and wide, for he soon succeeded in subjecting all the surrounding provinces. Denmark alone was too powerful for him, for its kings, Hrodrik and Helge, were famous for their noble deeds of prowess.

Iwar therefore, seeing that he could not overcome them in battle, determined to conquer them by cunning.

It chanced that Hrodrik loved Iwar's fair daughter Auda, and sued for her hand. Her father gladly gave his consent to the marriage, which was duly solemnized. Not long after, Iwar, whilst cruising about in his vessel, landed on the coast of Denmark. Now was his time to carry out his base plot: he persuaded Hrodrik that his brother Helge was in love with Auda, and urged him to lose no time avenging his tarnished honour. In vain did the virtuous Auda strive to persuade her husband of her father's treachery, Hrodrik was deaf to her entreaties and, fully persuaded of his brother's guilt, he stabbed him with his sword during a tournament.

Auda, in terror, fled from her husband's court, and taking with her her little son Harald, sought refuge in a garrisoned castle.

In the meantime Iwar, once more landing on the Danish coast, accused Hrodrik of the murder of his brother. Attacking him with his powerful army, he easily conquered the Danish forces, Hrodrik himself falling by his sword.

Iwar now called together the men of Denmark, bidding them choose a new king. To his surprise, however, his own daughter Auda advanced into their midst; at sight of her, the Danes instantly rallied round their beloved queen, declaring themselves ready to protect their country from the invasion of the stranger. Iwar, unprepared for such a determined resistance, had no choice but to embark in his vessel, and return to his own country.

During the winter, however, he made extensive preparations for a new invasion of Denmark. Auda, hearing of this, felt that without help she would not be able to resist her father's attack; she therefore embarked with her little son and the royal treasure, and accompanied by a numerous retinue sailed for Russia; for here she hoped to find an asylum at the court of King Radbard.

The king made her welcome, surrounding her with every luxury his court could supply; but it was out of his power to give her any aid in winning back her kingdom, of which her father Iwar had already taken possession; for though he had a large army of brave soldiers, he did not dare to send his puny fleet against the seafaring Northmen.

But ere long he learnt to love the beautiful and virtuous queen, and besought her to become his wife, to which she, after some hesitation, consented.

Iwar was much afraid when the news of this marriage reached him, for he knew his daughter's determined spirit. Resolved therefore to anticipate King Radbard, he sailed for Russia with a large army and a numerous fleet. One night during the voyage he had a strange dream, in which he saw a vision of a frightful dragon coming over the sea, whose huge wings disturbed the waters, raising great waves as he swam along. Then in the north rose a dark thundercloud, which advanced towards the dragon. No sooner had the monster come in contact with it, than a fearful clap of thunder broke over the land, the lightning flashed, the storm-wind howled, and the earth trembled and shook. Nothing more could be seen, only the crashes and peals of thunder could be heard as they rolled over the northern countries, echoing and re-echoing in the distance.

Iwar awoke. He lay beneath a purple tent, which had been placed for him on the deck of his beautiful vessel. The sun rose, sending his golden rays over land and sea; but the beauty of nature had no power to send peace into the troubled heart of the king. He commanded that Hord, his foster-father, should be brought to him to interpret his dream. Hord obeyed the summons, but stood on a projecting rock on the shore, refusing to come on board the king's vessel. He was a tall, imposing man, but his face was scarcely visible, for he wore a large hat, which was pulled down low over his forehead, while his shoulders were enveloped in a flowing mantle.

Iwar, after relating to him his dream, demanded an interpretation of the same. The old man replied that he thought the dream signified that King Iwar would soon wander in the pale halls of Hel. "Tell me," cried Iwar, "how am I esteemed by the gods?" "They regard thee as their bitter foe," replied Hord; "thou art to them the dragon of the South." When the king heard these words, he was beside himself with rage. "Thou prophesiest death to me," cried he; "but thou shalt precede me to Hel!" So saying, he rushed with drawn sword towards the old man, but in doing so he fell headlong over the side of the vessel into the sea. Hord springing after him, likewise disappeared beneath the waves, and neither was destined ever again to behold the light of day.

As soon as the news of the king's death became known to his warriors, they determined to abandon the war against King Radbard, and returned peaceably to their own country.

HARALD AND SIGURD RING

ONE of King Iwar's vessels, with the flag of truce hoisted at her mast-head, was now sent to the shore, to land the chief of the army, formerly a guest of King Radbard, who was to acquaint him with what had happened. The king received the messenger and his retinue at the court with much hospitality. Auda herself filled their goblets at the banquet given in their honour, at which her son Harald was also present. When the warriors saw the young prince they were much pleased with his noble bearing, and when he requested to be allowed to accompany them to the land of his fathers, they one and all arose and greeted him as their king.

Harald took a tender farewell of his beloved mother, who blessed her son, praying that Odin might soon place him upon the throne of his forefathers. She then took from a chest two swords with golden hilts; these she gave to Harald, bidding him use them only in honourable warfare, for then they would not fail to ensure him the victory.

Soon after Harald stood upon the deck of his vessel, which, with the little fleet which accompanied him, bounded lightly over the crested waves towards Hledra, the palace of the Danish kings. But by-and-by they were overtaken by a terrible storm; the waves rose mountain-high; the masts split; courage and hope alike forsook the hearts of the sailors, while the fear of death was depicted on every face. Harald alone was undaunted; he seized the rudder, crying, "Courage, friends! Odin is ever a protector of the brave!" Hardly had he spoken when he perceived, standing beside him, an old warrior of tall stature, with a large hat drawn low over his forehead. The stranger, in loud clear tones, rebuked the storm: in an instant the waves subsided, the wind was hushed, and all was calm and peaceful. He then took the rudder, and under his guidance the vessel cut through the water with wonderful swiftness, while the rest of the fleet, collecting together, followed its lead.

The sailors knew well who it was that had come amongst them to save them from destruction, but they dared not so much as breathe his name. Moreover, as soon as the vessels had touched the strand, the stranger suddenly disappeared, though no one knew whither he had gone.

Harald found his country in a troubled state, for while some of his subjects were loyal to him, many were still adherents of Iwar. He therefore called the people together, and in a noble speech reminded them how long the country had flourished under the rule of his forefathers, telling them, too, how Odin had protected him and his fleet during the voyage. While he was yet speaking, a pair of eagles came flying down from the clouds, and fluttered round the head of the noble youth, who looked so bright and beautiful as he stood proudly urging his claim upon the assembled multitude that they arose, crying to a man: "Harald shall be our king! Hail to our king!" Then, lifting him upon the royal shield, they bore him in triumph to the palace, and placed him. upon the throne of his forefathers.

Ere long great numbers of brave warriors gathered round the banner of the young king, with whose help he soon succeeded in conquering the whole of Gothland, which still adhered to Iwar.

On one occasion, when he was about to do battle with the Goths, he offered up sacrifices to Odin, beseeching the god to grant him the victory. As he did so he saw approaching him the same old man with the big hat drawn over his forehead and the flowing mantle, who had befriended him on his voyage to Denmark, by saving his fleet from destruction during the storm. The stranger carried a blood-red cloak, which he threw around King Harald's shoulders, while on his head he placed a new helmet bidding him carry no shield in battle, for the cloak and the helmet would protect him from injury. Having thus spoken, he disappeared from view.

When the horns sounded for the attack, Harald rushed at his adversaries, scattering them like chaff, while he himself was safe from hurt, for neither sword nor spear could penetrate his wonderful mantle.

Thus the victory was easily gained, and from that time forth the blood-red cloak protected him in all his campaigns.

Harald's court at Hledra was the most magnificent of any king of his time; it was famous also as being the home of many great and noble men.

One day a stranger, who was no other than the king's half-brother, Randwer, the son of Radbard and Auda, arrived at the palace. Harald received his brother with open arms, but Randwer had sad news to tell, for both his father and mother were dead, and his elder brother, now the king, had banished him from the country out of jealousy.

So Randwer remained at Harald's court, fighting his battles with him, and showing himself to be a good and brave man. Harald therefore made him king of Upsala and West Gothland, which countries he was to hold as his vassal.

Randwer, however, did not live long to enjoy his good fortune; he died in the arms of his brave young son, Sigurd Ring, who had accompanied him on an expedition against Britain.

Sigurd Ring was now with one accord chosen king in his father's stead. For full fifty years the peace of the country was unbroken, until at length the coast of Harald's domains was invaded and overrun by a swarm of pirates. Harald, in spite of age and infirmity, marched against them, riding at the head of his soldiers, wrapped in Odin's blood-red mantle, and holding in either hand a golden-hilted sword, the parting gift, of his mother, the fair Auda.

The battle raged long and fiercely, but at length the pirates were forced to fly over the border into King Sigurd Ring's domain.

As Harald stood in his chariot, watching their flight, a suspicion suddenly flashed upon him- that these pirates had invaded his territory with the consent of his brother-king. As he thus pondered, Bruni, one of the bravest of his warriors, approached him, having just returned from the pursuit of the enemy. He told the king that he had been stopped on the way by a detachment of soldiers under the banner of Upsala, and that there was therefore no doubt but that the pirates had invaded the country under the protection, or perhaps at the instigation, of King Sigurd Ring. These words aroused the just wrath of the aged monarch.

"Tell my treacherous kinsman", he cried, "that I command him, as my vassal, instantly to appear before the tribunal of this country, to answer for his base conduct."

"Thy commands shall be obeyed," replied Bruni, who at once departed to fulfil the behest of his sovereign.

He set out for Upsala, accompanied by a brilliant retinue. When he arrived at the palace he found much feasting and revelry going on, while in the midst of the courtiers sat King Sigurd Ring himself. To him Bruni delivered his message, whereupon the king replied in astonishment.

"I deny the right of King Harald to call me his vassal; it is true that it has been my wont to send yearly gifts to Hledra, but never either taxes or tribute-money. Go, tell thy master that the sword alone shall be judge between him and me in this matter."

"Well spoken, O king!" cried Bruni. "Odin will rejoice to hear thy noble answer!" Sigurd Ring looked at the messenger in unfeigned astonishment, but as he did so he recognized in the stranger one of the brave warriors who had often fought in battle at his father's side. He therefore bade him be seated beside him, feasted him at his board, and loaded him with rich gifts at his departure.

Bruni delivered Sigurd Ring's message to Harald, who vowed that he would soon find means to punish the presumption of the Swedish king.

After much communication it was at length arranged that in seven years' time the two sovereigns should join in battle, thus to decide to which of them belonged the supremacy.

THE BATTLE OF BRAVALLA

SEVEN years soon elapsed, during which time both Harald and Sigurd Ring, collecting their forces, made preparations for the great battle which was finally to decide the sovereignty of one country over the other.

At the appointed time the two mighty fleets sailed for the Bay of Brawik, for the battle was to be fought close by, on the Common of Bravalla, which separated Harald's kingdom of Denmark from Sweden, the territory of King Sigurd Ring.

Early in the morning, when the rising sun was sending forth his golden rays over land and sea, the two great hostile armies drew themselves up for battle. Then the noble but aged Harald, mounting his war-chariot, gave the signal for the attack. Instantly the horns were sounded, the battle-cry of the multitudes rose on the wind, echoing over hill and vale; arrows and javelins whistled through the air; spears crashed against shields and breast-plates.

At the head of the Swedish soldiers fought the brave Ragwald, who forced his way into the ranks of the enemy, felling the Danish soldiers to the ground with his mighty sword. Then Ubbi the Dane, seeing the distress of his countrymen, hastened to their aid; he rushed upon the Swedish hero, and the two crossed swords together. The fight was desperate, but at length Ragwald fell, pierced to the heart by Ubbi's hand. The victor then pressed forward, urging his soldiers to follow. They broke through the ranks of the enemy, carrying all before them as they went, for the Swedish soldiers dared not await the onset of the mighty hero.

When King Sigurd Ring perceived the triumph of the Danes, he cried out, "Is there no one amongst my warriors who will do battle with this destroyer?"

"I will!" cried one of the bravest of his soldiers, and pressing through the crowd, he rushed with drawn sword upon the advancing Ubbi. The tumult became so great, however, that they were soon separated. Ubbi, whose shield had been destroyed, seized his mighty sword with both hands, and made for himself a passage through the ranks of the enemy by felling to the ground all who stood in his way, while his brave soldiers protected him from attack in the rear.

Then the Swedes, seeing that this mighty man was not to be overcome by the sword, rained down arrows upon him from the distance. Numbers of brave warriors fell, while fighting fiercely at his side, until at length one arrow hit its mark, piercing the heart of the hero whom no sword could conquer. With Ubbi sank Denmark's glory and might.

The battle continued to rage fiercely, but from the moment that the brave Ubbi fell, fortune seemed to turn against the Danes. Starkad, one of Sigurd Ring's warriors, followed by many of his bravest soldiers, broke through the Danish ranks, spreading terror and confusion as they advanced.

A cry of woe was echoed along the lines as the brave Danish soldiers saw that their cause was lost. Harald, however, rallying all his energies for a last effort to save the honour of his country, drove his chariot into the midst of the Swedish army, whilst, with a mighty sword in either hand, he struck down his enemies as he advanced, his followers fighting bravely round him. He was soon prevented from advancing, however, by the corpses of the slain, which covered the battle-field. The soldiers of both sides fought the more desperately round the royal chariot, till at length a mighty blow from a club aimed at the king instantly felled him to the ground. The fighting continued, however, over the corpse of the slain monarch, until Sigurd Ring, wishing now to put an end to the bloody battle, ordered a truce to be proclaimed. The horns were sounded on both sides for a cessation and the shattered remnants of the armies retired to their respective camps.

The defeat of the Danes was unquestionable, for the number of their slain and wounded was just double that of the Swedes.

On the evening of the same day the victorious king, accompanied by a retinue of soldiers, appeared in the Danish camp. Summoning the leaders of their army, he explained to them his rights to the sovereignty of Denmark and Gothland. The Danes, knowing that they had no choice but to submit to the will of the conqueror, consented, though unwillingly, to acknowledge him as their king.

The following day Sigurd Ring commanded the body of the slain monarch to be placed upon his war-chariot, and drawn by his own richly caparisoned charger to the funeral pile, on which had been placed Harald's stately vessel, which was to receive his corpse.

The flames rose high and wrapt themselves about the vessel. Then King Sigurd Ring, mounting his steed, cried: "Let the great monarch who has died the death of a noble hero depart from this world to the halls of Valhalla laden with rich gifts, and covered with kingly honour."

With these words he rode round the funeral pile, accompanied by many princes and warriors, while each and all of them, following the king's example, cast rich gifts of jewels and wrought gold on the burning mass.

By the king's command the ashes of the departed hero were placed in a golden urn, which was taken to Hledra, and there buried, a costly monument being raised over the spot.

Sigurd Ring then ordered a grand banquet to be prepared in Harald's memory, to which he invited the princes and nobles of Denmark and Gothland, and whilst his guests feasted, he sat at the board, praising the noble deeds of the departed king.

By this wise policy he won the hearts of the Danish people, who now willingly acknowledged him as their ruler.

Thus did the battle of Bravalla end the struggle for supremacy between King Sigurd Ring of Sweden and King Harald of Denmark. Sigurd Ring's rule was wise and mild. He reigned long and happily as king of Denmark and Sweden, beloved by his subjects of both countries, and died at length full of years and honour, but by foul assassination, when asleep on board his ship, the *Dragon*.

THE STORY OF GUNNLAUG THE WORM-TONGUE AND RAVEN THE *SKALD*

as told by Eirikr Magnusson and William Morris

CHAPTER I. OF THORSTEIN EGILSON AND HIS KIN

THERE was a man called Thorstein, the son of Egil, the son of Skallagrim, the son of Kveldulf the Hersir of Norway. Asgerd was the mother of Thorstein; she was the daughter of Biorn Hold. Thorstein dwelt at Burg in Burg-firth; he was rich of fee, and a great chief, a wise man, meek and of measure in all wise. He was nought of such wondrous growth and strength as his father Egil had been; yet was he a right mighty man, and much beloved of all folk.

Thorstein was goodly to look on, flaxen-haired and the best-eyed of men; and so say men of lore that many of the kin of the Mere-men, who are come of Egil, have been the goodliest folk; yet, for all that, this kindred have differed much herein, for it is said that some of them have been accounted the most ill-favoured of men; but in that kin have been also many men of great prowess in many wise, such as Kiartan, the son of Olaf Peacock, and Slaying-Bardi, and Skuli, the son of Thorstein. Some have been great bards, too, in that kin, as Biorn, the champion of Hit-dale, priest Einar Skulison, Snorri Sturluson and many others.

Now, Thorstein had to wife Jofrid, the daughter of Gunnar, the son of Hlifar. This Gunnar was the best-skilled in weapons, and the lithest of limb of all bonderfolk who have been in Iceland; the second was Gunnar of Lithend; but Steinthor of Ere was the third. Jofrid was eighteen winters old when Thorstein wedded her; she was a widow, for

Gunnar, a skilled fighter and master swordsman, in battle

Thorodd, son of Odd of Tongue, had had her to wife aforetime. Their daughter was Hungerd, who was brought up at Thorstein's at Burg. Jofrid was a very stirring woman; she and Thorstein had many children betwixt them, but few of them come into this tale. Skuli was the eldest of their sons, Kollsvein the second, Egil the third.

CHAPTER II. OF THORSTEIN'S DREAM

ONE summer, it is said, a ship came from over the main into Gufaros. Bergfinn was he named who was the master thereof, a Northman of kin, rich in goods, and somewhat stricken in years, and a wise man he was withal.

Now, goodman Thorstein rode to the ship, as it was his wont mostly to rule the market, and this he did now. The Eastmen got housed, but Thorstein took the master to himself, for thither he prayed to go. Bergfinn was of few words throughout the winter, but Thorstein treated him well. The Eastman had great joy of dreams.

One day in spring-tide Thorstein asked Bergfinn if he would ride with him up to Hawkfell, where at that time was the Thing-stead of the Burg-firthers; for Thorstein had been told that the walls of his booth had fallen in. The Eastman said he had good will to go, so that day they rode, some three together, from home, and the house-carles of Thorstein withal, till they came up under Hawkfell to a farmstead called Foxholes. There dwelt a man of small wealth called Atli, who was Thorstein's tenant. Thorstein bade him come and work with them, and bring with him hoe and spade. This he did, and when they came to the tofts of the booth, they set to work all of them, and did out the walls.

The weather was hot with sunshine that day, and Thorstein and the Eastman grew heavy; and when they had moved out the walls, those two sat down within the tofts, and Thorstein slept, and fared ill in his sleep. The Eastman sat beside him, and let him have his dream fully out, and when he awoke he was much wearied. Then the Eastman asked him what he had dreamt, as he had had such an ill time of it in his sleep.

Thorstein said, "Nay, dreams betoken nought."

But as they rode homeward in the evening, the Eastman asked him again what he had dreamt.

Thorstein said, "If I tell thee the dream, then shalt thou unriddle it to me, as it verily is."

The Eastman said he would risk it.

Then Thorstein said: "This was my dream; for methought I was at home at Burg, standing outside the men's-door, and I looked up at the house-roof, and on the ridge I saw a swan, goodly and fair, and I thought it was mine own, and deemed it good beyond all things. Then I saw a great eagle sweep down from the mountains, and fly thitherward and alight beside the swan, and chuckle over her lovingly; and methouht the swan seemed well content thereat; but I noted that the eagle was black-eyed, and that on him were iron claws: valiant he seemed to me.

"After this I thought I saw another fowl come flying from the south quarter, and he, too, came hither to Burg, and sat down on the house beside the swan, and would fain be fond with her. This also was a mighty eagle.

"But soon I thought that the eagle first-come ruffled up at the coming of the other. Then they fought fiercely and long, and this I saw that both bled, and such was the end of their play, that each tumbled either way down from the house-roof, and there they lay both dead.

"But the swan sat left alone, drooping much, and sad of semblance.

"Then I saw a fowl fly from the west; that was a falcon, and he sat beside the swan and made fondly towards her, and they flew away both together into one and the same quarter, and therewith I awoke.

"But a dream of no mark this is," he says, "and will in all likelihood betoken gales, that they shall meet in the air from those quarters whence I deemed the fowl flew."

The Eastman spake: "I deem it nowise such," saith he.

Thorstein said, "Make of the dream, then, what seemeth likest to thee, and let me hear."

Then said the Eastman: "These birds are like to be fetches of men: but thy wife sickens now, and she will give birth to a woman-child fair and lovely; and dearly thou wilt love her; but high-born men shall woo thy daughter, coming from such quarters as the eagles seemed to fly from, and shall love her with overweening love, and shall fight about her, and both lose their lives thereby. And thereafter a third man, from the quarter whence came the falcon, shall woo her, and to that man shall she be wedded. Now, I have unravelled thy dream, and I think things will befall as I have said."

Thorstein answered: "In evil and unfriendly wise is the dream interpreted, nor do I deem thee fit for the work of unriddling dreams."

Then Eastman said, "Thou shalt find how it will come to pass."

But Thorstein estranged himself from the Eastman thenceforward, and he left that summer, and now he is out of the tale.

CHAPTER III. OF THE BIRTH AND FOSTERING OF HELGA THE FAIR

THIS summer Thorstein got ready to ride to the Thing, and spake to Jofrid his wife before he went from home. "So is it," he says, "that thou art with child now, but thy child shall be cast forth if thou bear a woman; but nourished if it be a man."

Now, at this time when all the land was heathen, it was somewhat the wont of such men as had little wealth, and were like to have many young children on their hands, to have them cast forth, but an evil deed it was always deemed to be.

And now, when Thorstein had said this, Jofrid answers, "This is a word all unlike thee, such a man as thou art, and surely to a wealthy man like thee it will not seem good that this should be done."

Thorstein answered: "Thou knowest my mind, and that no good will hap if my will be thwarted."

So he rode to the Thing; but while he was gone Jofrid gave birth to a woman-child wondrous fair. The women would fain show her to the mother; she said there was little need thereof, but had her shepherd Thorvard called to her, and spake to him:

"Thou shalt take my horse and saddle it, and bring this child west to Herdholt, to Thorgerd, Egil's daughter, and pray her to nourish it secretly, so that Thorstein may not know thereof. For with such looks of love do I behold this child that surely I cannot bear to have it cast forth. Here are three marks of silver, have them in reward of thy work; but west there Thorgerd will get thee fare and food over the sea."

Then Thorvard did her bidding; he rode with the child to Herdholt, and gave it into Thorgerd's hands, and she had it nourished at a tenant's of hers who dwelt at Freedmans-stead up in Hvamfirth; but she got fare for Thorvard north in Steingrims-firth, in Shell-creek, and gave him meet outfit for his sea-faring: he went thence abroad, and is now out of the story.

Now when Thorstein came home from the Thing, Jofrid told him that the child had been cast forth according to his word, but that the herdsman had fled away and stolen her horse. Thorstein said she had done well, and got himself another herdsman. So six winters passed, and this matter was nowise wotted of.

Now in those days Thorstein rode to Herdholt, being bidden there as guest of his brother-in-law, Olaf Peacock, the son of Hoskuld, who was then deemed to be the chief highest of worth among all men west there. Good cheer was made Thorstein, as was like to be; and one day at the feast it is said that Thorgerd sat in the high-seat talking with her brother Thorstein, while Olaf was talking to other men; but on the bench right over against them sat three little maidens. Then said Thorgerd, "How dost thou, brother, like the look of these three little maidens sitting straight before us?"

"Right well," he answers, "but one is by far the fairest; she has all the goodliness of Olaf, but the whiteness and the countenance of us, the Mere-men."

Thorgerd answered: "Surely this is true, brother, wherein thou sayest that she has the fairness and countenance of us Mere-folk, but the goodliness of Olaf Peacock she has not got, for she is not his daughter."

"How can that be," says Thorstein, "being thy daughter none the less?"

She answered: "To say sooth, kinsman," quoth she, "this fair maiden is not my daughter, but thine."

And therewith she told him all as it had befallen, and prayed him to forgive her and his own wife that trespass.

Thorstein said: "I cannot blame you two for having done this; most things will fall as they are fated, and well have ye covered over my folly: so look I on this maiden that I deem it great good luck to have so fair a child. But now, what is her name?"

"Helga she is called," says Thorgerd.

"Helga the Fair," says Thorstein. "But now shalt thou make her ready to come home with me."

She did so, and Thorstein was led out with good gifts, and Helga rode with him to his home, and was brought up there with much honour and great love from father and mother and all her kin.

CHAPTER IV. OF GUNNLAUG WORM-TONGUE AND HIS KIN

NOW at this time there dwelt at Gilsbank, up in White-water-side, Illugi the Black, son of Hallkel, the son of Hrosskel. The mother of Illugi was Thurid Dandle, daughter of Gunnlaug Worm-tongue.

Illugi was the next greatest chief in Burg-firth after Thorstein Egilson. He was a man of broad lands and hardy of mood, and wont to do well to his friends; he had to wife Ingibiorg, the daughter of Asbiorn Hordson, from Ornolfsdale; the mother of Ingibiorg was Thorgerd, the daughter of Midfirth-Skeggi. The children of Illugi and Ingibiorg were many, but few of them have to do with this story. Hermund was one of their sons, and Gunnlaug another; both were hopeful men, and at this time of ripe growth.

It is told of Gunnlaug that he was quick of growth in his early youth, big and strong; his hair was light red, and very goodly of fashion; he was dark-eyed, somewhat ugly-nosed, yet of lovesome countenance; thin of flank he was, and broad of shoulder, and the best-wrought of men; his whole mind was very masterful; eager was he from his youth up, and in all wise unsparing and hardy; he was a great *skald*, but somewhat bitter in his rhyming, and therefore was he called Gunnlaug Worm-tongue.

Hermund was the best beloved of the two brothers, and had the mien of a great man.

When Gunnlaug was fifteen winters old he prayed his father for goods to fare abroad withal, and said he had will to travel and see the manners of other folk. Master Illugi was slow to take the matter up, and said he was unlike to be deemed good in the out-lands "when I can scarcely shape thee to my own liking at home".

On a morning but a very little afterwards it happened that Illugi came out early, and saw that his storehouse was opened, and that some sacks of wares, six of them, had been brought out into the road, and therewithal too some pack-gear. Now, as he wondered at this, there came up a man leading four horses, and who should it be but his son Gunnlaug. Then said he:

"I it was who brought out the sacks."

Illugi asked him why he had done so. He said that they should make his faring goods.

Illugi said: "In nowise shalt thou thwart my will, nor fare anywhere sooner than I like!" And in again he swung the ware-sacks therewith.

Then Gunnlaug rode thence and came in the evening down to Burg, and goodman Thorstein asked him to bide there, and Gunnlaug was fain of that proffer. He told Thorstein how things had gone betwixt him and his father, and Thorstein offered to let him bide there as long as he liked, and for some seasons Gunnlaug abode there, and learned law-craft of Thorstein, and all men accounted well of him.

Now Gunnlaug and Helga would be always at the chess-playing together, and very soon each found favour with the other, as came to be proven well enough afterwards: they were very nigh of an age.

Helga was so fair that men of lore say that she was the fairest woman of Iceland, then or since; her hair was so plenteous and long that it could cover her all over, and it was as fair as a band of gold; nor was there any so good to choose as Helga the Fair in all Burg-firth, and far and wide elsewhere.

Now one day, as men sat in the hall at Burg, Gunnlaug spake to Thorstein: "One thing in law there is which thou hast not taught me, and that is how to woo me a wife."

Thorstein said, "That is but a small matter," and therewith taught him how to go about it.

Then said Gunnlaug, "Now shalt thou try if I have understood all: I shall take thee by the hand and make as if I were wooing thy daughter Helga."

"I see no need of that," says Thorstein. Gunnlaug, however, groped then and there after his hand, and seizing it said, "Nay, grant me this though."

"Do as thou wilt, then," said Thorstein; "but be it known to all who are hereby that this shall be as if it had been unspoken, nor shall any guile follow herein."

Then Gunnlaug named for himself witnesses, and betrothed Helga to him, and

Gunnlaug is brought before Earl Eric

asked thereafter if it would stand good thus. Thorstein said that it was well; and those who were present were mightily pleased at all this.

CHAPTER V. OF RAVEN AND HIS KIN

THERE was a man called Onund, who dwelt in the south at Mossfell: he was the wealthiest of men, and had a priesthood south there about the nesses. He was married, and his wife was called Geirny. She was the daughter of Gnup, son of Mold-Gnup, who settled at Grindwick, in the south country. Their sons were Raven, and Thorarin, and Eindridi; they were all hopeful men, but Raven was in all wise the first of them. He was a big man and a strong, the sightliest of men and a good *skald*; and when he was fully grown he fared between sundry lands, and was well accounted of wherever he came.

Thorod the Sage, the son of Eyvind, then dwelt at Hjalli, south in Olfus, with Skapti his son, who was then the spokesman-at-law in Iceland. The mother of Skapti was Ranveig, daughter of Gnup, the son of Mold-Gnup; and Skapti and the sons of Onund were sisters' sons. Between these kinsmen was much friendship as well as kinship.

At this time Thorfin, the son of Selthorir, dwelt at Red-Mel, and had seven sons, who were all the hopefullest of men; and of them were these – Thorgils, Eyjolf and Thorir; and they were all the greatest men out there. But these men who have now been named lived all at one and the same time.

Next to this befell those tidings, the best that ever have befallen here in Iceland, that the whole land became Christian, and that all folk cast off the old faith.

CHAPTER VI. HOW HELGA WAS VOWED TO GUNNLAUG, AND OF GUNNLAUG'S FARING ABROAD

GUNNLAUG Worm-tongue was, as is aforesaid, whiles at Burg with Thorstein, whiles with his father Illugi at Gilsbank, three winters together, and was by now eighteen winters old; and father and son were now much more of a mind.

There was a man called Thorkel the Black; he was a house-carle of Illugi, and near akin to him, and had been brought up in his house. To him fell an heritage north at As, in Water-dale, and he prayed Gunnlaug to go with him thither. This he did, and so they rode, the two together, to As. There they got the fee; it was given up to them by those who had the keeping of it, mostly because of Gunnlaug's furtherance.

But as they rode from the north they guested at Grimstongue, at a rich bonder's who dwelt there; but in the morning a herdsman took Gunnlaug's horse, and it had sweated much by then he got it back. Then Gunnlaug smote the herdsman, and stunned him; but the bonder would in nowise bear this, and claimed boot therefor. Gunnlaug offered to pay him one mark. The bonder thought it too little.

Then Gunnlaug sang:

> "Bade I the middling mighty
> To have a mark of waves' flame;
> Giver of grey seas? Glitter,
> This gift shalt thou make shift with.
> If the elf sun of the waters
> From out of purse thou lettest,
> O waster of the worm's bedy
> Awaits thee sorrow later."

So the peace was made as Gunnlaug bade, and in such wise the two rode south.

Now, a little while after, Gunnlaug asked his father a second time for goods for going abroad.

Illugi says, "Now shalt thou have thy will, for thou hast wrought thyself into something better than thou wert." So Illugi rode hastily from home, and bought for Gunnlaug half a ship which lay in Gufaros, from Audun Festargram – this Audun was he who would not flit abroad the sons of Oswif the Wise, after the slaying of Kiartan Olafson, as is told in the story of the Laxdalemen, which thing though betid later than this. And when Illugi came home, Gunnlaug thanked him well.

Thorkel the Black betook himself to seafaring with Gunnlaug, and their wares were brought to the ship; but Gunnlaug was at Burg while they made her ready, and found more cheer in talk with Helga than in toiling with chapmen.

Now one day Thorstein asked Gunnlaug if he would ride to his horses with him up to Long-water-dale. Gunnlaug said he would. So they ride both together till they come to the mountain-dairies of Thorstein, called Thorgils-stead. There were stud-horses of Thorstein, four of them together, all red of hue. There was one horse very goodly, but little tried: this horse Thorstein offered to give Gunnlaug. He said he was in no need of horses, as he was going away from the country; and so they ride to other stud-horses. There was a grey horse with four mares, and he was the best of horses in Burg-firth. This one, too, Thorstein offered to give Gunnlaug, but he said, "I desire these in no wise more than the others; but why dost thou not bid me what I will take?"

"What is that?" said Thorstein.

"Helga the Fair, thy daughter," says Gunnlaug.

"That rede is not to be settled so hastily," said Thorstein; and therewithal got on other talk. And now they ride homewards down along Long-water.

Then said Gunnlaug, "I must needs know what thou wilt answer me about the wooing."

Thorstein answers: "I heed not thy vain talk," says he.

Gunnlaug says, "This is my whole mind, and no vain words."

Thorstein says, "Thou shouldst first know thine own will. Art thou not bound to fare abroad? And yet thou makest as if thou wouldst go marry. Neither art thou an even match for Helga while thou art so unsettled, and therefore this cannot so much as be looked at."

Gunnlaug says, "Where lookest thou for a match for thy daughter, if thou wilt not give her to the son of Illugi the Black; or who are they throughout Burg-firth who are of more note than he?"

Thorstein answered: "I will not play at men-mating," says he, "but if thou wert such a man as he is, thou wouldst not be turned away."

Gunnlaug said, "To whom wilt thou give thy daughter rather than to me?"

Said Thorstein, "Hereabout are many good men to choose from. Thorfin of Red-Mel hath seven sons, and all of them men of good manners."

Gunnlaug answers, "Neither Onund nor Thorfin are men as good as my father. Nay, thou thyself clearly fallest short of him – or what hast thou to set against his strife with Thorgrim the Priest, the son of Kiallak, and his sons, at Thorsness Thing, where he carried all that was in debate?"

Thorstein answers, "I drave away Steinar, the son of Onund Sioni, which was deemed somewhat of a deed."

Gunnlaug says, "Therein thou wast holpen by thy father Egil; and, to end all, it is for few bonders to cast away my alliance."

Said Thorstein, "Carry thy cowing away to the fellows up yonder at the mountains; for down here, on the Meres, it shall avail thee nought."

Now in the evening they come home; but next morning Gunnlaug rode up to Gilsbank, and prayed his father to ride with him a-wooing out to Burg.

Illugi answered, "Thou art an unsettled man, being bound for faring abroad, but makest now as if thou wouldst busy thyself with wife-wooing; and so much do I know, that this is not to Thorstein's mind."

Gunnlaug answers, "I shall go abroad all the same, nor shall I be well pleased but if thou further this."

So after this Illugi rode with eleven men from home down to Burg, and Thorstein greeted him well. Early in the morning Illugi said to Thorstein, "I would speak to thee."

"Let us go, then, to the top of the Burg, and talk together there," says Thorstein; and so they did, and Gunnlaug went with them.

Then said Illugi, "My kinsman Gunnlaug tells me that he has begun a talk with thee on his own behalf, praying that he might woo thy daughter Helga; but now I would fain know what is like to come of this matter. His kin is known to thee, and our possessions; from my hand shall be spared neither land nor rule over men, if such things might perchance further matters."

Thorstein said, "Herein alone Gunnlaug pleases me not, that I find him an unsettled man; but if he were of a mind like thine, little would I hang back."

Illugi said, "It will cut our friendship across if thou gainsayest me and my son an equal match."

Thorstein answers, "For thy words and our friendship then, Helga shall be vowed, but not betrothed, to Gunnlaug, and shall bide for him three winters: but Gunnlaug shall go abroad and shape himself to the ways of good men; but I shall be free from all these matters if he does not then come back, or if his ways are not to my liking."

Thereat they parted; Illugi rode home, but Gunnlaug rode to his ship. But when they had wind at will they sailed for the main, and made the northern part of Norway, and sailed landward along Thrandheim to Nidaros; there they rode in the harbour, and unshipped their goods.

CHAPTER VII. OF GUNNLAUG IN THE EAST AND THE WEST

IN those days Earl Eric, the son of Hakon, and his brother Svein ruled in Norway. Earl Eric abode as then at Hladir, which was left to him by his father, and a mighty lord he was. Skuli, the son of Thorstein, was with the earl at that time, and was one of his court, and well esteemed.

Now they say that Gunnlaug and Audun Festargram, and seven of them together, went up to Hladir to the earl. Gunnlaug was so clad that he had on a grey kirtle and white long-hose; he had a boil on his foot by the instep, and from this oozed blood and matter as he strode on. In this guise he went before the earl with Audun and the rest of them, and greeted him well. The earl knew Audun, and asked him tidings from Iceland. Audun told him what there was toward. Then the earl asked Gunnlaug who he was, and Gunnlaug told him his name and kin. Then the earl said: "Skuli Thorstein's son, what manner of man is this in Iceland?"

"Lord," says he, "give him good welcome, for he is the son of the best man in Iceland, Illugi the Black of Gilsbank, and my foster-brother withal."

The earl asked, "What ails thy foot, Icelander?"

"A boil, lord," said he.

"And yet thou wentest not halt?"

Gunnlaug answers, "Why go halt while both legs are long alike?"

Then said one of the earl's men, called Thorir: "He swaggereth hugely, this Icelander! It would not be amiss to try him a little."

Gunnlaug looked at him and sang:

> "A courtman there is
> Full evil I wis,

A bad man and black,

Belief let him lack."

Then would Thorir seize an axe. The earl spake: "Let it be," says he; "to such things men should pay no heed. But now, Icelander, how old a man art thou?"

Gunnlaug answers: "I am eighteen winters old as now," says he.

Then says Earl Eric, "My spell is that thou shalt not live eighteen winters more."

Gunnlaug said, somewhat under his breath: "Pray not against me, but for thyself rather."

The earl asked thereat, "What didst thou say, Icelander?"

Gunnlaug answers, "What I thought well befitting, that thou shouldst bid no prayers against me, but pray well for thyself rather."

"What prayers, then?" says the earl.

"That thou mightest not meet thy death after the manner of Earl Hakon, thy father."

The earl turned red as blood, and bade them take the rascal in haste; but Skuli stepped up to the earl, and said: "Do this for my words, lord, and give this man peace, so that he depart at his swiftest."

The earl answered, "At his swiftest let him be off then, if he will have peace, and never let him come again within mv realm."

Then Skuli went out with Gunnlaug down to the bridges, where there was an England-bound ship ready to put out; therein Skuli got for Gunnlaug a berth, as well as for Thorkel, his kinsman; but Gunnlaug gave his ship into Audun's ward, and so much of his goods as he did not take with him.

Now sail Gunnlaug and his fellows into the English main, and come at autumntide south to London Bridge, where they hauled ashore their ship.

Now at that time King Ethelred, the son of Edgar, ruled over England, and was a good lord; this winter he sat in London. But in those days there was the same tongue in England as in Norway and Denmark; but the tongues changed when William the Bastard won England, for thenceforward French went current there, for he was of French kin.

Gunnlaug went presently to the king, and greeted him well and worthily. The king asked him from what land he came, and Gunnlaug told him all as it was. "But", said he, "I have come to meet thee, lord, for that I have made a song on thee, and I would that it might please thee to hearken to that song." The king said it should be so, and Gunnlaug gave forth the song well and proudly; and this is the burden thereof:

"As God are all folk fearing
The free lord King of England,
Kin of all kings and all folk,
To Ethelred the head tow."

The king thanked him for the song, and gave him as song-reward a scarlet cloak lined with the costliest of furs, and golden-broidered down to the hem; and made him his man; and Gunnlaug was with him all the winter, and was well accounted of.

One day, in the morning early, Gunnlaug met three men in a certain street, and Thororm was the name of their leader; he was big and strong, and right evil to deal with. He said, "Northman, lend me some money."

Gunnlaug answered, "That were ill counselled to lend one's money to unknown men."

He said, "I will pay it thee back on a named day."

"Then shall it be risked," says Gunnlaug; and he lent him the fee withal.

But some time afterwards Gunnlaug met the king, and told him of the money-lending. The king answered, "Now hast thou thriven little, for this is the greatest robber and reiver; deal with him in no wise, but I will give thee money as much as thine was."

Gunnlaug said, "Then do we, your men, do after a sorry sort, if, treading sackless folk under foot, we let such fellows as this deal us out our lot. Nay, that shall never be."

Soon after he met Thororm and claimed the fee of him. He said he was not going to pay it.

Then sang Gunnlaug:

"Evil counselled art thou,
Gold from us withholding;
The reddener of the edges,
Pricking on with tricking.
Wot ye what they called me?
Worm-tongue, yet a youngling;
Nor for nought so hight I;
Now is time to show it!"

"Now I will make an offer good in law," says Gunnlaug; "that thou either pay me my money, or else that thou go on holm with me in three nights' space."

Then laughed the viking, and said, "Before thee none have come to that, to call me to holm, despite of all the ruin that many a man has had to take at my hands. Well, I am ready to go."

Thereon they parted for that time.

Gunnlaug told the king what had befallen; and he said, "Now, indeed, have things taken a right hopeless turn; for this man's eyes can dull any weapon. But thou shalt follow my rede; here is a sword I will give thee – with that thou shalt fight, but before the battle show him another."

Gunnlaug thanked the king well therefor.

Now when they were ready for the holm, Thororm asked what sort of a sword it was that he had. Gunnlaug unsheathed it and showed him, but had a loop round the handle of the king's sword, and slipped it over his hand; the bearserk looked on the sword, and said, "I fear not that sword."

But now he dealt a blow on Gunnlaug with his sword, and cut off from him nigh all his shield; Gunnlaug smote in turn with the king's gift; the bearserk stood shieldless before him, thinking he had the same weapon he had shown him, but Gunnlaug smote him his deathblow then and there.

The king thanked him for this work, and he got much fame therefor, both in England and far and wide elsewhere.

In the spring, when ships sailed from land to land, Gunnlaug prayed King Ethelred for leave to sail somewhither; the king asks what he was about then. Gunnlaug said, "I would fulfil what I have given my word to do," and sang this stave withal:

"My ways must I be wending
Three kings' walls to see yet,
And earls twain, as I promised
Erewhile to land-sharers.
Neither will I wend me
Back, the worms' bed lacking,

By war-lord's son, the wealth-free,

For work done gift well given."

"So be it, then, *skald*," said the king, and withal he gave him a ring that weighed six ounces. "But", said he, "thou shalt give me thy word to come back next autumn, for I will not let thee go altogether, because of thy great prowess."

CHAPTER VIII. OF GUNNLAUG IN IRELAND

THEREAFTER Gunnlaug sailed from England with chapmen north to Dublin. In those days King Sigtrygg Silky-beard, son of King Olaf Kvaran and Queen Kormlada, ruled over Ireland; and he had then borne sway but a little while. Gunnlaug went before the king, and greeted him well and worthily. The king received him as was meet. Then Gunnlaug said, "I have made a song on thee, and I would fain have silence therefor."

The king answered, "No men have before now come forward with songs for me, and surely will I hearken to thine." Then Gunnlaug brought the song, whereof this is the burden:

"Swaru's steed

Doth Sigtrygg feed."

And this is therein also:

"Praise-worth I can

Well measure in man,

And kings, one by one –

Lo here, Kvaran's son!

Gruageth the king

Gift of gold ring?

I, singer, know

His wont to bestow.

Let the high king say,

Heard he or this day,

Song *drapa*-measure

Dearer a treasure?"

The king thanked him for the song, and called his treasurer to him, and said, "How shall the song be rewarded?"

"What hast thou will to give, lord?" says he.

"How will it be rewarded if I give him two ships for it?" said the king.

Then said the treasurer, "This is too much, lord; other kings give in regard of songs good keepsakes, fair swords or golden rings."

So the king gave him his own raiment of new scarlet, a gold-embroidered kirtle and a cloak lined with choice furs and a gold ring which weighed a mark. Gunnlaug thanked him well.

He dwelt a short time here, and then went thence to the Orkneys.

Then was lord in Orkney, Earl Sigurd, the son of Hlodver; he was friendly to Icelanders. Now Gunnlaug greeted the earl well, and said he had a song to bring him. The earl said he would listen thereto, since he was of such great kin in Iceland.

Then Gunnlaug brought the song; it was a shorter lay, and well done. The earl gave him for lay-reward a broad axe, all inlaid with silver, and bade him abide with him.

Gunnlaug thanked him both for his gift and his offer, but said he was bound east for Sweden; and thereafter he went on board ship with chapmen who sailed to Norway.

In the autumn they came east to King's Cliff, Thorkel, his kinsman, being with him all the time. From King's Cliff they got a guide up to West Gothland, and came upon a cheaping-stead, called Skarir: there ruled an earl called Sigurd, a man stricken in years. Gunnlaug went before him, and told him he had made a song on him; the earl gave a willing ear hereto, and Gunnlaug brought the song, which was a shorter lay.

The earl thanked him, and rewarded the song well, and bade him abide there that winter.

Earl Sigurd had a great Yule-feast in the winter, and on Yule-eve came thither men sent from Earl Eric of Norway, twelve of them together, and brought gifts to Earl Sigurd. The earl made them good cheer, and bade them sit by Gunnlaug through the Yule-tide; and there was great mirth at drinks.

Now the Gothlanders said that no earl was greater or of more fame than Earl Sigurd; but the Norwegians thought that Earl Eric was by far the foremost of the two. Hereon would they bandy words, till they both took Gunnlaug to be umpire in the matter.

Then he sang this stave:

"Tell ye, staves of spear-din,
How on sleek-side sea-horse
Oft this earl hath proven
Over-toppling billows;
But Eric, victory's ash tree,
Oft hath seen in east seas
More of high blue billows
Before the bows a-roaring."

Both sides were content with his finding, but the Norwegians the best. But after Yule-tide those messengers left with gifts of goodly things, which Earl Sigurd sent to Earl Eric.

Now they told Earl Eric of Gunnlaug's finding: the earl thought that he had shown upright dealing and friendship to him herein, and let out some words, saying that Gunnlaug should have good peace throughout his land. What the earl had said came thereafter to the ears of Gunnlaug.

But now Earl Sigurd gave Gunnlaug a guide east to Tenthland, in Sweden, as he had asked.

CHAPTER IX. OF THE QUARREL BETWEEN GUNNLAUG AND RAVEN BEFORE THE SWEDISH KING

IN those days King Olaf the Swede, son of King Eric the Victorious, and Sigrid the High-counselled, daughter of Skogul Tosti, ruled over Sweden. He was a mighty king and renowned, and full fain of fame.

Gunnlaug came to Upsala towards the time of the Thing of the Swedes in spring-tide; and when he got to see the king, he greeted him. The king took his greeting well, and asked who he was. He said he was an Iceland-man.

Then the king called out: "Raven," says he, "what man is he in Iceland?"

Then one stood up from the lower bench, a big man and a stalwart, and stepped up before the king, and spake: "Lord," says he, "he is of good kin, and himself the most stalwart of men."

"Let him go, then, and sit beside thee," said the king.

Then Gunnlaug said, "I have a song to set forth before thee, king, and I would fain have peace while thou hearkenest thereto."

"Go ye first, and sit ye down," says the king, "for there is no leisure now to sit listening to songs."

So they did as he bade them.

Now Gunnlaug and Raven fell a-talking together, and each told each of his travels. Raven said that he had gone the summer before from Iceland to Norway, and had come east to Sweden in the forepart of winter. They soon got friendly together.

But one day, when the Thing was over, they were both before the king, Gunnlaug and Raven.

Then spake Gunnlaug, "Now, lord, I would that thou shouldst hear the song."

"That I may do now," said the king.

"My song too will I set forth now," says Raven.

"Thou mayst do so," said the king.

Then Gunnlaug said, "I will set forth mine first if thou wilt have it so, king."

"Nay," said Raven, "it behoveth me to be first, lord, for I myself came first to thee."

"Whereto came our fathers forth, so that my father was the little boat towed behind? Whereto, but nowhere?" says Gunnlaug. "And in likewise shall it be with us."

Raven answered, "Let us be courteous enough not to make this a matter of bandying of words. Let the king rule here."

The king said, "Let Gunnlaug set forth his song first, for he will not be at peace till he has his will."

Then Gunnlaug set forth the song which he had made to King Olaf, and when it was at an end the king spake. "Raven," says he, "how is the song done?"

"Right well," he answered; "it is a song full of big words and little beauty; a somewhat rugged song, as is Gunnlaug's own mood."

"Well, Raven, thy song," said the king.

Raven gave it forth, and when it was done the king said, "How is this song made, Gunnlaug?"

"Well it is, lord," he said; "this is a pretty song, as is Raven himself to behold, and delicate of countenance. But why didst thou make a short song on the king, Raven? Didst thou perchance deem him unworthy of a long one?"

Raven answered, "Let us not talk longer on this; matters will be taken up again, though it be later."

And thereat, they parted.

Soon after Raven became a man of King Olaf's, and asked him leave to go away. This the king granted him. And when Raven was ready to go, he spake to Gunnlaug, and said, "Now shall our friendship be ended, for that thou must needs shame me here before great men; but in time to come I shall cast on thee no less shame than thou hadst will to cast on me here."

Gunnlaug answers: "Thy threats grieve me nought. Nowhere are we likely to come where I shall be thought less worthy than thou."

King Olaf gave to Raven good gifts at parting, and thereafter.

CHAPTER X. HOW RAVEN CAME HOME TO ICELAND, AND ASKED FOR HELGA TO WIFE

NOW this spring Raven came from the east to Thrandheim, and fitted out his ship, and sailed in the summer to Iceland. He brought his ship to Leiruvag, below the Heath, and his friends and kinsmen were right fain of him. That winter he was at home with his father, but the summer after he met at the Althing his kinsman, Skapti the law-man.

Then said Raven to him, "Thine aid would I have to go a-wooing to Thorstein Egilson, to bid Helga his daughter."

Skapti answered, "But is she not already vowed to Gunnlaug Worm-tongue?"

Said Raven, "Is not the appointed time of waiting between them passed by? And far too wanton is he withal, that he should hold or heed it aught."

"Let us then do as thou wouldst," said Skapti.

Thereafter they went with many men to the booth of Thorstein Egilson, and he greeted them well.

Then Skapti spoke: "Raven, my kinsman, is minded to woo thy daughter Helga. Thou knowest well his blood, his wealth and his good manners, his many mighty kinsmen and friends."

Thorstein said, "She is already the vowed maiden of Gunnlaug, and with him shall I hold all words spoken."

Skapti said, "Are not the three winters worn now that were named between you?"

"Yes," said Thorstein; "but the summer is not yet worn, and he may still come out this summer."

Then Skapti said, "But if he cometh not this summer, what hope may we have of the matter then?"

Thorstein answered, "We are like to come here next summer, and then may we see what may wisely be done, but it will not do to speak hereof longer as at this time."

Thereon they parted. And men rode home from the Althing. But this talk of Raven's wooing of Helga was nought hidden.

That summer Gunnlaug came not out.

The next summer, at the Althing, Skapti and his folk pushed the wooing eagerly, and said that Thorstein was free as to all matters with Gunnlaug.

Thorstein answered, "I have few daughters to see to, and fain am I that they should not be the cause of strife to any man. Now I will first see Illugi the Black." And so he did.

And when they met, he said to Illugi, "Dost thou not think that I am free from all troth with thy son Gunnlaug?"

Illugi said, "Surely, if thou wiliest it. Little can I say herein, as I do not know clearly what Gunnlaug is about."

Then Thorstein went to Skapti, and a bargain was struck that the wedding should be at Burg, about winter-nights, if Gunnlaug did not come out that summer; but that Thorstein should be free from all troth with Raven if Gunnlaug should come and fetch his bride.

After this men ride home from the Thing, and Gunnlaug's coming was long drawn out. But Helga thought evilly of all these redes.

CHAPTER XI. OF HOW GUNNLAUG MUST NEEDS ABIDE AWAY FROM ICELAND

NOW it is to be told of Gunnlaug that he went from Sweden the same summer that Raven went to Iceland, and good gifts he had from King Olaf at parting.

King Ethelred welcomed Gunnlaug worthily, and that winter he was with the king, and was held in great honour.

In those days Knut the Great, son of Svein, ruled Denmark, and had new-taken his father's heritage, and he vowed ever to wage war on England, for that his father had won a great realm there before he died west in that same land.

And at that time there was a great army of Danish men west there, whose chief was Heming, the son of Earl Strut-Harald, and brother to Earl Sigvaldi, and he held for King Knut that land that Svein had won.

Now in the spring Gunnlaug asked the king for leave to go away, but he said, "It ill beseems that thou, my man, shouldst go away now, when all bodes such mighty war in the land."

Gunnlaug said, "Thou shalt rule, lord; but give me leave next summer to depart, if the Danes come not."

The king answered, "Then we shall see."

Now this summer went by, and the next winter, but no Danes came; and after midsummer Gunnlaug got his leave to depart from the king, and went thence east to Norway, and found Earl Eric in Thrandheim, at Hladir, and the earl greeted him well, and bade him abide with him. Gunnlaug thanked him for his offer, but said he would first go out to Iceland, to look to his promised maiden.

The earl said, "Now all ships bound for Iceland have sailed."

Then said one of the court, "Here lay, yesterday, Hallfred Troublous-*Skald*, out tinder Agdaness."

The earl answered, "That may well be; he sailed hence five nights ago."

Then Earl Eric had Gunnlaug rowed put to Hallfred, who greeted him with joy; and forthwith a fair wind bore them from land, and they were right merry.

This was late in the summer: but now Hallfred said to Gunnlaug, "Hast thou heard of how Raven, the son of Onund, is wooing Helga the Fair?"

Gunnlaug said he had heard thereof but dimly. Hallfred tells him all he knew of it, and therewith, too, that it was the talk of many men that Raven was in nowise less brave a man than Gunnlaug. Then Gunnlaug sang this stave:

> "Light the weather wafteth;
> But if this east wind drifted
> Week-long, wild upon us
> Little were I recking;
> More this word I mind of
> Me with Raven mated,
> Than gain for me the gold-foe
> Of days to make me grey-haired."

Then Hallfred said, "Well, fellow, may'st thou fare better in thy strife with Raven than I did in mine. I brought my ship some winters ago into Leiruvag, and had to pay a half-mark in silver to a house-carle of Raven's, but I held it back from him. So Raven rode at us with sixty men, and cut the moorings of the ship, and she was driven up on the shallows, and we were bound for a wreck. Then I had to give selfdoom to Raven, and a whole mark I had to pay; and that is the tale of my dealings with him."

Then they two talked together alone of Helga the Fair, and Gunnlaug praised her much for her goodliness; and Gunnlaug sang:

> "He who brand of battle
> Beareth over-wary,
> Never love shall let him
> Hold the linen-folded;
> For we when we were younger
> In many a way were playing
> On the outward nesses
> From golden land outstanding."

"Well sung!" said Hallfred.

CHAPTER XII. OF GUNNLAUG'S LANDING, AND HOW HE FOUND HELGA WEDDED TO RAVEN

THEY made land north by Fox-Plain, in Hraunhaven, half a month before winter, and there unshipped their goods. Now there was a man called Thord, a bonder's son of the Plain, there. He fell to wrestling with the chapmen, and they mostly got worsted at his hands.

Then a wrestling was settled between him and Gunnlaug. The night before Thord made vows to Thor for the victory; but the next day, when they met, they fell to wrestling. Then Gunnlaug tripped both feet from under Thord, and gave him a great fall; but the foot that Gunnlaug stood on was put out of joint, and Gunnlaug fell together with Thord.

Then said Thord, "Maybe that other things go no better for thee."

"What then?" says Gunnlaug.

"Thy dealings with Raven, if he wed Helga the Fair at winter-nights. I was anigh at the Thing when that was settled last summer."

Gunnlaug answered naught thereto.

Now the foot was swathed, and put into joint again, and it swelled mightily; but he and Hallfred ride twelve in company till they come to Gilsbank, in Burg-firth, the very Saturday night when folk sat at the wedding at Burg. Illugi was fain of his son Gunnlaug and his fellows; but Gunnlaug said he would ride then and there down to Burg. Illugi said it was not wise to do so, and to all but Gunnlaug that seemed good. But Gunnlaug was then unfit to walk, because of his foot, though he would not let that be seen. Therefore there was no faring to Burg.

On the morrow Hallfred rode to Hreda-water, in North-water dale, where Galti, his brother and a brisk man, managed their matters.

CHAPTER XIII. OF THE WINTER WEDDING AT SKANEY, AND HOW GUNNLAUG GAVE THE KING'S CLOAK TO HELGA

TELLS the tale of Raven that he sat at his wedding-feast at Burg, and it was the talk of most men that the bride was but drooping; for true is the saw that saith, "Long we remember what youth gained us," and even so it was with her now.

But this new thing befell at the feast, that Hungerd, the daughter of Thorod and Jofrid, was wooed by a man named Sverting, the son of Hafr-Biorn, the son of Mold-Gnup, and the wedding was to come off that winter after Yule, at Skaney, where dwelt Thorkel, a kinsman of Hungerd, and son of Torn Valbrandsson; and the mother of Torn was Thorodda, the sister of Odd of the Tongue.

Now Raven went home to Mossfell with Helga his wife. When they had been there a little while, one morning early before they rose up, Helga was awake, but Raven slept, and fared ill in his sleep. And when he woke Helga asked him what he had dreamt. Then Raven sang:

"In thine arms, so dreamed I,
Hewn was I, gold island!
Bride, in blood I bled there,
Bed of thine was reddened.
Never more then mightst thou,
Mead-bowl's pourer speedy,
Bind my gashes bloody –
Lind-leek-bough thou likst it."

Helga spake: "Never shall I weep therefor," quoth she; "ye have evilly beguiled me, and Gunnlaug has surely come out." And therewith she wept much.

But, a little after, Gunnlaug's coming was bruited about, and Helga became so hard with Raven that he could not keep her at home at Mossfell; so that back they had to go to Burg, and Raven got small share of her company.

Now men get ready for the winter-wedding. Thorkel of Skaney bade Illugi the Black and his sons. But when master Illugi got ready, Gunnlaug sat in the hall, and stirred not to go. Illugi went up to him and said, "Why dost thou not get ready, kinsman?"

Gunnlaug answered, "I have no mind to go."

Says Illugi, "Nay, but certes thou shalt go, kinsman," says he; "and cast thou not grief over thee by yearning for one woman. Make as if thou knewest nought of it, for women thou wilt never lack."

Now Gunnlaug did as his father bade him; so they came to the wedding, and Illugi and his sons were set down in the high-seat; but Thorstein Egilson, and Raven his son-in-law, and the bridegroom's following, were set in the other high-seat, over against Illugi.

The women sat on the dais, and Helga the Fair sat next to the bride. Oft she turned her eyes on Gunnlaug, thereby proving the saw, "Eyes will bewray if maid love man."

Gunnlaug was well arrayed, and had on him that goodly raiment that King Sigtrygg had given him; and now he was thought far above all other men, because of many things, both strength, and goodliness, and growth.

There was little mirth among folk at this wedding. But on the day when all men were making ready to go away the women stood up and got ready to go home. Then went Gunnlaug to talk to Helga, and long they talked together: but Gunnlaug sang:

"Light-heart lived the Worm-tongue
All day long no longer
In mountain-home, since Helga
Had name of wife of Raven;
Nought foresaw thy father,
Hardener white of fight-thaw,
What my words should come to –
The maid to gold was wedded."

And again he sang:

"Worst reward I owe them,
Father thine, O wine-may,
And mother, that they made thee

So fair beneath thy maid-gear;
For thou, sweet field of sea-flame,
All joy hast slain within me.
Lo, here, take it, loveliest
E'er made of lord and lady!"

And therewith Gunnlaug gave Helga the cloak, Ethelred's gift, which was the fairest of things, and she thanked him well for the gift.

Then Gunnlaug went out, and by that time riding-horses had been brought home and saddled, and among them were many very good ones; and they were all tied up in the road. Gunnlaug leaps on to a horse, and rides a hand-gallop along the homefield up to a place where Raven happened to stand just before him; and Raven had to draw out of his way. Then Gunnlaug said:

"No need to slink aback, Raven, for I threaten thee nought as at this time; but thou knowest, forsooth, what thou hast earned."

Raven answered and sang:

"God of wound-flamed glitter,
Glorier of fight-goddess,
Must we fall a-fighting
For fairest kirtle-bearer?
Death-staffs many such-like
Fair as she is are there
In south-lands o'er the sea floods.
Sooth saith he who knoweth."

"Maybe there are many such, but they do not seem so to me," said Gunnlaug. Therewith Illugi and Thorstein ran up to them, and would not have them fight. Then Gunnlaug sang:

"The fair-hued golden goddess
For gold to Raven sold they
(Raven my match as men say)
While the mighty isle-king,
Ethelred, in England

From eastward way delayed me,

Wherefore to gold-waster

Waneth tongue's speech-hunger."

Hereafter both rode home, and all was quiet and tidingless that winter through; but Raven had nought of Helga's fellowship after her meeting with Gunnlaug.

CHAPTER XIV. OF THE *HOLMGANG* AT THE ALTHING

NOW in summer men ride a very many to the Althing: Illugi the Black and his sons with him, Gunnlaug and Hermund; Thorstein Egilson and Kolsvein his son; Onund, of Mossfell, and his sons all, and Sverting, Hafr-Biorn's son. Skapti yet held the spokesmanship-at-law.

One day at the Thing, as men went thronging to the Hill of Laws, and when the matters of the law were done there, then Gunnlaug craved silence, and said:

"Is Raven, the son of Onund, here?"

He said he was.

Then spake Gunnlaug, "Thou well knowest that thou hast got to wife my avowed bride, and thus hast thou made thyself my foe. Now for this I bid thee to holm here at the Thing, in the holm of the Axe-water, when three nights are gone by."

Raven answers, "This is well bidden, as was to be looked for of thee, and for this I am ready, whenever thou wiliest it."

Now the kin of each deemed this a very ill thing. But, at that time it was lawful for him who thought himself wronged by another to call him to fight on the holm.

So when three nights had gone by they got ready for the *holmgang*, and Illugi the Black followed his son thither with a great following. But Skapti, the lawman, followed Raven, and his father and other kinsmen of his.

Now before Gunnlaug went upon the holm he sang:

"Out to isle of eel-field

Dight am I to hie me:

Give, O God, thy singer

With glaive to end the striving.

Here shall I the head cleave
Of Helga's love's devourer,
At last my bright sword bringeth
Sundering of head and body."
Then Raven answered and sang:
"Thou, singer, knowest not surely
Which of us twain shall gain it;
With edge for leg-swathe eager,
Here are the wound-scythes bare now.
In whatso-wise we wound us,
The tidings from the Thing here,
And fame of thanes' fair doings,
The fair young maid shall hear it."

Hermund held shield for his brother, Gunnlaug; but Sverting, Hafr-Biorn's son, was Raven's shield-bearer. Whoso should be wounded was to ransom himself from the holm with three marks of silver.

Now, Raven's part it was to deal the first blow, as he was the challenged man. He hewed at the upper part of Gunnlaug's shield, and the sword brake asunder just beneath the hilt, with so great might he smote; but the point of the sword flew up from the shield and struck Gunnlaug's cheek, whereby he got just grazed; with that their fathers ran in between them, and many other men.

"Now," said Gunnlaug, "I call Raven overcome, as he is weaponless."

"But I say that thou art vanquished, since thou art wounded," said Raven.

Now, Gunnlaug was nigh mad, and very wrathful, and said it was not tried out yet.

Illugi, his father, said they should try no more for that time.

Gunnlaug said, "Beyond all things I desire that I might in such wise meet Raven again, that thou, father, wert not anigh to part us."

And thereat they parted for that time, and all men went back to their booths.

But on the second day after this it was made law in the law-court that, henceforth, all *holmgang*s should be forbidden; and this was done by the counsel of all the wisest men that were at the Thing; and there, indeed, were all the men of most counsel in all the land. And this was the last *holmgang* fought in Iceland, this, wherein Gunnlaug and Raven fought.

But this Thing was the third most thronged Thing that has been held in Iceland; the first was after Njal's burning, the second after the Heath-slaughters.

Now, one morning, as the brothers Hermund and Gunnlaug went to Axe-water to wash, on the other side went many women towards the river, and in that company was Helga the Fair. Then said Hermund:

"Dost thou see thy friend Helga there on the other side of the river?"

"Surely, I see her," says Gunnlaug, and withal he sang:

"Born was she for men's bickering:
Sore bale hath wrought the war-stemy
And I yearned ever madly
To hold that oak tree golden.
To me then, me destroyer
Of swan-mead's flame, unneedful
This looking on the dark-eyed,
This golden land's beholding."

Therewith they crossed the river, and Helga and Gunnlaug spake awhile together, and as the brothers crossed the river eastward back again, Helga stood and gazed long after Gunnlaug.

Then Gunnlaug looked back and sang:

"Moon of linen-lapped one,
Leek-sea-bearing goddess,
Hawk-keen out of heaven
Shone all bright upon me;
But that eyelid's moonbeam
Of gold-necklaced goddess
Her hath all undoing
Wrought, and me made nought of."

CHAPTER XV. HOW GUNNLAUG AND RAVEN AGREED TO GO EAST TO NORWAY, TO TRY THE MATTER AGAIN

NOW after these things were gone by men rode home from the Thing, and Gunnlaug dwelt at home at Gilsbank.

On a morning when he awoke all men had risen up, but he alone still lay abed; he lay in a shut-bed behind the seats. Now into the hall came twelve men, all full armed, and who should be there but Raven, Onund's son; Gunnlaug sprang up forthwith, and got to his weapons.

But Raven spake, "Thou art in risk of no hurt this time," quoth he, "but my errand hither is what thou shalt now hear: thou didst call me to a *holmgang* last summer at the Althing, and thou didst not deem matters to be fairly tried therein; now I will offer thee this, that we both fare away from Iceland, and go abroad next summer, and go on holm in Norway, for there our kinsmen are not like to stand in our way."

Gunnlaug answered, "Hail to thy words, stoutest of men! This thine offer I take gladly; and here, Raven, mayest thou have cheer as good as thou mayest desire."

"It is well offered," said Raven, "but this time we shall first have to ride away." Thereon they parted.

Now the kinsmen of both sore misliked them of this, but could in no wise undo it, because of the wrath of Gunnlaug and Raven; and, after all, that must betide that drew towards.

Now it is to be said of Raven that he fitted out his ship in Leiruvag; two men are named that went with him, sisters' sons of his father Onund, one named Grim, the other Olaf, doughty men both. All the kinsmen of Raven thought it great scathe when he went away, but he said he had challenged Gunnlaug to the *holmgang* because he could have no joy soever of Helga; and he said, withal, that one must fall before the other.

So Raven put to sea, when he had wind at will, and brought his ship to Thrandheim, and was there that winter and heard nought of Gunnlaug that winter through; there lie abode him the summer following: and still another winter was he in Thrandheim, at a place called Lifangr.

Gunnlaug Worm-tongue took ship with Hallfred Troublous-*Skald*, in the north at the Plain; they were very late ready for sea.

They sailed into the main when they had a fair wind, and made Orkney a little before the winter. Earl Sigurd Lodverson was still lord over the isles, and Gunnlaug went to him and abode there that winter, and the earl held him of much account.

In the spring the earl would go on warfare, and Gunnlaug made ready to go with him; and that summer they harried wide about the South-isles and Scotland's firths, and had many fights, and Gunnlaug always showed himself the bravest and doughtiest of fellows, and the hardiest of men wherever they came.

Earl Sigurd went back home early in the summer, but Gunnlaug took ship with chapmen, sailing for Norway, and he and Earl Sigurd parted in great friendship.

Gunnlaug fared north to Thrandheim, to Hladir, to see Earl Eric, and dwelt there through the early winter; the earl welcomed him gladly, and made offer to Gunnlaug to stay with him, and Gunnlaug agreed thereto.

The earl had heard already how all had befallen between Gunnlaug and Raven, and he told Gunnlaug that he laid ban on their fighting within his realm; Gunnlaug said the earl should be free to have his will herein.

So Gunnlaug abode there the winter through, ever heavy of mood.

CHAPTER XVI. HOW THE TWO FOES MET AND FOUGHT AT DINGNESS

BUT on a day in spring Gunnlaug was walking abroad, and his kinsman Thorkel with him; they walked away from the town, till on the meads. before them they saw a ring of men, and in that ring were two men with weapons fencing; but one was named Raven, the other Gunnlaug, while they who stood by said that Icelanders smote light, and were slow to remember their words.

Gunnlaug saw the great mocking hereunder, and much jeering was brought into the play; and withal he went away silent.

So a little while after he said to the earl that he had no mind to bear any longer the jeers and mocks of his courtiers about his dealings with Raven, and therewith he prayed the earl to give him a guide to Lifangr: now before this the earl had been told that Raven had left Lifangr and gone east to Sweden; therefore, he granted Gunnlaug leave to go, and gave him two guides for the journey.

Now Gunnlaug went from Hladir with six men to Lifangr; and, on the morning of the very day whereas Gunnlaug came in in the evening, Raven had left Lifangr with four men. Thence Gunnlaug went to Vera-dale, and came always in the evening to where Raven had been the night before.

So Gunnlaug went on till he came to the uppermost farm in the valley, called Sula, wherefrom had Raven fared in the morning; there he stayed not his journey, but kept on his way through the night.

Then in the morning at sun-rise they saw one another. Raven had got to a place where were two waters, and between them flat meads, and they are called Gleipni's meads: but into one water stretched a little ness called Dingness. There on the ness Raven and his fellows, five together, took their stand. With Raven were his kinsmen, Grim and Olaf.

Now when they met, Gunnlaug said, "It is well that we have found one another."

Raven said that he had nought to quarrel with therein.

"But now," says he, "thou mayest choose as thou wilt, either that we fight alone together, or that we fight all of us man to man."

Gunnlaug said that either way seemed good to him.

Then spake Raven's kinsmen, Grim and Olaf, and said that they would little like to stand by and look on the fight, and in like wise spake Thorkel the Black, the kinsman of Gunnlaug.

Then said Gunnlaug to the earl's guides, "Ye shall sit by and aid neither side, and be here to tell of our meeting." And so they did.

So they set on, and fought dauntlessly, all of them. Grim and Olaf went both against Gunnlaug alone, and so closed their dealings with him that Gunnlaug slew them both and got no wound. This proves Thord Kolbeinson in a song that he made on Gunnlaug the Worm-tongue:

> "Grim and Olaf great-hearts
> In Gondul's din, with thin sword

> First did Gunnlaug fell there
> Ere at Raven fared he;
> Bold, with blood be-drifted
> Bane of three the thane was;
> War-lord of the wave-horse
> Wrought for men-folks' slaughter."

Meanwhile Raven and Thorkel the Black, Gunnlaug's kinsman, fought until Thorkel fell before Raven and lost his life; and so at last all their fellowship fell. Then they two alone fought together with fierce onsets and mighty strokes, which they dealt each the other, falling on furiously without stop or stay.

Gunnlaug had the sword, Ethelred's gift, and that was the best of weapons. At last Gunnlaug dealt a mighty blow at Raven, and cut his leg from under him; but none the more did Raven fall, but swung round up to a tree-stem, whereat he steadied the stump.

Then said Gunnlaug, "Now thou art no more meet for battle, nor will I fight with thee any longer, a maimed man."

Raven answered: "So it is", said he, "that my lot is now all the worser lot, but it were well with me yet, might I but drink somewhat."

Gunnlaug said, "Bewray me not if I bring thee water in my helm."

"I will not bewray thee," said Raven. Then went Gunnlaug to a brook and fetched water in his helm, and brought it to Raven; but Raven stretched forth his left hand to take it, but with his right hand drave his sword into Gunnlaug's head, and that was a mighty great wound.

Then Gunnlaug said, "Evilly hast thou beguiled me, and done traitorously wherein I trusted thee."

Raven answers, "Thou sayest sooth, but this brought me to it, that I begrudged thee to lie in the bosom of Helga the Fair."

Thereat they fought on, recking of nought; but the end of it was that Gunnlaug overcame Raven, and there Raven lost his life.

Then the earl's guides came forward and bound the head-wound of Gunnlaug, and in meanwhile, he sat and sang:

"O thou sword-storm stirrer,
Raven, stem of battle
Famous, fared against me
Fiercely in the spear din.
Many a flight of metal
Was borne on me this morning,
By the spear-walls' builder,
Ring-bearer, on hard Dingness."

After that they buried the dead, and got Gunnlaug on to his horse thereafter, and brought him right down to Lifangr. There he lay three nights, and got all his rights of a priest, and died thereafter, and was buried at the church there.

All men thought it great scathe of both of these men, Gunnlaug and Raven, amid such deeds as they died.

CHAPTER XVII. THE NEWS OF THE FIGHT BROUGHT TO ICELAND

NOW this summer, before these tidings were brought out hither to Iceland, Illugi the Black, being at home at Gilsbank, dreamed a dream: he thought that Gunnlaug came to him in his sleep, all bloody, and he sang in the dream this stave before him; and Illugi remembered the song when he woke, and sang it before others:

"Knew I of the hewing
Of Raven's hilt-finned steel-fish
Byrny-shearing – sword-edge
Sharp clave leg of Raven.
Of warm wounds drank the eagle,
When the war-rod slender,
Cleaver of the corpses,
Clave the head of Gunnlaug."

This portent befell south at Mossfell, the self-same night, that Onund dreamed how

Raven came to him, covered all over with blood, and sang:

> "Red is the sword, but I now
> Am undone by Sword-Odin.
> 'Gainst shields beyond the sea-flood
> The ruin of shields was wielded.
> Methinks the blood-fowl blood-stained
> In blood o'er men's heads stood there,
> The wound-erne yet wound-eager
> Trod over wounded bodies?"

Now the second summer after this, Illugi the Black spoke at the Althing from the Hill of Laws, and said:

"Wherewith wilt thou make atonement to me for my son, whom Raven, thy son, beguiled in his troth?"

Onund answers, "Be it far from me to atone for him, so sorely as their meeting hath wounded me. Yet will I not ask atonement of thee for my son."

"Then shall my wrath come home to some of thy kin," says Illugi. And withal after the Thing was Illugi at most times very sad.

Tells the tale how this autumn Illugi rode from Gilsbank with thirty men, and came to Mossfell early in the morning. Then Onund got into the church with his sons, and took sanctuary; but Illugi caught two of his kin, one called Biorn and the other Thorgrim, and had Biorn slain, but the feet smitten from Thorgrim. And thereafter Illugi rode home, and there was no righting of this for Onund.

Hermund, Illugi's son, had little joy after the death of Gunnlaug his brother, and deemed he was none the more avenged even though this had been wrought.

Now there was a man called Raven, brother's son to Onund of Mossfell; he was a great sea-farer, and had a ship that lay up in Ramfirth; and in the spring Hermund Illugison rode from home alone north over Holt-beacon Heath, even to Ramfirth, and out as far as Board-ere to the ship of the chapmen. The chapmen were then nearly ready for sea; Raven, the ship-master, was on shore, and many men with him; Hermund rode up to him, and thrust him through with his spear, and rode away forthwith: but all Raven's men were bewildered at seeing Hermund.

No atonement came for this slaying, and therewith ended the dealings of Illugi the Black and Onund of Mossfell.

CHAPTER XVIII. THE DEATH OF HELGA THE FAIR

AS time went on, Thorstein Egilson married his daughter Helga to a man called Thorkel, son of Hallkel, who lived west in Hraundale. Helga went to his house with him, but loved him little, for she cannot cease to think of Gunnlaug, though he be dead. Yet was Thorkel a doughty man, and wealthy of goods, and a good *skald*.

They had children together not a few; one of them was called Thorarin, another Thorstein, and yet more they had.

But Helga's chief joy was to pluck at the threads of that cloak, Gunnlaug's gift, and she would be ever gazing at it.

But on a time there came a great sickness to the house of Thorkel and Helga, and many were bed-ridden for a long time. Helga also fell sick, and yet she could not keep abed.

So one Saturday evening Helga sat in the fire-hall, and leaned her head upon her husband's knees, and had the cloak Gunnlaug's gift sent for; and when the cloak came to her she sat up and plucked at it, and gazed thereon awhile, and then sank back upon her husband's bosom, and was dead. Then Thorkel sang this:

"Dead in mine arms she droopeth,
My dear one, gold-rings bearer,
For God hath changed the life-days
Of this Lady of the linen.
Weary pain hath pined her,
But unto me, the seeker
Of hoard of fishes highway,
Abiding here is wearier."

Helga was buried in the church there, but Thorkel dwelt yet at Hraundale: but a great matter seemed the death of Helga to all, as was to be looked for.